Wise Publications
London / New York / Paris / Sydney / Copenhagen / Madrid

Exclusive Distributors:
Music Sales Limited
8/9 Frith Street,
London W1V 5TZ, England.
Music Sales Pty Limited
120 Rothschild Avenue, Rosebery,
NSW 2018, Australia.

Order No. AM951973
ISBN 0-7119-7347-4
This book © Copyright 1999 by
    Wise Publications.

Compiled by Peter Evans & Peter Lavender.
Music arranged by Peter Lavender.
Music processed by
    MSS Studios & Hillmob Music Services.
Cover & prelims design by Michael Bell Design.
Printed & bound in Singapore.

www.musicinprint.com

Two more mega songbooks
for singers and all musicians...
The Busker's Fake Book:
1001 All-Time Hit Songs
AM84047
The New Busker's Fake Book:
1001 All-Time Hit Songs
AM91528

The Best Busker's Book Ever!

CHRISTMAS SONGS & CAROLS

CLASSICAL

CLASSIFIED INDEX
With Song Numbers

COMEDY & NOVELTY SONGS

COUNTRY MUSIC

DISNEY SONGS

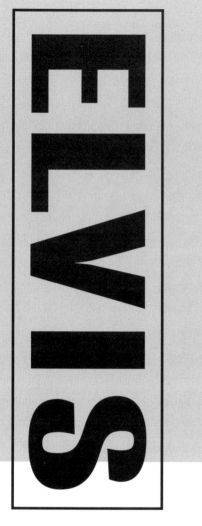

HYMNS
SPIRITUALS
GOSPELS

JAZZ & BLUES

THE BEATLES

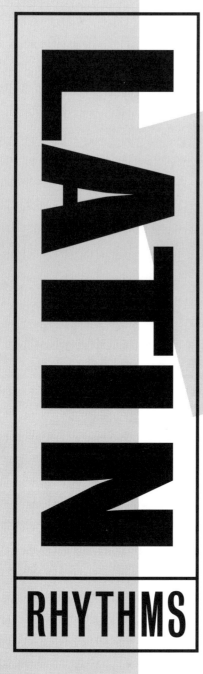

STANDARDS

1. A-Tisket A-Tasket

Traditional

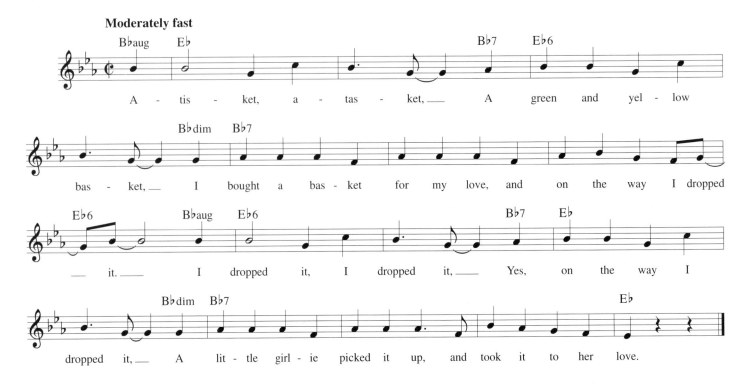

2. Abide With Me

Words & Music by Henry Lyte & William Monk

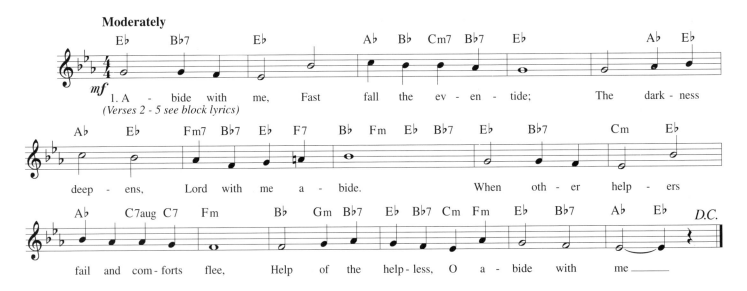

2. Swift to its close ebbs out life's little day
Earth's joys grow dim, its glories pass away
Change and decay in all around I see
O Thou who changes not, abide with me.

3. I need Thy presence ev'ry passing hour
What but Thy grace can foil the tempter's power?
Who like Thyself my guide and stay can be?
Through cloud and sunshine, O abide with me.

4. I fear no foe, with Thee at hand to bless
Ills have no weight and tears no bitterness
Where is death's sting? Where, grave, thy victory?
I triumph still if Thou abide with me.

5. Hold Thou Thy cross before my closing eyes
Shine through the gloom and point me to the skies
Heaven's morning breaks, and earth's vain shadows flee
In life, in death, O Lord, abide with me.

3. Alfie

Music by Burt Bacharach. Lyric by Hal David

4. Adagio

By Tomaso Giovanni Albinoni

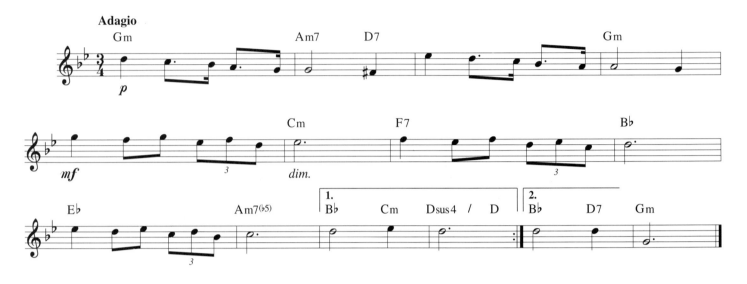

5. Across The Alley From The Alamo

Words & Music by Joe Greene

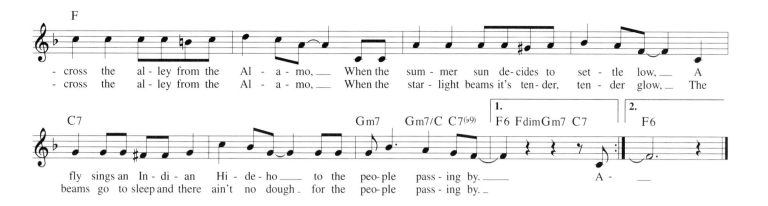

-cross the al- ley from the Al - a- mo, ___ When the sum- mer sun de-cides to set- tle low, ___ A
-cross the al- ley from the Al - a- mo, ___ When the star - light beams it's ten- der, ten - der glow, ___ The

fly sings an In - di - an Hi - de - ho ___ to the peo- ple pass- ing by. ___ A -
beams go to sleep and there ain't no dough _ for the peo- ple pass- ing by. ___

6. All Right Now

Words & Music by Paul Rodgers & Andy Fraser

© Copyright 1970 Blue Mountain Music Limited, 47 British Grove, London W4.
All Rights Reserved. International Copyright Secured.

Moderately

(instrumental)

1. There she
2. I took her

stood in the street, ___ smil- ing from her head ___ to her feet, I said
home to my place, ___ watch- ing ev - 'ry move on her face, she said

"Hey, what is this?" Now ba- by, may- be may- be she's in need ___ of a kiss. I said
"Look, what's your game ba- by, are you tryin' to put me in shame?" I said

"Hey, what's your name ba- by, may- be we can see things the same, now don't you
"Slow, don't go so fast, don't you think that love ___ can last?" She said ___

wait or hes- i - tate, ___ let's move ___ be - fore they raise the park- ing rate."
"Love, ___ Lord a - bove, ___ now ___ you're tryin' to trick me in love."

All right now ___ ba - by, it's all ___ right ___ now.

All right now ___ ba - by, it's all ___ right ___ now.

Repeat to fade

All right now ___ ba - by, it's all ___ right ___ now.

21

7. The Addams Family Waltz

By Marc Shaiman

Moderately fast

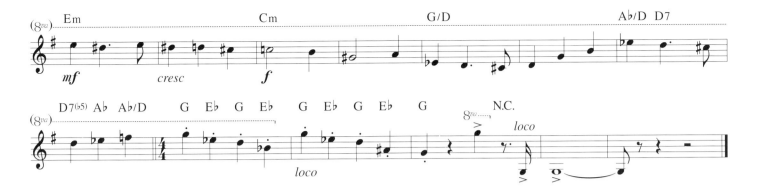

8. Almost In Your Arms

Words & Music by Jay Livingston & Ray Evans

Slowly, freely and intimately

9. Afton Water

Music Traditional. Words by Robert Burns

1. Flow gent-ly sweet Af-ton a-mong thy green braes, Flow gent-ly, I'll sing thee a song in thy praise. My Ma-ry's a-sleep by thy mur-mur-ing stream, Flow gent-ly sweet Af-ton, dis-turb not her dream.

(Verses 2 - 4 see block lyrics)

2. Thou
3. Thy
4. Flow

2. Thou stock dove whose echo resounds thro' the glen
Ye wild whistling blackbirds in yon thorny den
Thou green crested lapwing, thy screaming for bear
I charge you disturb not my slumbering fair.

3. Thy crystal stream Afton, how lovely it glides
And winds by the cot where my Mary resides
How wanton thy waters her snowy feet lave
As, gath'ring sweet flow'rets she stems thy clear wave.

4. Flow gently, sweet Afton among thy green braes
Flow gently, sweet river, the theme of my lays
My Mary's asleep by thy murmuring stream
Flow gently, sweet Afton, disturb not her dream.

10. All I Want For Christmas Is My Two Front Teeth

Words & Music by Donald Gardner

Moderately *(Christmas is pronounced "Chrithmath")*

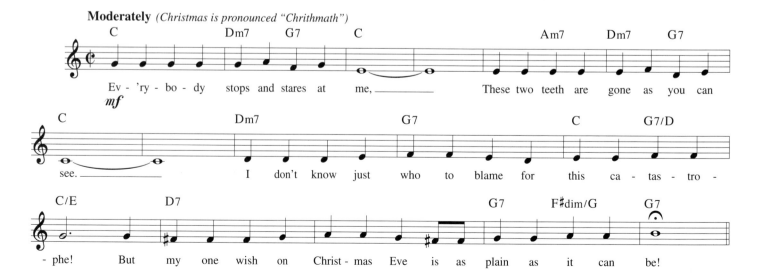

Ev-'ry-bo-dy stops and stares at me, _____ These two teeth are gone as you can see. _____ I don't know just who to blame for this ca-tas-tro-phe! But my one wish on Christ-mas Eve is as plain as it can be!

All I want for Christ-mas is my two front teeth, My two front teeth, See my two front teeth!

Gee, if I could on-ly have my two front teeth, Then I could wish you "Mer-ry Christ-mas!" It

seems so long since I could say "Sis-ter Su-sie sit-ting on a this-tle!" —

Gosh oh gee, How hap-py I'd be, If I could on-ly whis-tle! — "Thhhh..."

All I want for Christ-mas is my two front teeth, My two front teeth, See my two front teeth!

Gee, if I could on-ly have my two front teeth, Then I could wish you "Mer-ry Christ-mas!"

11. All Things Bright And Beautiful

Traditional

Moderately

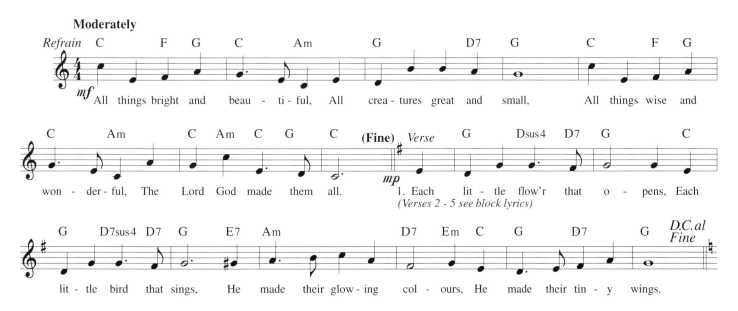

All things bright and beau-ti-ful, All crea-tures great and small, All things wise and

won-der-ful, The Lord God made them all. (Fine) *Verse* 1. Each lit-tle flow'r that o-pens, Each
(Verses 2 - 5 see block lyrics)

lit-tle bird that sings, He made their glow-ing col-ours, He made their tin-y wings.

2. The purple-headed mountain
The river running by
The sunset, and the morning
That brightens up the sky.

3. The cold wind in the winter
The pleasant summer sun
The ripe fruits in the garden
He made them every one.

4. He gave us eyes to see them
And lips that we might tell
How great is God Almighty
Who has made all things well.

12. Ain't Nobody

Words & Music by David Wolinski

you.

At first you put your arms a-round me,

then you put your charms a-round me, I've got

a feel-ing most would trea-sure, and a love so deep we can-not mea-sure.

2. I've been waiting for you
   It's been so long
   I knew just what I would do
   When I heard your song
   You filled my heart with a kiss
   You gave me freedom
   You knew I could not resist
   I needed someone
   And now we're flying through the stars
   And hope this night will last forever.

3. I wait for night time to come
   To bring you to me
   I can't believe I'm the one
   I was so lonely
   I feel like no-one before
   I must be dreaming
   I want this dream to be real
   I need this feeling
   I make my wish upon a star
   And hope this night will last forever.

13. Angels From The Realms Of Glory

Traditional Christmas Carol

1. An - gels from the realms of glo - ry, Wing your flight o'er all the earth,

Ye who sang cre - a - tion's sto - ry, Now pro - claim Mes - si - ah's birth.

Come and wor - ship, wor - ship Christ the new - born King.

2. Shepherds in the field abiding
   Watching o'er your flocks by night
   God with man is now residing
   Yonder shines the infant light
   Come and worship
   Worship Christ the new-born King.

3. Sages leave your contemplations
   Brighter visions beam afar
   Seek the great desire of nations
   Ye have seen His natal star
   Come and worship
   Worship Christ the new-born King.

4. Saints, before the altar bending
   Watching long with hope and fear
   Suddenly the Lord descending
   In His temple shall appear
   Come and worship
   Worship Christ the new-born King.

5. Sinner, wrung with true repentance
   Doomed for guilt to endless pains
   Justice now revokes the sentence
   Mercy calls you, break your chains
   Come and worship
   Worship Christ the new-born King.

14. All At Once

Words by Jeffrey Osborne & Michael Masser. Music by Michael Masser

D.%.

2, 3. etc.   *Repeat ad lib. and fade*

    2. All   at   once ___   ___ than it   shows.   All   at   once

2. All at once
   I looked around and found
   That you were with another love
   In someone else's arms
   And all my dreams were shattered
   All at once
   All at once
   The smile that used to greet me
   Brightens someone else's day
   She took your smile away
   And left me with just mem'ries
   All at once
   (To Bridge:)

15. All Our Tomorrows

Words & Music by Jimmy Kennedy

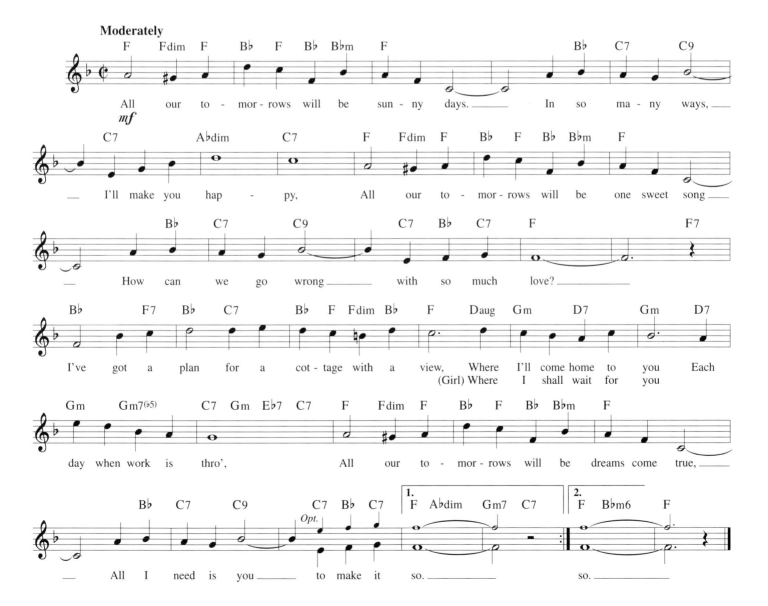

16. All I Really Want

Music by Alanis Morissette & Glenn Ballard. Words by Alanis Morissette

17. All Shook Up

Words & Music by Otis Blackwell & Elvis Presley

32

yeah! I'm all shook up! — Mm — mm oh, oh, yeah, — yeah! I'm all shook up!

18. All Of Me

Words & Music by Seymour Simons & Gerald Marks

Moderately

You took my kiss- es and you took my love, — You taught me how to care.

Am I to be — just the rem - nant of — a one - sid - ed love — af - fair?

All you took I glad - ly gave, There's noth - ing left for me to save. All of me, —

— Why not take all of me? Can't you see — I'm no good with -

- out you? — Take my lips, — I want to lose them,

Take my arms, — I'll nev - er use them. Your good - bye

— left me with eyes that cry. — How can I go on, dear, with -

- out you? — You took the part that once was my

heart, So why not take all of me? —

19. All That She Wants

Words & Music by Buddha & Joker

ba - by. She's gone to - mor - row, boy, all ____ that she wants ____ is ____ an - oth - er

ba - by, yeah. ____

All that she wants. All that she wants. So if ____ you

are in - side and the day is right, ____ she's the hun - ter, you're the fox. ____ A

gen - tle voice that talks ____ to you won't talk for - ev - er.

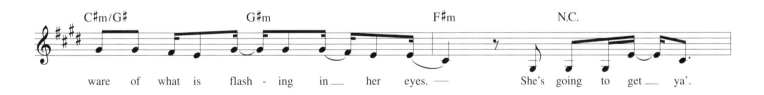

It is a night for pas - sion where the morn - ing means good - bye. Be -

ware of what is flash - ing in ____ her eyes. ____ She's going to get ____ ya'.

Repeat to fade

All ____ that she wants ____ is an - oth - er ba - by. She's gone to - mor - row, boy,

all ____ that she wants ____ is an - oth - er ba - by, yeah. ____

20. Alone

Words & Music by Barry Gibb, Robin Gibb & Maurice Gibb

lone. — Gone — but not out of sight, — I'm caught in the rain — and there's no one home. ——
Face — the heat of the night, — the one that you love's — got a heart that's made of —
stone. — Shine — and search for the light — and soon-er or la-ter you'll be cruising on your o-cean.

2. Well, since I got no message on your answer phone,
   Since you're ringing every minute I just stay at home
   I make believe you care, I feel you everywhere
   But I'm still alone
   I'm on a wheel of fortune with a twist of fate
   Cause I know it isn't heaven, is it love or hate
   Am I the subject of the pain, am I the stranger in the rain?
   I am alone.

   And is there glory there to behold?
   Maybe it's my imagination
   Another story there to be told
   So I play, I'll wait
   And I pray it's not too late
   You know we came so far
   Just the beat of a lonely heart
   And it's mine
   I don't want to be alone.

3. (%) And all the wonders made for the earth
   And all the hearts in all creation
   Another story there to be told
   So I play, I'll wait
   And I pray it's not too late
   We came so far
   Just the beat of a lonely heart
   And it's mine
   I don't want to be alone.

21. All My Love (Solo Tu)

Music by F. Monti Arduini. English Lyric by Peter Callander

Moderately slow

mf All my love —— came to no-thing at all, my love —— when I woke up to

find you were no long-er mine. All my love —— thrown a-way af-ter

Last time to fade all this time, —— now there's no place for me in the fu-ture, you

see. I don't un-der-stand you I've done all I can do, Tell me how could I

1. give you more. —— more than all my love.
2. give you more, ——

D.%. al Fade

—— more than all my love —— came to no-thing at

22. Always

Words & Music by Jon Bon Jovi

2. Now your pictures that you left behind
    Are just memories of a different life
    Some that made us laugh, some that made us cry
    One that made you have to say goodbye.

    What I'd give to run my fingers through your hair
    To touch your lips, to hold you near
    When you say your prayers
    Try to understand, I've made mistakes, I'm just a man.

    When he holds you close, when he pulls you near
    When he says the words you've been needing to hear
    I'll wish I was him, 'cause those words are mine
    To say to you till the end of time.

23. All I've Ever Wanted

Words & Music by Mariah Carey & Walter Afanasieff

is you, _____ you.

24. And Your Bird Can Sing

Words & Music by John Lennon & Paul McCartney

1. Tell me that you've got ev-'ry thing you want, And your bird can sing, but you don't get me, ___
2. You say you've seen sev-en won-ders, And your bird is green, but you can't see me, ___

You don't get me.
You can't see me.

When your prized ___ pos-ses-sions start to weigh ___ you down, ___
When your bird ___ is bro-ken, will it bring ___ you down? ___

Look in my ___ di-rec-tion, I'll be 'round, ___ I'll be 'round. ___ on %: 3. You
You may be ___ a-wo-ken, I'll be 'round, ___ I'll be 'round. ___

To Coda ⊕

D.%.al Coda

⊕ Coda

tell me that you've heard ev-'ry sound there is, And your bird can sing, but you can't hear me, ___

___ you can't hear me.

25. Ain't That A Shame

Words & Music by Antoine Domino & Dave Bartholomew

2. You broke my heart
Now we're apart
Ain't that a shame
You're the one to blame *(etc.)*

3. So long, goodbye
Although I cry
Ain't that a shame
You're the one to blame *(etc.)*

26. Ah! Sweet Mystery Of Life

Music by Victor Herbert. Words by Rida Johnson Young

27. Arabian Nights
(From Walt Disney Pictures' "Aladdin")

Music by Alan Menken. Lyrics by Howard Ashman

28. All People That On Earth Do Dwell

Traditional

2. The Lord, ye know, is God indeed
Without our aid He did us make
We are His folk, He doth us feed
And for His sheep He doth us take.

3. O enter then His gates with praise
Approach with joy His courts unto
Praise, laud and bless His name always
For it is seemly so to do.

4. For why? The Lord our God is good
His mercy is for ever sure
His truth at all times firmly stood
And shall from age to age endure.

5. To Father, Son, and Holy Ghost
The God whom heaven and earth adore
From men and from the angel host
Be praise and glory evermore.

29. Almost Paradise

Words & Music by Dean Pitchford & Eric Carman

pa - ra - dise. __ How could we ask __ for more? I swear that I __ can see __ for - ev - er

in your __ eyes. Pa - ra - dise.

To Coda ⊕

1.

2.

(Male:) And in your arms, __ sal - va - tion's not so far a - way. __

D.%.al Coda

It's get - ting clos - er. (Both:) Clos - er ev - 'ry day. __ Al - most

⊕ Coda

Pa - ra - dise. __ Pa - ra - dise. __

30. America The Beautiful

Music by Samuel A. Ward. Words by Katherine Lee Bates

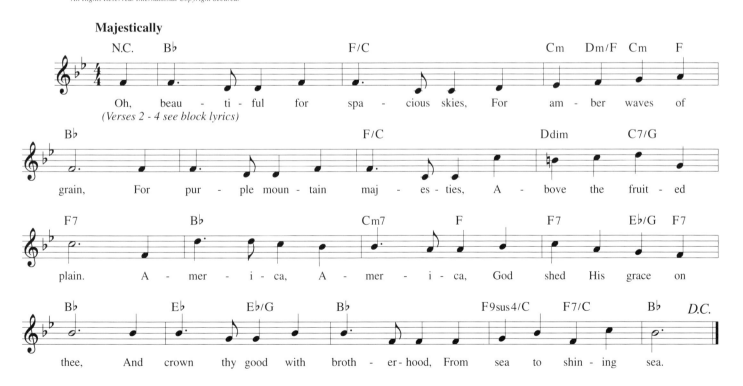

Majestically

Oh, beau - ti - ful for spa - cious skies, For am - ber waves of
(Verses 2 - 4 see block lyrics)

grain, For pur - ple moun - tain maj - es - ties, A - bove the fruit - ed

plain. A - mer - i - ca, A - mer - i - ca, God shed His grace on

thee, And crown thy good with broth - er - hood, From sea to shin - ing sea.

2. Oh, beautiful for pilgrim feet
   Whose stern impassioned stress
   A thoroughfare for freedom beat
   Across the wilderness.
   America, America
   God mend thine ev'ry flaw
   Confirm thy soul in self-control
   Thy liberty in law.

3. Oh, beautiful for heroes proved
   In liberating strife
   Who more than self their country loved
   And mercy more than life.
   America, America
   May God thy gold refine
   Till all success be nobleness
   And ev'ry gain divine.

4. Oh, beautiful for patriot dream
   That sees beyond the years
   Thine alabaster cities gleam
   Undimmed by human tears.
   America, America
   God shed His grace on thee
   And crown thy good with brotherhood
   From sea to shining sea.

31. Always Be My Baby

Words by Mariah Carey. Music by Jermaine Dupri, Mariah Carey & Manuel Seal

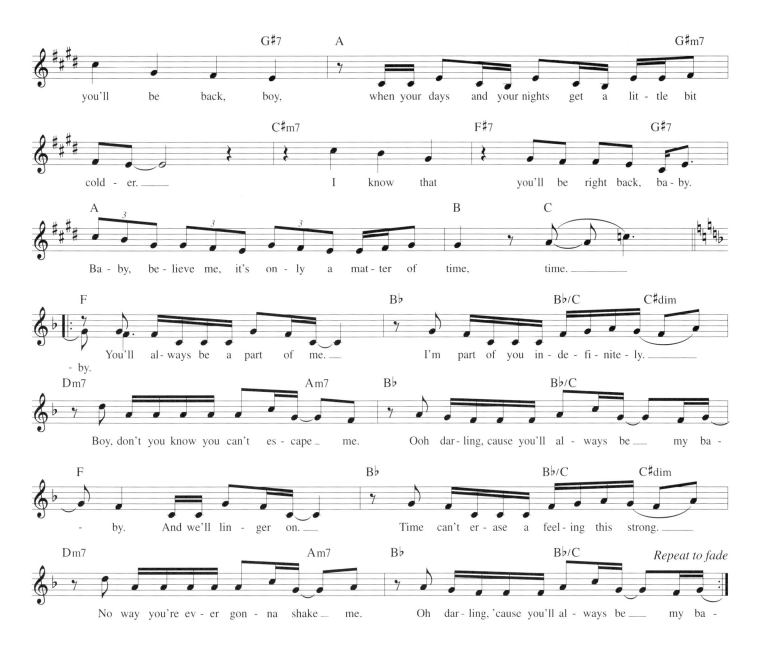

you'll be back, boy, when your days and your nights get a lit - tle bit cold - er. ___ I know that you'll be right back, ba - by.

Ba - by, be - lieve me, it's on - ly a mat - ter of time, time. ___

You'll al - ways be a part of me. ___ I'm part of you in - de - fi - nite - ly. ___

- by. Boy, don't you know you can't es - cape ___ me. Ooh dar - ling, cause you'll al - ways be ___ my ba -

- by. And we'll lin - ger on. ___ Time can't er - ase a feel - ing this strong. ___

No way you're ev - er gon - na shake ___ me. Oh dar - ling, 'cause you'll al - ways be ___ my ba -

Repeat to fade

32. Anchors Aweigh

Music by Chas A. Zimmerman

Brightly

33. Among My Souvenirs

Words by Edgar Leslie. Music by Horatio Nicholls

34. And I Love You So

Words & Music by Don McLean

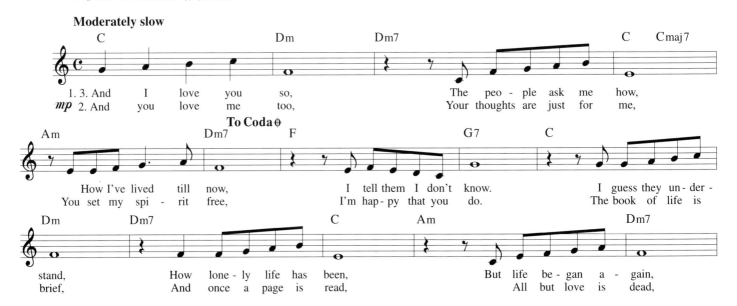

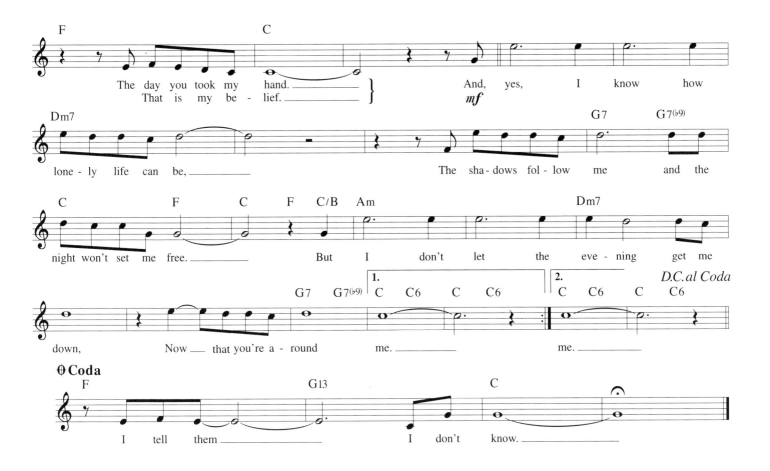

The day you took my hand. ___
That is my be - lief. ___
And, yes, I know how lone - ly life can be, ___ The sha - dows fol - low me and the night won't set me free. ___ But I don't let the eve - ning get me down, Now ___ that you're a - round me. me.

D.C. al Coda

⊕ Coda

I tell them ___ I don't know. ___

35. Alice In Wonderland

Music by Sammy Fain. Words by Bob Hilliard

Moderately slow

Al - ice in Won - der - land, How do you get to Won - der - land? O - ver the hill or
When clouds go roll - ing by, They roll a - way and leave the sky. Where is the land be -

un - der - land or just be - hind the tree. yond the eye that peo - ple can - not see. ___

___ Where can it be? Where do stars go? Where is the cres - cent moon? They

a tempo

rit.

must be some - where in the sun - ny aft - er - noon. Al - ice in Won - der - land,

rit.

Where is the path to Won - der - land o - ver the hill or here or there? I won - der where.

36. Amorita (Fue Mentira)

Words & Music by Carlos Barberena. English Lyrics by Len Lawson

37. Anthropology

By Dizzy Gillespie & Charlie Parker

51

38. Any Time At All

Words & Music by John Lennon & Paul McCartney

39. Theme From August

By Anthony Hopkins

40. Anticipation Blues
(I'm Gonna Be A Daddy Now)

Words & Music by Tennessee Ernie & Cliffie Stone

Moderately slow

1. She just got home from the doc-tor's, ___ I just got home from the mill; ___ She
mf (Verses 2 & 3 see block lyrics)
looked a lit-tle peak-ed, Her eyes were kind-a streak-ed, I could-n't fig-ure out what made her
ill; ___ She looked a lit-tle weep-ish, Smiled kind a sheep-ish, The an-swer hit me like a hick-'ry
mall; ___ I threw my din-ner buck-et down, Yelled like my trail-in' hound, I was
gon-na be a dad-dy af-ter all. Now the wait-in', ___ An-tic-i-
pat-in'; ___ Rock-a-bye, ___ I'm gon-na be ___ a dad-dy

1, 2.
now! ___ 2. Well,
 3. Well,

3.
now! ___

2. Well, the weeks went by kinda sweetly, then, all at once, I thought she'd lost her mind
   She would rant, she would rave for the things she would crave
   Like ice cream and sauerkraut combined
   She wanted watermelon, it was wintertime
   Dill pickles set around the house in jars
   My, how she'd eat that stuff, she never seemed to get enough
   And, at 3.00 a.m., she'd want candy bars
      Oh! the waitin', anticipatin'; rock-a-bye, I'm gonna be a daddy now!

3. Well, at last the time was drawin' near, I began to walk and pace and sweat
   The doctor said, "Now son, I know this ain't no fun
   But we ain't never lost a daddy yet."
   I stood up and set down, I even thought of leavin' town
   The doctor and the nurse came out all grins
   They said, "Buck up, my boy, you should shout with joy
   You're the daddy of a pair of bouncin' twins!"
      No more waitin', anticipatin'; rock-a-bye, I'm a daddy now!

41. Ashby De La Zouch (Castle Abbey)

Words & Music by Al Hoffman, Milton Drake & Jerry Livingston

Moderately slow

42. April Played The Fiddle

Words by Johnny Burke. Music by James Monaco

43. The Aristocats

Words & Music by Richard M. Sherman & Robert B. Sherman

44. Ah! So Pure

Composed by Felix Von Flotow

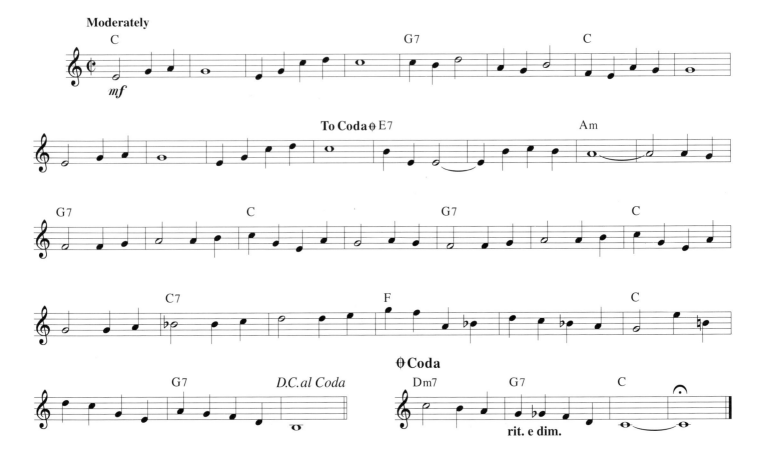

45. Another Tear Falls

Music by Burt Bacharach. Words by Hal David

heart. *mp* Ev - 'ry time I go with some - one new ___ I tell my - self

I've got - ten ov - er you, but just ___ when I think I'm ___ all cried ___ out ___

mf an - oth - er tear ___ falls, ___ an - oth - er tear ___ falls, ___

and ___ then I'd know ___ you are still here in my ___ heart, ___

you are still here in my bro - ken heart. ___

46. Annie Laurie

Music by Lady John Scott. Words by William Douglas

Moderately

1. Max - wel - ton braes are bon - nie, where ear - ly fa's the dew, And it's
mf *(Verses 2 & 3 see block lyrics)*

there that An - nie Lau - rie gie'd me her prom - ise true. Gie'd

me her prom - ise true, which ne'er for - got will be, And for

bon - nie An - nie ___ Lau - rie, I'd ___ lay ___ me doon and dee. 2. Her ___ dee.
3. Like ___

2. Her brow is like the snaw-drift
   Her neck is like the swan
   Her face it is the fairest
   That e'er the sun shone on
   That e'er the sun shone on
   And dark blue is her e'e
   And for bonnie Annie Laurie
   I'd lay me doon and dee.

3. Like dew on the gowan lying
   Is the fa' o' her fairy feet
   And like winds in summer sighing
   Her voice is low and sweet
   Her voice is low and sweet
   And she's a' the world to me
   And for bonnie Annie Laurie
   I'd lay me doon and dee.

59

47. Around The World

Words & Music by Mortimer, Harvey, Rowebottom & Stannard

Spoken: Shout to the north, to the south, to the east, to the west, to the home I love the best.

where my soul can rest yes.

2. Been above the clouds
   That paint the sky
   Stood below the cosmos
   And pondered on a why.

   Back to the track in fact I'm breaking
   Though I never knew that you would turn and walk away to stay
   And leave me standing on my own
   Far from home, like a normal, sad bad
   Dreams about togetherness that we never had.

48. Are You Really Mine?

Words & Music by Al Hoffman, Dick Manning & Mark Markwell

49. As Long As You Love Me

Words & Music by Max Martin

2. Every little thing that you have said and done
   Feels like it's deep within me
   Doesn't really matter if you're on the run
   It seems like we're meant to be.

   I don't care etc.

50. Avalon Of The Heart

Words & Music by Van Morrison

2. Oh the Avalon sunset
   Avalon of the heart
   Me and my lady
   Goin' down by Avalon.

   Instrumental 8 bars

   Well I came upon
   The enchanted vale
   Down by the viaducts of my dreams
   Near Camelot hangs the tale
   Of the enchanted vale.

3. *(D.S.)* In the upper room
   There the cup does stand
   In the upper room
   Down by Avalon.

   Going down by Avalon
   Oh my Avalon of the heart
   Goin' down by Avalon
   Gonna make a brand new start.

51. Are My Ears On Straight

Words & Music by Mel Leven

52. Aranjuez, Mon Amour

Music by Joaquin Rodrigo. Words by Hal Shaper

53. Anything For Your Love

Words & Music by Jerry Lynn Williams

54. Arthur Murray Taught Me Dancing In A Hurry

Words & Music by Victor Schetzinger & Johnny Mercer

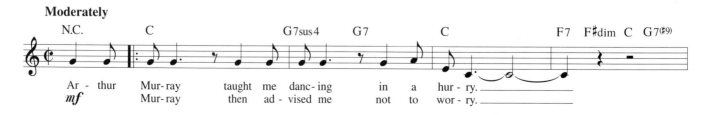

I had a week — to spare. _____ He showed me the ground-work, the walk a-round — work, and
It -'d come out _____ all right. _____ To my way of think-in', it came out stink-in', I

told me to take — it from there. _____ Ar - thur don't know my left _____ from my

right. _____ The peo-ple a-round — me can all sing _____ a-one and a-two — and a-three.

_____ But an-y re-sem-blance to waltz-ing is just co-in-ci-den-tal with me, — 'Cause Ar-thur

Mur-ray taught me danc-ing in a hur-ry.

And so I take — a chance _____ To me it re-sem-bles the nine day trem-bles But

he guar - an - tees _____ it's a dance. _____

55. Blow Away The Morning Dew

Traditional English Song

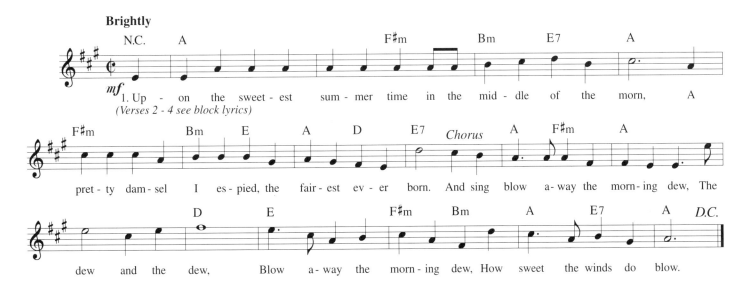

Brightly

mf
1. Up — on the sweet-est sum-mer time in the mid-dle of the morn, A
(Verses 2 - 4 see block lyrics)

pret-ty dam-sel I es-pied, the fair-est ev-er born. And sing blow a-way the morn-ing dew, The

dew and the dew, Blow a-way the morn-ing dew, How sweet the winds do blow.

2. She gathered up her lovely flowers
And spent her time in sport
As if in pretty Cupid's bowers
She daily did resort.

3. The yellow cowslip by the brim
The daffodil as well
The timid primrose, pale and trim
The pretty snow-drop bell.

4. She's gone with all those flowers sweet
Of white, of red, of blue
And unto me about my feet
Is only left the rue.

56. Attitude Dancing

Words & Music by Carly Simon & Jacob Brackman

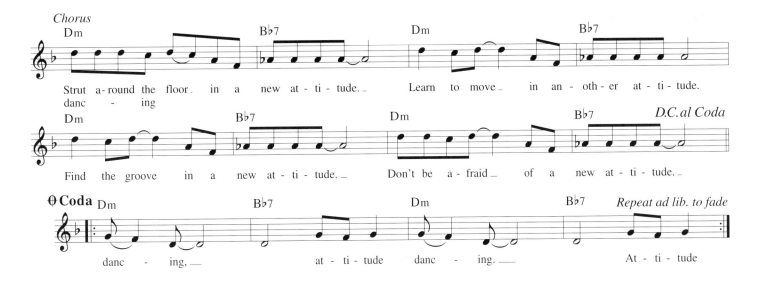

D.C.al Coda

Find the groove in a new at-ti-tude. Don't be a-fraid of a new at-ti-tude.

Coda Dm

Repeat ad lib. to fade

danc - ing, at-ti-tude danc - ing. At-ti-tude

57. Baby's In Black

Words & Music by John Lennon & Paul McCartney

Slowly, with a strong beat

Oh dear, what can I do? Ba-by's in black and I'm feel-ing blue. Tell me

oh, what can I do? 1, 3. She thinks of him and so she dress-es in black, And
2. I think of her but she thinks on-ly of him, And

though he'll nev-er come back, she's dressed in black. him
though it's on-ly a whim, she thinks of

Oh, how long will it take 'till she sees the mis-take she has made? Dear what can I do?

Ba-by's in black and I'm feel-ing blue. Tell me oh, what can I do?

oh, what can I do? black Oh dear, what can I do?

Ba-by's in black and I'm feel-ing blue. Tell me oh, what can I do?

71

58. Barbie Girl

Words & Music by Soren Rasted, Claus Norreen, Rene Dif, Lene Nystrom, Johnny Pederson & Karsten Dahlgaard

Spoken: Ooh, I'm having so much fun! Well Barbie, we're just getting started. Ooh, I love you Ken!

59. Baby Let's Play House

Words & Music by Arthur Gunter

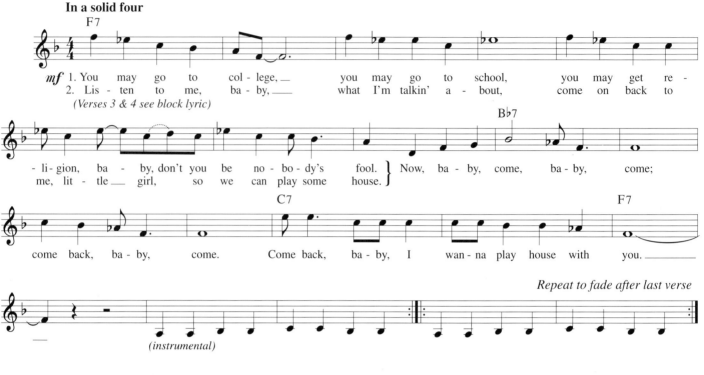

In a solid four

mf 1. You may go to col - lege, __ you may go to school, you may get re -
2. Lis - ten to me, ba - by, __ what I'm talkin' a - bout, come on back to

(Verses 3 & 4 see block lyric)

- li - gion, ba - by, don't you be no - bo - dy's fool. } Now, ba - by, come, ba - by, come;
me, lit - tle __ girl, so we can play some house.

come back, ba - by, come. Come back, ba - by, I wan - na play house with you. __

Repeat to fade after last verse

(instrumental)

3. This is one thing, baby
   What I want you to know:
   Come on back and let's play a little house
   So we can do what we did before:
   Now, baby, come, *etc.*

4. Listen, I'm telling you, baby,
   Don't you understand?
   I'd rather see you dead, little girl,
   That to be with another man.
   Now, baby, come, *etc.*

60. Baby, It's You

Words & Music by Hal David, Burt Bacharach & Barney Williams

Moderately slow

mp It's not the way you smile __ that touched my heart, __ It's not the way you

(Verse 2 see block lyric)

kiss that tears me a - part. __ Ma - ny ma - ny nights roll by, __

I sit a - lone __ at home and cry __ ov - er you. What can I do?

I can't help my - self, __ 'Cause, ba - by, it's you. __ Ba - by, it's

mf

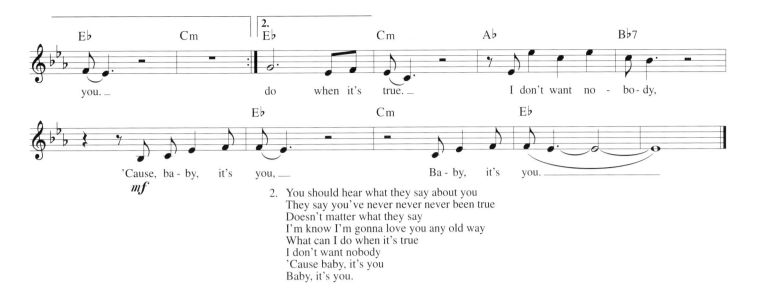

you. _ | do when it's true. _ | I don't want no - bo - dy,

'Cause, ba - by, it's you, _ | Ba - by, it's you. _

mf

2. You should hear what they say about you
They say you've never never never been true
Doesn't matter what they say
I'm know I'm gonna love you any old way
What can I do when it's true
I don't want nobody
'Cause baby, it's you
Baby, it's you.

61. (Baby) You Don't Have To Tell Me

Words & Music by Pater Antell

♩ = 112

mf

1. You don't have to tell me girl, be - cause I know. _
(Verses 2 & 3 see block lyrics)

Ba - by don't you think I knew it long _ a - go. _ Oh, _

ba - by _ you _ don't have to tell _ me ba - by, 'cos I al - read - y know you see

ba - by _ you _ don't have to tell me good - bye. _ bye. _

Have a lit - tle mer - cy now ba - by _ try _ to be a lit - tle kind ba - by well I know _

_ what is on your mind ba - by _ you _ don't have to tell me good - bye _

D.C. repeat chorus to fade

2. There is someone new who gets your kiss now
What about the times before, don't they exist now?

Oh baby you don't have to tell me *(etc.)*

3. Go ahead and tell me that's life you'd stay if you could
You are giving me a taste of life but good.

Oh baby you don't have to tell me *(etc.)*

62. Baby Elephant Walk

Music by Henry Mancini. Words by Hal David

63. Theme From Back To The Future

By Alan Silvestri

64. Billy Boy

Traditional

♩ = 112

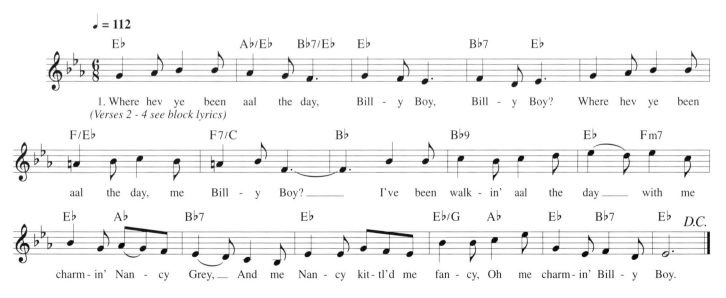

1. Where hev ye been aal the day, Bill - y Boy, Bill - y Boy? Where hev ye been
(Verses 2 - 4 see block lyrics)

aal the day, me Bill - y Boy? _____ I've been walk - in' aal the day _____ with me

charm - in' Nan - cy Grey, _ And me Nan - cy kit - tl'd me fan - cy, Oh me charm - in' Bill - y Boy.

2. Is she fit to be yor wife
Billy Boy, Billy Boy?
Is she fit to be yor wife, me Billy Boy?
She's as fit to be me wife
As the fork is to the knife
And me Nancy… *etc.*

3. Can she cook a bit o' steak
Billy Boy, Billy Boy?
Can she cook a bit o' steak, me Billy Boy?
She can cook a bit o' steak
Aye, and myek a gairdle cake
And me Nancy… *etc.*

4. Can she myek an Irish stew
Billy Boy, Billy Boy?
Can she myek an Irish stew, me Billy Boy?
She can myek an Irish stew
Aye, and "Singin' Hinnies" too
And me Nancy… *etc.*

77

65. Bank Holiday

Words & Music by Damon Albarn, Graham Coxon, Alex James & David Rowntree

2. Barbecue is cooking
Sausages and chicken
The patio is buzzing
The neighbours they are looking

John is down the fun pub
Drinking lots of lager
Girls and boys are on the game
All the high streets look the same.

66. Theme From Barbarella

Music by Charles Fox. Words by Bob Crewe

67. Baia (Na Baixa Do Sapateiro)

Music by Ary Barroso. English Lyric by Ray Gilbert

Moderate rhumba

Oh! _____ Ba - i - a - yah! _____ When twi-light is deep in the sky, Ba -
Ai! _____ Q a - mô, ai, ai! _____ A mô bo - ba - ge que a gen - te não ex -
Oi! _____ Ba - i a ai, ai! _____ Ba - i - a que nâo me sa he do pen - sa -

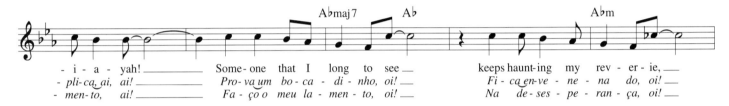

- i - a - yah! _____ Some - one that I long to see ___ keeps haunt-ing my rev - er - ie, ___
- pli - ca ai, ai! _____ Pro - va um bo - ca - di - nho, oi! ___ Fi - ca en - ve - ne - na do, oi! ___
- men - to, ai! _____ Fa - ço o meu la - men - to, oi! ___ Na de - ses - pe - ran - ça, oi! ___

And so the lone - li - ness deep in my heart calls to you, calls to
E pro res - to da vi - da é um tal de so - ffer, o la - rá, o le -
De en - can - trá pré - sse mun - do o a - mô que eu per - di na Ba - ía, vô con -

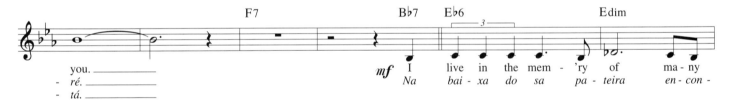

you. _____ I live in the mem - 'ry of ma - ny
- ré. _____ Na bai - xa do sa pa - teira en - con -
- tá. _____

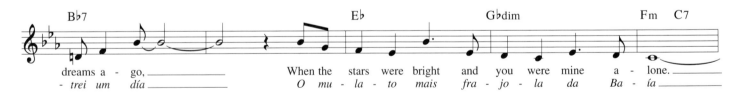

dreams a - go, ___ When the stars were bright and you were mine a - lone. ___
- trei um día ___ O mu - la - to mais fra - jo - la da Ba - ía

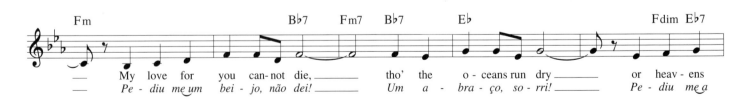

My love for you can-not die, ___ tho' the o - ceans run dry ___ or heav - ens
Pe - diu me um bei - jo, não dei! ___ Um a - bra - ço, so - rri! ___ Pe - diu me a

fall from the sky. ___ Now you're gone! ___ Ba - í - a,
mão, nûo quiz dar! ___ Fu - gi! ___ Ba - í - a,

68. Baker Street

Words & Music by Gerry Rafferty

Verse 2. This city desert makes you feel so cold
He's got so many people but he's got no soul
And it's taking so long to find out you were wrong
When you thought it held everything.

Verse 3. Way down the street there's a lot in his place
He opens the door he's got that look on his face
And he asks you where you've been
You tell him who you've seen and you talk about anything.

Verse 4. He's got this dream about buyin' some land he's gonna
Give up the booze and the one night stands and
Then you'll settle down with some quiet little town
And forget about everything.

Chorus 3. But you know you'll always keep movin'
You know he's never gonna stop movin'
'Cause he's rollin' he's the rollin' stone.

Chorus 4. When you wake up it's a new mornin'
The sun shinin'; it's a new mornin'
And you're goin', you're goin' home.

69. Beside The Alamo

Music by Frank Skinner. Words by Victor Kirk

70. (You're So Square) Baby I Don't Care

Words & Music by Jerry Leiber & Mike Stoller

71. Bali Ha'i

Words by Oscar Hammerstein II. Music by Richard Rodgers

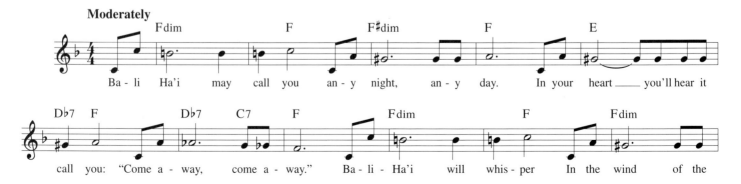

sea: Here am I ___ your spe-cial is - land! Come to me, come to me!" Your own spe - cial

hopes, Your own spe - cial dreams. Bloom on the hill - side and shine in the

streams. If you try, You'll find me where the sky meets the sea. Here am I ___ your spe-cial

is - land! "Come to me, come to me!" Ba - li Ha'i, Ba - li Ha'i, Ba - li Ha'i. ___

72. Be-Bop Boogie Boy

Words & Music by Gene Vincent

Moderate rock

Well there's Dan - ny boy ___

lives down the street, ___ And he say ___ this ev - 'ry time we meet: Well I'm the Be - Bop

Boo - gie Boy, Well - a Be - Bop Boo - gie Boy, Well - a Be - Bop Boo - gie's done

gone all ov - er this town. ___ Well when he sees a boy ___ that - a does it good, ___

He does ___ it ev - 'ry - bo - dy should, He's a Be - Bop Boo - gie Boy, Well - a Be - Bop

Boo - gie Boy, Well - a Be - Bop Boo - gie's done gone all ov - er this town. ___

73. The Bear Went Over The Mountain

Traditional

74. The Bare Necessities

Words & Music by Terry Gilkyson

tree to make some hon-ey just for me. You look un-der the rocks and plants and
paw, when you pick a pear, try to use the claw. But you don't need to use the claw when you
-round for some-thing you want that can't be found. When you find out you can live with-out it and

take a glance at the fan-cy ants, ___ then may-be try a few. The bare ne -
pick a pear of the big paw - paw. ___ Have I giv - en you a clue?
go a-long not think-in' a-bout it. I'll tell you some-thing true.

- ces - si - ties of life will come to you, ___ they'll come to you! ___

75. Big Love, Big Heartache

Words & Music by Dolores Fuller, Lee Morris & Sonny Hendrix

Moderately

Big love, big heart - ache. Big love, big heart-ache. Big love, big heart - ache,

Oh yes, I know it's true. The more you ___ fall in ___ love, The more your heart can

break in two. ___ Big love, big heart - ache, Now that you said good - bye, ___

For ev - 'ry ___ ten - der kiss, I count the tears I cry. I gave my heart ___ and

soul, All the love I knew. Oh, how much it hurts me now ___ to

know ___ that we ___ were through. Big love, big heart - ache, I'll al - ways feel this way,

My arms will be so emp - ty Till you re - turn some - day and say, ___ Your love, ___

___ yes, your big love ___ will be here to stay. ___

76. Beautiful People

Words & Music by Melanie Safka

tell you some-thing. We have so much in com-mon. I go the same di-rec-tion that you do.

So if you take care of me, may-be I'll take care of you.

Beau-ti-ful peo-ple, you look like friends of mine and it's a-bout time

D.%.al Fine

that some-one said it here and now. I make a vow that some-time, some-how...

77. Bernie's Tune

By Bernie Miller

Moderately

78. Better Than Ever

Music by Marvin Hamlisch. Words by Carole Bayer Sager.

Bet-ter than ev - er, _____ bet-ter than ev - er. _____

Coda

_____ my - self. Say hel - lo _____ to an old _____ ro - mance, say hel - lo _____

_____ to a se-cond chance. Where you been _____ so long, _____ my love? _____ Come on

back where you be - long. You and me _____ Bet - ter than

ev - er. Bet - ter than ev - er, _____ (I'm) Bet - ter than ev - er. _____

79. Theme From Breakfast At Tiffany's

By Henry Mancini

80. Betty Boop

Music by John W. Green. Words by Edward Heyman

81. Big Mistake

Words & Music by Natalie Imbruglia & Matt Goldenberg

2. Got a buzz in my head
   And my flowers are dead
   Can't figure out a way to rectify this situation
   Don't believe what you said.

   You forgotten how it started *etc.*

3. I could sing like a bee
   Careful how you treat me
   Baby I don't think I'll accept your sorry invitation
   Close the door as you leave.

   You forgotten how it started *etc.*

82. Bella Notte

Words & Music by Sonny Burke & Peggy Lee

Moderately slow

This — is the night, It's a beau - ti - ful night, — And we call it Bel - la Not - te,

Look — at the skies, They have stars — in their eyes — on this love - ly Bel - la Not - te. So

take the love — of your loved one, You'll need it a - bout this time, To

keep from fall - ing like a star — when you make that diz - zy climb, For

this — is the night, — And the heav - ens are right, — On this love - ly Bel - la Not - te.

83. Baby, Please Don't Go

Words & Music by Joe Williams

Moderately slow

1. Ba - by, please don't go, — Ba - by, please don't go, —
   lamp down low, — Turn the lamp down low, —

Ba - by, please don't go — down to New Or - leans, — I know I
Turn the lamp down low, — I beg you all night long, — Ba - by,

love you so. — 2. Be - fore I be your dog, —
please don't go. — 4. You know your man done gone, —

Be - fore I be your dog, — Be - fore I be your dog, — I get you
You know your man done gone. — You know your man done gone — down — the

84. Being For The Benefit Of Mr Kite

Words & Music by John Lennon & Paul McCartney

85. Blaze Of Glory

Words & Music by Jon Bon Jovi

dev-il's son call me Young Gun. Each

night I go to bed, I pray the Lord my soul to keep. No I ain't look-ing for for-give-ness but be-

-fore I'm six-feet deep. Lord, I got to ask a fa-vour and I

hope you'll un-der-stand. 'Cause I've lived life to the full-est, let this boy die like a man.

D.%.al Coda

Star-ing down a bul-let, let me make my fin-al stand. Shot

⊕ Coda

no-one's son, call me Young Gun. I'm a Young Gun.

Young Gun, yeah, yeah, yeah Young Gun.

Additional Lyrics (Album version)

2. When you're brought into this world
   They say you're born to sin
   Well, at least they gave me something
   I didn't have to steal or have to win
   Well, they tell me that I'm wanted
   Yeah, I'm a wanted man
   I'm a colt in your stable
   I'm what Cain was to Abel
   Mister, catch me if you can.

86. Botch-A-Me (Ba-Ba-Baciami Piccina)

Original Words & Music by Riccardo Morbelli & Luigi Astore.
English Words & Music Adaptation by Eddie Y. Stanley

87. Buttons And Bows

Words & Music by Jay Livingston & Ray Evans

88. Both Sides Of The Story

Words & Music by Phil Collins

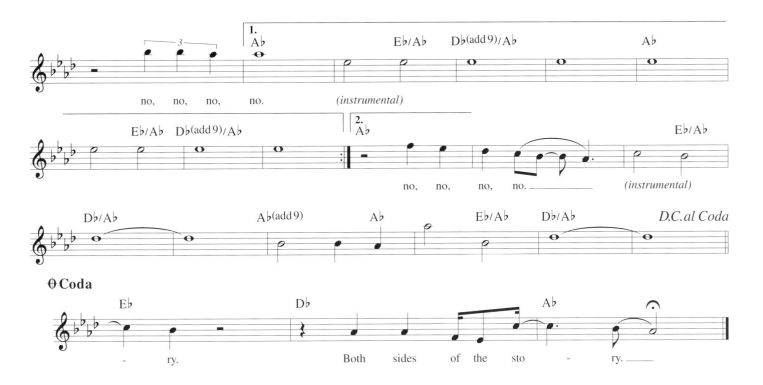

no, no, no, no. *(instrumental)*

no, no, no, no. ——— *(instrumental)*

D.C. al Coda

⊕ Coda

-ry. Both sides of the sto - ry. ———

2. A neighbourhood peace is shattered, it's the middle of the night
Young faces hide in the shadows, while they watch their mother and father fight
He says she's been unfaithful, she says her love for him has gone
And the brother shrugs to his sister, and says "Looks like it's just us from now on".

3. Here we are all gathered in what seems to be the centre of the storm
Neighbours once friendly now stand each side of the line that has been drawn
They've been fighting here for years, but now there's killing on the streets
While small coffins are lined up sadly, now united in defeat.

4. White man turns the corner, finds himself within a different world
Ghetto kid grabs his shoulder, throws him up against the wall
He says "Would you respect me if I didn't have this gun
'Cos without it, I don't get it, and that's why I carry one.

89. Boston Come-All-Ye

Traditional

Brightly

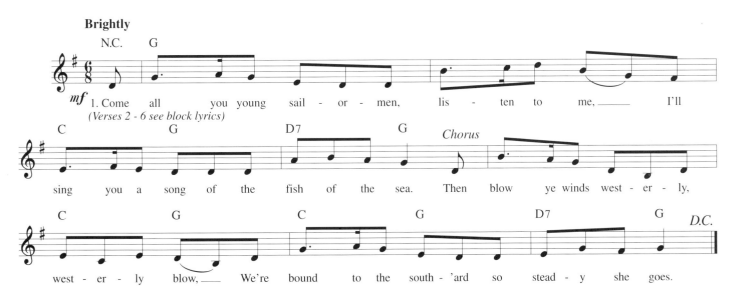

1. Come all you young sail - or - men, lis - ten to me, —— I'll
(Verses 2 - 6 see block lyrics)

sing you a song of the fish of the sea. Then blow ye winds west - er - ly,

west - er - ly blow, We're bound to the south - 'ard so stead - y she goes.

2. Oh, first came the whale, he's the biggest of all
He climb'd up aloft and let every sail fall.

3. Next was the mack'rel with his striped back
He hauled aft the sheets and then boarded each tack.

4. The porpoise came next with his little snout
He gripped the wheel, hailing "Turn her about!"

5. Then came the minnow, the smallest of all,
He leapt o'er the deck singing "Haul, men, haul!"

6. Up jumped the tuna saying "I am the king
"Pull on the line and let the bell ring!"

90. The Boys Are Back In Town

Words & Music by Phil Lynott

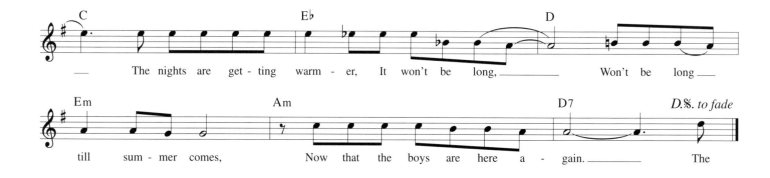

The nights are get-ting warm-er, It won't be long, ___ Won't be long ___

till sum-mer comes, Now that the boys are here a-gain. ___ The

91. Barefoot In The Park

Music by Neal Hefti. Words by Johnny Mercer

Go-ing bare-foot in the park ___ where it says, "Keep off the grass," ___

___ is-n't rec-om-men-ded for the ver-y old. ___ But

when you're young and you're in love the world is beau-ti-ful ___ and

I'm not a bit a-fraid of you catch-ing cold. ___ Run-ning

bare-foot through the park, ___ stroll-ing bare-head-ed in the rain ___ just to

look for a dai-sy seems kind o' cra-zy to do. ___ But come a-

-long, my bare-foot love, ___ to the fields that shine with spring. ___ Let me

laugh and play all the way, knee deep in dai-sies with you. ___

92. Brazilian Summer

Original Words & Music by Caetano Zama. English Lyrics by Michael Vaughan

93. Berceuse (from 'The Dolly Suite')

Composed by Gabriel Fauré

94. Bibbidi-Bobbidi-Boo (The Magic Song)

Words by Jerry Livingston. Music by Mack David and Al Hoffman

bib - bi - di - bob - bi - di - boo. Sa - la - ga - doo - la means men - chic - ka boo - le - roo, But the

thing - a - ma - bob that does the job is bib - bi - di - bob - bi - di - boo. Sa - la - ga - doo - la men - chic - ka boo - la

bib - bi - di - bob - bi - di - boo Put 'em to - geth - er and what have you got

bib - bi - di - bob - bi - di bib - bi - di - bob - bi - di bib - bi - di - bob - bi - di - boo.

95. Blue Christmas

Words & Music by Billy Hayes & Jay Johnson

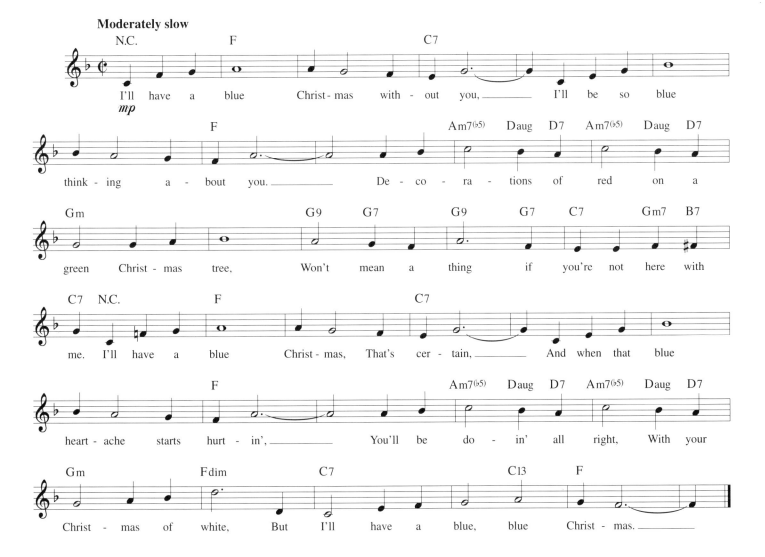

I'll have a blue Christ - mas with - out you, _____ I'll be so blue

think - ing a - bout you. _____ De - co - ra - tions of red on a

green Christ - mas tree, Won't mean a thing if you're not here with

me. I'll have a blue Christ - mas, That's cer - tain, _____ And when that blue

heart - ache starts hurt - in', _____ You'll be do - in' all right, With your

Christ - mas of white, But I'll have a blue, blue Christ - mas.

96. Beyond The Blue Horizon

Words & Music by Leo Robin, Richard Whiting & Franke W. Harling

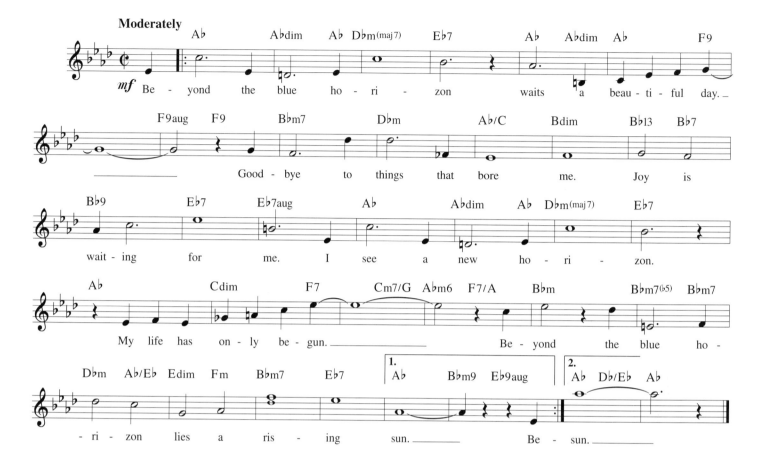

97. Brown Suede

Music by Mercer Ellington. Words by Mercer Ellington & Ted Persons

rayed in your new brown suede. It's strange how we cling ___ To some lit-tle thing ___ to serve as a sou-ven-ir, ___ A trin-ket, a key ___ But as for me, ___ Brown suede ___ makes thoughts of ___ you ap-pear. ___ Fash-ions go, and you know, An-y-thing new won your re-gard. That is why you were quick to dis-card ___ Your old love with your old brown suede.

98. Black Is The Colour Of My True Love's Hair

Traditional American Song

Tenderly

Black, black, black is the col-our ___ of my true love's
(Verses 2 & 3 see block lyrics)
hair. Her lips ___ are some-thing ros-y fair. The ___ pur-est eyes and the pret-ti-est hands, I love the grass where-on she stands. Black, black, black is the col-our ___ of my true love's hair. ___

2. Black, black, black is the colour of my true love's hair
Her face is something truly rare
I know my love and well she knows
I love the grass whereon she goes
Black, black, black is the colour of my true love's hair.

3. Black, black, black is the colour of my true love's hair
Alone, my life would be so bare
If she on earth no more I see
My life would quickly fade away
Black, black, black is the colour of my true love's hair.

99. Believe Me If All Those Endearing Young Charms

Music by Matthew Locke. Words by Thomas Moore

Moderately slow

1. Be - lieve me, if all those en - dear - ing young charms, Which I gaze on so fond - ly to -
(Verse 2 see block lyric)
day, _____ Were to change by to - mor - row, and fleet in my arms, Like _ fair - y gifts, fad - ing a -
way. _____ Thou wouldst still be a - dored as this mo - ment thou art, Let thy love - li - ness fade as it
will, _____ And a - round the dear ru - in, each wish of my heart, Would en - twine it - self ver - dant - ly still. _____

2. It is not while beauty and youth are thine own
   And thy cheeks unprofan'd by a tear
   And the fervour and faith of a soul can be known
   To which time will but make thee more dear.

   No, the heart that has truly loved never forgets
   But as truly loves on to the close
   As the sunflower turns on her god when he sets
   The same look which she turn'd when he rose.

100. The Bell That Couldn't Jingle

Words & Music by Burt Bacharach & Lary Kusik

Moderately

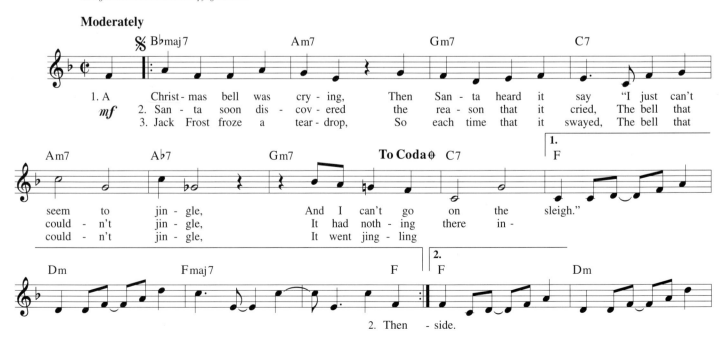

1. A Christ - mas bell was cry - ing, Then San - ta heard it say "I just can't
2. San - ta soon dis - cov - ered the rea - son that it cried, The bell that
3. Jack Frost froze a tear - drop, So each time that it swayed, The bell that

seem to jin - gle, And I can't go on the sleigh."
could - n't jin - gle, It had noth - ing there in -
could - n't jin - gle, It went jing - ling

2. Then - side.

101. Blue Snowfall

Words & Music by Dave Coleman

102. Big Fun

Words & Music by Rudy Taylor & Lonnie Simmons

2. And if you want my love, come and get it girl
   And if you want to be my friend, through thick and thin
   You can fill in, that's no sin
   Having big fun

103. Big Boots

Words & Music by Sherman Edwards & Sid Wayne

"Big Boots," Wher-ev-er sol-diers are, ___ 'Cause he can han-dle an arm-ored car Just like a kid-die car. So sleep ___ lit-tle sol-dier; don't you cry. Loo ___ loo loo loo ___ loo loo loo. Gen - er-al Sand-man soon ___ com-ing by. Loo ___ loo loo loo ___ loo loo loo. Gon-na tell you a lit - tle se-cret; You won't be-lieve it's true. ___ Did you know your ___ dad-dy "Big Boots" ___ Once wore lit-tle boots like you? They you?

104. Theme From Ballade Op.23

Composed by Frédéric Chopin

Moderato

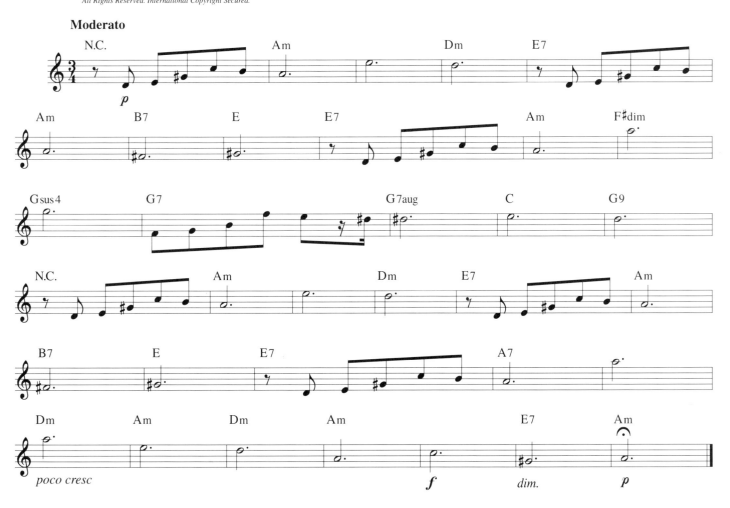

105. Blue Hawaii

Words & Music by Leo Robin & Ralph Rainger

106. Big Rock Candy Mountain

Traditional

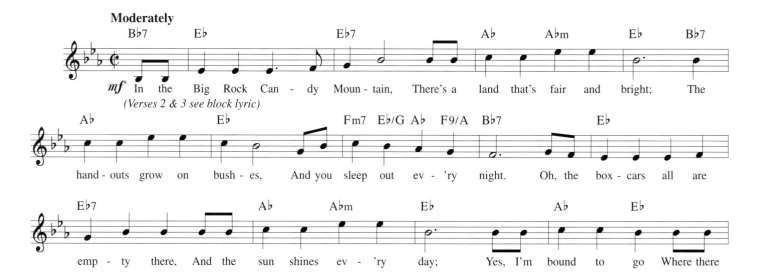

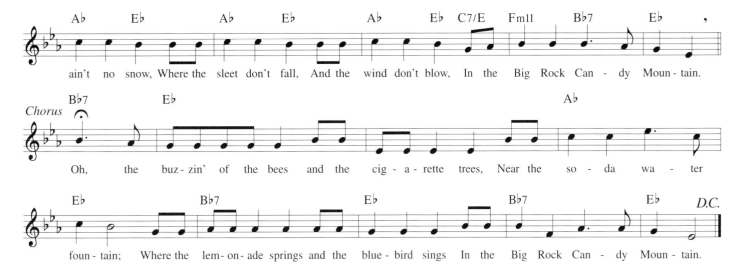

ain't no snow, Where the sleet don't fall, And the wind don't blow, In the Big Rock Can- dy Moun- tain.

Chorus

Oh, the buz- zin' of the bees and the cig- a- rette trees, Near the so- da wa- ter

foun- tain; Where the lem- on- ade springs and the blue- bird sings In the Big Rock Can- dy Moun- tain.

2. In the Big Rock Candy Mountain
The cops have wooden legs
The bulldogs all have rubber teeth
And the hens lay soft-boiled eggs
The farmers' trees are full of fruit
And the barns are full of hay
Yes, I want to go
Where there ain't no snow
Where the sleet don't fall
And the wind don't blow
In the Big Rock Candy Mountain.
Chorus

3. In the Big Rock Candy Mountain
The jails are made of tin
And you can bust right out again
As soon as you get in
There ain't no hoes or shovels
No axes, saws, nor picks
Oh, I'm going to stay
Where you sleep all day
Where they hung the jerk
Who invented work
In the Big Rock Candy Mountain.
Chorus

107. Theme From Bleak House

By Geoffrey Burgon

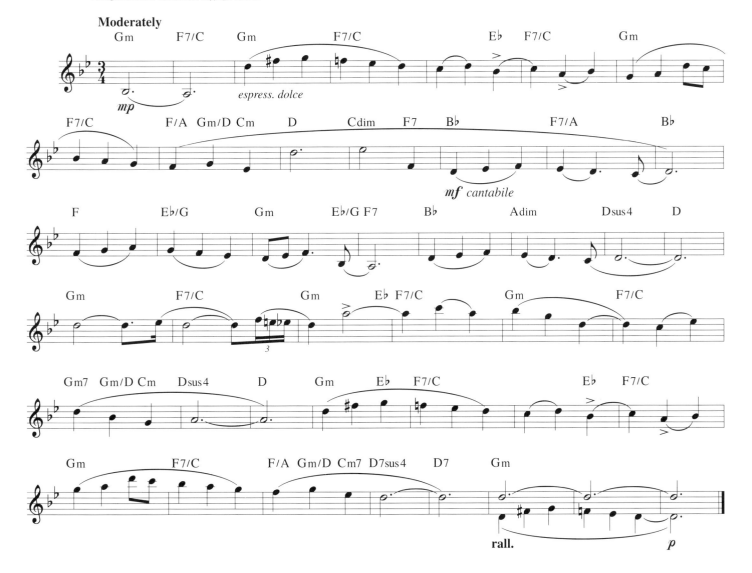

108. Brazil

Music by Ary Barroso. English Lyric by S. K. Russell

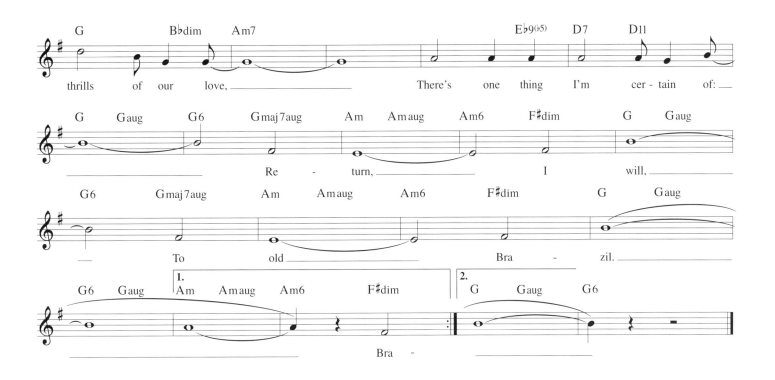

109. Brideshead Revisited

By Geoffrey Burgon

110. Bop! Goes My Heart

Music by Jule Styne. Words by Walter Bishop

111. Borsalino

Words by Pierre Delanoe. Music by Claude Bolling

112. Born To Be Wild

Words & Music by Mars Bonfire

113. Bossa Nova Baby

Words & Music by Jerry Leiber & Mike Stoller

Moderately Bossa Nova

I said, "Take it eas - y, ba - by, I worked all day __ and my feet feel just like lead. __
"Hey, __ lit - tle ma - ma, __ let's sit down, have a drink and dig the band."
"Come _ on, _ ba - by, it's hot in here __ and it's oh, so cool out - side. __

You got my shirt - tails fly - in' all __ ov - er the place _ and __ the sweat pop - pin' out of my head."
She said, __ "Drink, drink, drink, _ oh, __ fid - dle - de - dink, _ I __ can dance with a drink in my hand."
If you __ lend me a dol - lar, I can buy _ some gas __ and we can go for a lit - tle ride."

She said, "Hey, Bos - sa No - va, ba - by, keep on a - work - in', child { this ain't no time to quit."
this ain't no time to drink."
I ain't got time for that."

She said, "Go, Bos - sa No - va, ba - by, keep on danc - in', { I'm a - bout to have my - self a fit." __
'cause I ain't __ got __ time to think."
or I'll find my - self an - oth - er cat." __

Bos - sa No - va, __ Bos - sa No - va. __

1, 2. **3.**

I said, __ Bos - sa No - va, __ Bos - sa

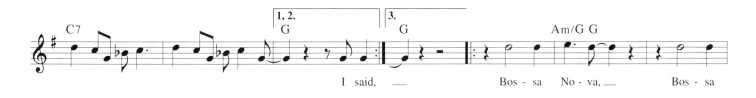

Repeat to fade

No - va. __

121

114. Buffalo Soldier

Words & Music by Bob Marley & Noel Williams

wo - yo - yo - yo-yo - yo-yo - yo.   Buf - fa - lo   sol - dier   trod - ding thro' the

land. _____   Said you wan - na   run   and then you make a   stand.   Trod - ding thro' the

land, _   yeah! _____   Said he was a   buf - fa - lo   sol - dier,   win the war for A - me - ri - ca.
(% *see block lyrics*)

Buf - fa - lo   sol - dier,   dread - lock Ras - ta.   Fight - ing on ar - ri - val,

fight - ing for sur - vi - val.   Driv - en from the main - land   to the

heart   of the Car - ib - be - an.   Sing - ing   Wo - yo - yo   yo - yo - yo - yo,

1.   D   A   2.   D   A   *D.%.*   3.   *Repeat to fade*   D   A

Wo - yo - yo - yo-yo - yo-yo - yo.   - yo-yo - yo.   - yo-yo - yo.

2. And he was taken from Africa
   Brought to America
   Fighting on arrival
   Fighting for survival
   Said he was a buffalo soldier
   Dreadlock Rasta
   Buffalo soldier in the heart of America
   If you know your history
   Then you would know know where you're coming from
   Then you wouldn't have to ask me
   Who the heck do I think I am
   I'm just a buffalo soldier *(etc.)*

% Trodding through San Juan
   In the arms of America
   Trodding through Jamaica
   The buffalo soldier
   Fighting on arrival
   Fighting for survival
   Buffalo soldier
   Dreadlock Rasta
   Wo-yo-yo-yo-yo-yo-yo *(etc.)*

115. Blue Velvet

Words & Music by Bernie Wayne & Lee Morris

She wore blue vel - vet, Blu - er than vel - vet was the night,
Soft - er than sat - in was the light from the stars. She wore blue vel - vet,
Blu - er than vel - vet were her eyes, Warm - er than May her ten - der sighs, love was
ours. Ours, a love I held tight - ly, Feel - ing the rap - ture grow,
Like a flame burn - ing bright - ly, But when she left, gone was the glow of blue
vel - vet, But in my heart there'll al - ways be, Pre - cious and warm a me - mo - ry thro' the
years, And I still can see blue vel - vet thro' my tears.

116. Blue Orchids

Words & Music by Hoagy Carmichael

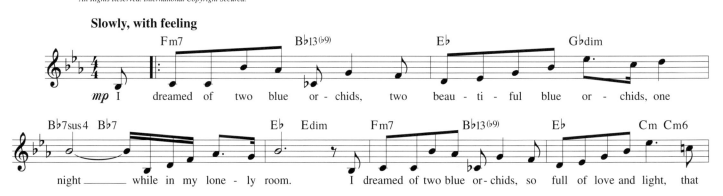

night while in my lone - ly room. I dreamed of two blue or - chids, so full of love and light, that

I want-ed to pos-sess each ten-der bloom. Then my dream took wings and through a thou-sand springs, blue or-chids seemed in a world a-part, But when I met you some-thing pale and blue ___ came steal-ing from the mead-ows of my heart. I saw my two blue or-chids, my beau-ti-ful blue or-chids, last night ___ and what a sweet sur-prise. When you looked at me it was plain to see, blue or-chids on-ly bloom in your eyes. ___ I eyes. ___

117. The Champ

Words & Music by Harry Palmer

Champ! Champ! Champ!

Champ! Champ!

Repeat several times and fade

118. But She's My Buddy's Chick

Words & Music by Sy Oliver & Cholly Atkinson

Moderately slow

Met a gal the oth-er night, Jack she's real-ly slick. An' she on-ly knocked me out but she's my bud-dy's chick. Start-ed once to move right in, changed my mind but quick She could send me yes, she could, but she's my bud-dy's chick. When she passed by look-in' cute an' fly, Man she real-ly caught my eye. From her quaint lit-tle hat down to her boots Was the fin-est of scen-ic routes, That's the way the sto-ry ends, I nixed out, but quick But I'm sor-ry to my soul that she's my bud-dy's chick.

119. Busy Line

Words & Music by Murray Semos & Frank Stanton

Rhythmically

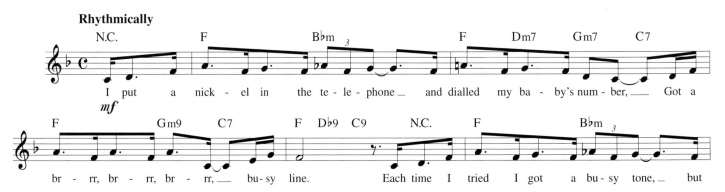

I put a nick-el in the te-le-phone and dialled my ba-by's num-ber, Got a br - rr, br - rr, br - rr, bu-sy line. Each time I tried I got a bu-sy tone, but

not my ba - by's num - ber, ___ Just a br - rr, br - rr, br - rr, bu - sy line. ___ Called her

un - cle in Ja - mai - ca, ___ left a mes - sage ___ with the bak - er, ___ Ev - en checked her num - ber in the te - le - phone

book, ___ The I got so awf - 'lly wor - ried, ___ To my ba - by's house I hur - ried, When I

looked in - side the 'phone was off the hook! And as I walked up to my ba - by, then ___ I

got my ba - by's num - ber, ___ She was bu - sy in the par - lour and do - in' fine, ___ Bu - sy

kiss - in' some - one else while I was keep - in' bu - sy, get - tin' a br - rr, br - rr, br - rr, ___ bu - sy line. ___

120. The Coventry Carol

Traditional

Moderately

mp

Lul - ly lul - lay, Thou lit - tle ti - ny Child, By by lul - ly lul - lay.

1. O sis - ters too, How may we do, For to pre - serve this

(Verses 2 & 3 see block lyrics)

day? This poor young - ling for whom we do sing, By by lul - ly lul - lay.

D.%.

2. Herod the king in his raging
   Charged he hath this day
   His man of might, in his own sight
   All children young to slay.

3. Then woe is me, poor Child, for Thee
   And ever mourn and say
   For Thy parting nor say nor sing
   By by lully lullay.

121. The Blue Danube Waltz

Composed by Johann Strauss

Tempo di valse

122. Chapel Of Dreams

Words & Music by Billy Myles

Slowly, with a strong beat

In the cha-pel of dreams _____ Ev - 'ry dream will come true, _____

_____ In the cha-pel of dreams _____ There's a dream there for you. _____ Thru' the dark of the

night ____ Tho' as strange as it seems, Ev-'ry heart finds de- light ____

In the cha- pel of dreams. ____ For un- til I found this

cha- pel of re- nown I searched and searched for peace __ of __ mind. I'm

glad ____ that at last my emp- ty days are past, Now I wor- ship there all the

time. It is hea- ven to know ____ Just what hap- pi- ness means,

1.
It is found at the door ____ In the cha- pel of dreams.

2.
In the cha- pel of In the cha- pel of dreams. ____

123. Cumberland Gap

Traditional

With Spirit

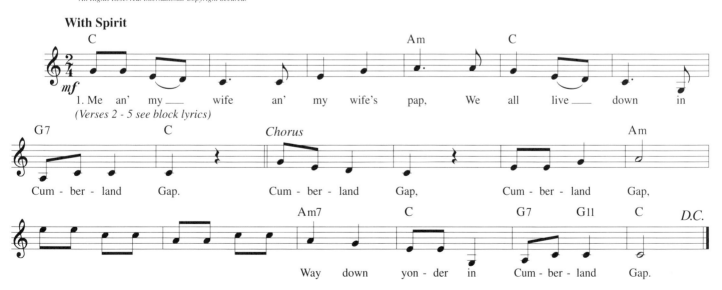

1. Me an' my __ wife an' my wife's pap, We all live __ down in
(Verses 2 - 5 see block lyrics)

Cum- ber- land Gap. Cum- ber- land Gap, Cum- ber- land Gap,

Way down yon- der in Cum- ber- land Gap.

2. I got a gal in Cumberland Gap
   She's got a baby that calls me pap.

3. Cumberland Gap is a noted place
   Three kinds of water to wash your face.

4. Cumberland Gap, it ain't very far
   It's just three miles from Middlesboro.

5. Lay down boys and take a little nap
   We're all goin' down to Cumberland Gap.

124. Bobby's Girl

Words & Music by Henry Hoffman & Gary Klein

1. When people ask of me ___ what would you like to be, ___ now that you're not a kid ___ any-more? ___ I know just what to say; ___ I an-swer right a-way, ___ there's just one thing I've been ___ wish-ing for. ___ I wan-na be ___ Bob-by's girl, ___ I wan-na be ___ Bob-by's girl. ___ That's the most ___ im-port-ant thing ___ to me. ___ And if ___ I was ___ Bob-by's girl; ___ if ___ I was ___ Bob-by's girl, ___ what a faith-ful, thank-ful girl I'd be. ___

2. Each night I sit at home ___ hop-ing that he will phone, ___ but I know Bob-by has ___ some-one else. ___ Still in my heart I pray, ___ there soon will come a day, ___ when I will have him all ___ to my-self. ___

125. Clair De Lune

Composed by Claude Debussy

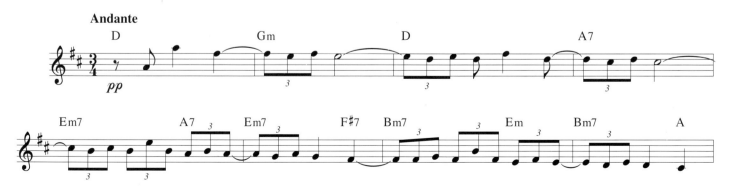

126. Cinderella

Words & Music by Mack David, Al Hoffman & Jerry Livingston

Slowly, with expression

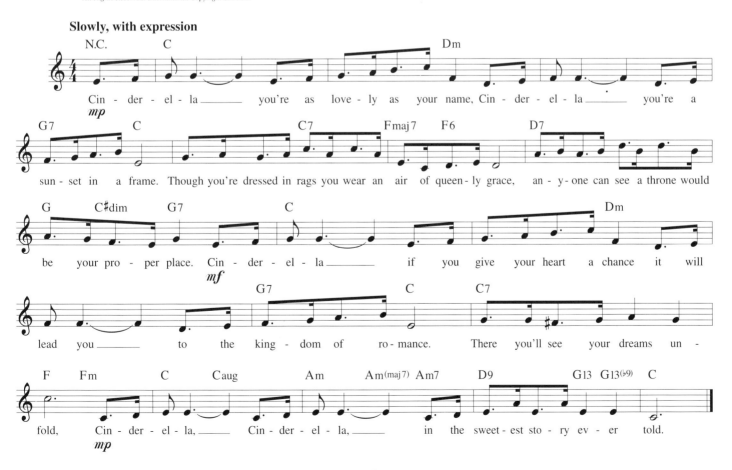

Cin - der - el - la____ you're as love - ly as your name, Cin - der - el - la____ you're a

sun - set in a frame. Though you're dressed in rags you wear an air of queen - ly grace, an - y-one can see a throne would

be your pro - per place. Cin - der - el - la_____ if you give your heart a chance it will

lead you____ to the king - dom of ro - mance. There you'll see your dreams un -

fold, Cin - der - el - la,_____ Cin - der - el - la,_____ in the sweet - est sto - ry ev - er told.

127. Call Me

Words & Music by Deborah Harry & Giorgio Moroder

Oo, _____ he speaks _ the lan - gua - ges _ of love.

Oo, _____ a - mo - re, chia - ma mi, _ *chia-ma mi.* Oo, _____

_ ap - pelle _ moi, mon cher - ie, _ *ap-pelle moi,* an - y - time, _ an - y - place, _ an - y - where, _

_ an - y - way, _____ an - y - time, _ an - y - place, _ an - y - where, _ an - y day.

_ (instrumental) Call me, _____ in my life call me, call me an - y, an - y - time. Call me,

128. Come Saturday Morning

Words & Music by Dory Previn & Fred Karlin

Moderately

mf Come Sat - ur - day morn - ing I'm go - ing a - way with my friend;
Come Sat - ur - day morn - ing I'm go - ing a - way with my friend;

We'll Sat - ur - day spend till the end of the day. _____
We'll Sat - ur - day laugh more than half of the day. _____

Just I and my friend. _____ We'll trav - el for miles in our Sat - ur - day
Just I and my friend. _____ dressed up in our rings and our Sat - ur - day

smiles, _____ and then we'll move on. _____ But we will re -
things, _____

mem - ber long af - ter Sat - ur - day's gone. Come Sat - ur - day morn - ing.

1.
Come Sat - ur - day morn - ing.

2. *Repeat to fade*
Come Sat - ur - day morn - ing.

129. Call Me Irresponsible

Words by Sammy Cahn. Music by Jimmy Van Heusen

130. Carry Me Back To Old Virginny

Words & Music by James A. Bland

heart am long'd to go.
life will pass a- way.
There's where I la- boured so hard for old mas- ter,
Mas- ter and Mis- sus have long gone be- fore me,

Day af- ter day in the field of yel- low corn,
Soon we will meet on that bright and gold- en shore,
No place on earth do I
There we'll be hap- py and

love more sin- cere- ly,
free from all sor- row,
Than old Vir- gin- ny, the state where I was born.
There's where we'll meet and we'll nev- er part no more.

131. Close To You

Words & Music by Al Hoffman, Jerry Livingston & Carl G. Lampl

Moderately slow

Close to you, I will al- ways stay close to

you, though you're far a- way. You'll al- ways be near

as though you were here by my side, no mat- ter where, in my

dreams I'll find you there, close to me, shar- ing your ca-

- ress, can't you see you're my hap- pi- ness. Where-

-ev- er you go my heart will go too, what can I do? It on- ly wants to

1. be close to you. **2.** Close to you.

132. Can You Feel The Love Tonight
(from Walt Disney Pictures' "The Lion King")

as performed by Elton John

Music by Elton John. Words by Tim Rice

133. Choo Choo Samba

Words by Jack Fishman. Music by B. P. Godinho

134. Colours

Words & Music by Donovan Leitch

2. Green is the colour of the sparkling corn
   In the morning when we rise
   In the morning when we rise
   That's the time
   That's the time I love the best.

3. Blue is the colour of the sky
   In the morning when we rise
   In the morning when we rise
   That's the time
   That's the time I love the best.

4. *Instrumental*

5. Mellow is the feeling that I get
   When I see her, mm
   When I see her, oh yeah
   That's the time
   That's the time I love the best.

6. Freedom is a word I rarely use
   Without thinking, oh yeah
   Without thinking, mm
   Of the time
   Of the time when I've been loved.

7. Yellow is the colour of my true love's hair
   In the morning when we rise
   In the morning when we rise
   That's the time
   That's the time I love the best.

135. Can't Get Indiana Off My Mind

Music by Hoagy Carmichael. Words by Robert De Leon

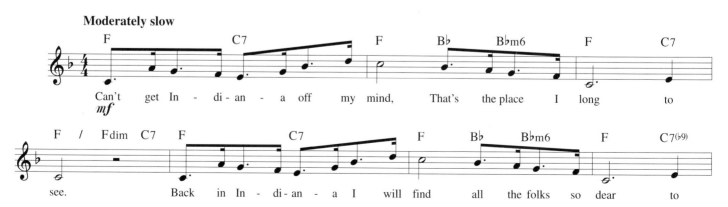

me. How I'd love to see that la-zy riv-er stop and give "her" my love, In my dreams I see a la-dy knit-tin' for the one she's think-ing of. Can't get In-di-an-a off my mind, An-y-where I chance to roam; The moon-light on the Wa-bash that I left be-hind calls me back home. home.

136. Can't Help Falling In Love

Words & Music by George Weiss, Hugo Peretti & Luigi Creatore

Moderately slow

mp Wise men say on-ly fools rush in, but I can't
Shall I stay? Would it be a sin if I can't

help fall-ing in love with you. Like a riv-er flows sure-ly to the sea, *mf*
help fall-ing in love with you?

dar-ling, so it goes some things are meant to be. Take my hand, take my *mp*

whole life too, for I can't help fall-ing in love with you.

you. For I can't help fall-ing in love with you. *mf*

137. Charmless Man

Words & Music by Damon Albarn, Alex James, Graham Coxon & Dave Rowntree

La la la la la la la _____ la la la la la la la la la. _____ La la la la la la la la la la _____

_____ la la la la la la la la, la la la la la la, la la la la la la la.

2. He knows the swingers and their cavalry
Says he can get in anywhere for free
I began to go a little cross-eyed
And from this charmless man I just had to hide.

La la la...

He talks at speed, he gets nose-bleeds
He doesn't see his days are tumbling down upon him
And yet he tries so hard to please
He's just so keen for you to listen, but no one is listening
And when you put it all together
There's the model of a charmless man.

He thinks his educated airs, those family shares
Will protect him, that you'll respect him
And yet he tries so hard to please
He's so keen for you to listen, but no one's listening
And when you put it all together
There's the model of a charmless man.

138. Christmas Is

Words & Music by Percy Faith & Spence Maxwell

Moderately slow

mp Christ-mas is sleigh bells, Christ-mas is shar-ing. Christ-mas is child-ren who
Christ-mas is hol-ly, Christ-mas is car-ing. Christ-mas is car-ols to

just can't ___ go to sleep, Christ-mas is mem-'ries, The kind you ___ al-ways keep.
warm you ___ in the snow, Christ-mas is bed-time where no one wants to go.

mf Deck the halls and ___ give a cheer, For all the things that Christ-mas is each
All the world is ___ tin-sel bright, So glad to know that Christ-mas is to-

year, *mf* Christ - mas, ___ Mer - ry Christ - mas, ___ When
- night, Christ - mas, ___ Mer - ry Christ - mas, ___ When

1. all your wish - es come true.
2. all your wish - es come true.

Christ - mas, ___ Mer - ry Christ - mas, ___ May all your wish - es come true.

139. Circle Of Life
(from Walt Disney Pictures' "The Lion King")

Music by Elton John. Lyrics by Tim Rice

From the day we ar - rive on the plan - et and blink - ing, step in - to the sun, ___ there's more to see ___ than can ev - er be seen, ___ more to do than can ev - er ___ be done. There's far too much ___ to take in ___ here, more to find than can ev - er be found. But the sun roll - ing high ___ through the sap - phi - re sky ___ keeps great and small on the end - less round. ___ It's the cir - cle ___ of life, and it moves us all ___

through de - spair and hope, through faith and love,

'til we find our place on the path un - wind - ing in the

cir - cle, the cir - cle of life. *(instrumental)*

It's the cir - cle of life, and it moves us all

through de - spair and hope, through faith and love,

'til we find our place on the path un - wind - ing

in the cir - cle, the cir - cle of life.

140. Candle On The Water

Words & Music by Al Kasha & Joel Hirschhorn

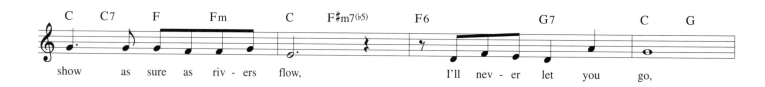

141. Christmas Rock 'n' Roll

Words by Hank Russell. Music by Buddy Brooks

When you're at a Christ - mas par - ty, And you're feel - ing blue,
Now you've got the par - ty rock - in', Ev - 'ry - bo - dy's gay,
When you catch your sweet - ie un - der - neath the mis - tle - toe,

Take a tip from me my friends, I'll show you what to do, Are you
Ev - en mum and dad are rock - in', Thro' the night and day, For the
Take her in your arms and tell her that you love her so, Get a

stea - dy, Get rea - dy, Let's get on the ball with a One! Two! One! Two! Three! Four!
beat's gon - na get ya, Sure it's gon - na get ya, One! Two! One! Two! Three! Four!
hold of ya ba - by, Then you start to count from One! Two! One! Two! Three! Four!

Come a - long with me, Rock a - long with me, Do the Christ - mas Rock 'n' Roll, ___

___ When you feel the drive, Man you're all a - live,

Get the rhy - thm in your soul, ___ Come on ev - 'ry - bo - dy, Let's all do the Christ - mas

1, 2.
Rock 'n' ___ Roll. ___

3.
Rock 'n' ___ Roll. ___

145

142. Chim Chim Cher-ee

Words & Music by Richard M. Sherman & Robert B. Sherman

143. The Circle

Words & Music by Simon Fowler, Steve Cradock, Oscar Harrison & Damon Minchella

2. If I walk by the trees
   I'll catch the falling leaves
   If the wind blows
   But I know all this means
   Is whiling on the hours
   Watching side-shows.

3. (D.S.) Fare you well, I'll carry me away
   And sing for those I know
   Upon their birthdays.

144. Cocktails For Two

Words & Music by Arthur Johnston & Sam Coslow

145. The Cradle Rock

Words & Music by Cy Chalmers

146. The Coffee Song

Words & Music by Bob Hilliard & Dick Miles

150

147. Coming Around Again

Words & Music by Carly Simon

2. You pay the grocer, fix the toaster
You kiss the host good-bye
Then you break a window, burn the souffle
Scream a lullaby.

148. The Colour Of My Love

Words & Music by David Foster & Arthur Janov

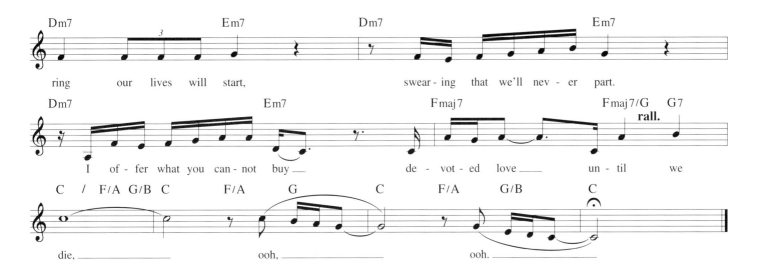

ring   our   lives   will   start,   swear- ing   that   we'll   nev- er   part.

I   of- fer   what   you   can- not   buy ___   de- vot- ed   love ___   un- til   we

die, ___   ooh, ___   ooh. ___

149. Come Back To Erin

Irish Traditional

Moderately

mp 1. Come   back   to   E- rin,   Ma- vour- neen,   Ma- vour- neen,   Come   back,   A- roon,   to   the   land   of   thy   birth, ___

(Verses 2 & 3 see block lyrics)

Come   with   the   sham- rocks   and   spring- time,   Ma- vour- neen.   And   it's   Kil- lar- ney   shall   ring   with   our   mirth.

Sure,   when   we   lent   ye   to   beau- ti- ful   Eng- land,   Lit- tle   we   thought   of   the   lone   win- ter   days,

Lit- tle   we   thought   of   the   hush   of   the   star- shine,   Ov- er   the   moun- tain,   the   buffs   and   the   bays.   Then   *mf*

come   back   to   E- rin,   Ma- vour- neen,   Ma- vour- neen,   Come   back   a- gain   to   the   land   of   thy   birth, ___

Come   back   to   E- rin,   Ma- vour- neen,   Ma- vour- neen,   And ___   it's   Kil- lar- ney   shall   ring   with   our   mirth.

2.   Over the green sea, Mavourneen, Mavourneen
     Long shone the white sail that bore thee away
     Riding the white waves that fair summer morning
     Just like a Mayflow'r afloat on the bay
     Oh, but my heart sank when clouds came between us
     Like a grey curtain, the rain falling down
     Hid from my sad eyes the path o'er the ocean
     Far, far away where my colleen had flown
     Then come back to Erin, Mavourneen, Mavourneen, *(etc.)*

3.   Oh, may the angels awakin' and sleepin'
     Watch o'er my bird in the land far away
     And it's my prayers will consign to their keepin'
     Care o' my jewel by night and by day
     When by the fireside I watch the bright embers
     Then all my heart flies to England and thee
     Cravin' to know if my darlin' remembers
     Or if her thoughts may be crossin' to me
     Then come back to Erin, Mavourneen, Mavourneen, *(etc.)*

153

150. Comes A-Long A-Love

Words & Music by Al Sherman

you dis-cov-er things that just a-maze you. You just be-gin to

live comes a-long a love. _____ just be-gin to

love and real-ly love each day you live, comes a-long a love. _____

151. Could I Have This Dance

Words & Music by Wayland Holyfield & Bob House

Moderately

I'll al-ways re-mem-ber the song they were play-ing the
al-ways re-mem-ber that mag-ic mo-ment. When

first time _____ we danced and I knew. As we swayed to the mu-sic _____ and
I held _____ you close _____ to me. As we moved to-geth-er, _____

held to each oth-er, _____ I fell in love with _____ you. } Could
I knew for-ev-er _____ you're all I'll ev-er _____ need.

I have this dance for the rest of my life? Would you be my part-ner _____

ev-'ry night? When we're to-geth-er, it feels _____ so right. Could

To Coda ⊕ | **1.** | **2.** | *D.%. al Coda*

I have _ this dance for the rest of my _ life? I'll life? Could

⊕**Coda**

rest of my _____ life? _____

152. Common People

Music by Pulp. Lyrics by Jarvis Cocker

'cos when you're laid — in bed — at night — watch-ing roach - es climb — the wall, —

If you called — your dad — he could stop — it all, — yeah! You'll nev - er live like

com - mon peo - ple, You'll nev - er do what - ev - er com - mon peo - ple do, — Nev - er fail like

com - mon peo - ple, You'll nev - er watch your life — slide out of view, — And dance

— and drink — and screw, — Be - cause there's no - thing else — to do. —

Play 6 times vocal ad lib.

Want to live with com - mon peo - ple like you.

Want to live with com - mon peo - ple like you. — La — la la — la,

Oh! — La — la la — la, Ooh! — La — la la la la, Oh you!

2. I took her to a supermarket
   I don't know why but I had to start it somewhere
   So it started there
   I said "Pretend you've got no money,"
   But she just laughed and said
   "Oh you're so funny!"
   I said "Yeah?"
   (Spoken): "Well,
   "I can't see anyone else smiling in here,"
   "Are you sure?"

   Chorus 1:
   You want to live like common people
   You want to see whatever common people see
   Want to sleep with common people
   You want to sleep with common people like me
   But she didn't understand
   She just held my hand.

3. *Guitar solo*

   Chorus 2:
   Sing along with the common people
   Sing along and it might just get you through
   Laugh along with the common people
   Laugh along even though they're laughing at you
   And the stupid things that you do
   Because you think that poor is cool.

153. Confide In Me

Words & Music by Steve Anderson, Dave Seaman & Anthony Barton

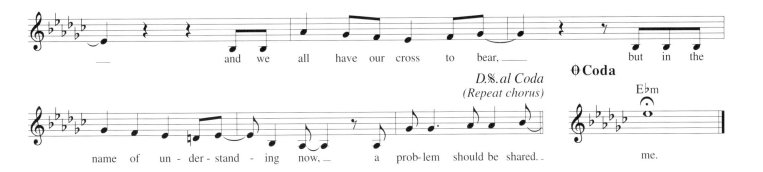

and we all have our cross to bear, — but in the

D.%.al Coda (Repeat chorus)

θ Coda

name of un-der-stand-ing now, — a prob-lem should be shared. — me.

154. The Crying Game

Words & Music by Geoff Stephens

Moderately slow

I know all there is to know — a-bout the cry-ing game, — I've had my

share of the cry-ing game. — First there are kiss-es, — Then there are

sighs, And then be-fore you know where you are you're say-ing good-bye. —

One day soon I'm gon-na tell the moon — a-bout the cry-ing game, — And if he

knows, may-be he'll ex-plain, — Why there are heart-aches, — Why there are

tears, And what to do to stop feel-ing blue when love — dis-ap-pears. —

θ Coda

Don't want no more — of the cry-ing game, — Don't want no more —

of the cry-ing game. —

155. Cotton Eye Joe

Traditional. Arranged by Jan Ericsson, Oban & Pat Reiniz

He came to town like a mid-win-ter storm, — He rode thro' the fields so
He brought di-sas-ter where-ev-er he went, — The hearts of the girls was

hand-some and strong. His eyes was his tools and his smile was his gun, — But
hell bro-ken sent. They all ran a-way so no-bo-dy would know, — And

all — he had come for was — hav-ing some fun, If it had-n't been for Cot-ton Eye Joe,
left — on-ly men — 'cause of Cot-ton Eye Joe.

I'd been mar-ried a long time a-go. Where did you come from, Where did you go,

Where did you come from, Cot-ton Eye Joe? —

156. Come Live Your Life With Me

Music by Nino Rota. Words by Billy Meshel & Larry Kusik

No one can buy to-mor-row, _____ No one can sell their
Here in our world to-geth-er, _____ Love will go on for-

sor-row, _____ But when you look in-to my eyes,
-ev-er, _____ Warm in the shel-ter of my arms,

Dar-ling, you'll al-ways see _____ Love, _____ I will give you
Dar-ling, you'll al-ways be _____

love, _____ Come live your life with me.

We'll have our good times and ev-en in sad times, with love, we will

find a way, _____ Noth-ing else mat-ters but

lov-ing each oth-er the way that we do to-day. _____

162

157. Cruella De Vil

Words & Music by Mel Leven

158. Country House

Words & Music by Damon Albarn, Graham Coxon, Alex James & David Rowntree

⊕ **Coda**

Blow, blow me out, ___ I am ___ so sad, ___ I don't ___ know why. ___

Oh, ___ he lives in a house, a
(Chorus 2, see block lyrics)

ve-ry big house in the coun-try, watch-ing af-ter-noon re-peats and the

food he eats ___ in the coun-try. He takes all man-ner of pills ___ and piles up

a-na-lyst's bills ___ in the coun-try; Ooh, ___ it's like an A-ni-mal Farm, ___ lots of

ru-ral charm ___ in the coun-try. Oh, ___ he - ry. ___

___ Ooh, la la (la.) *instrumental*

Play 3 times (quick fade 3rd)

Verse 2.   He's got morning glory
            And life's a different story
            Everything's going 'Jackanory'...
            In touch with his own mortality
            He's reading Balzac, knocking back Prozac-
            It's a helping hand that makes you feel wonderfully bland
            Oh, it's the century's remedy
            For the faint at heart, a new start.

Chorus 3.   He lives in a house, a very big house in the country
            He's got a fog in his chest
            So he needs a lot of rest in the country
            He doesn't drink, smoke, laugh
            Takes herbal baths in the country
            But you'll come to no harm
            On the Animal Farm in the country.

Verse 3.   *Instrumental*

165

159. Crazy Blues

Words & Music by Perry Bradford

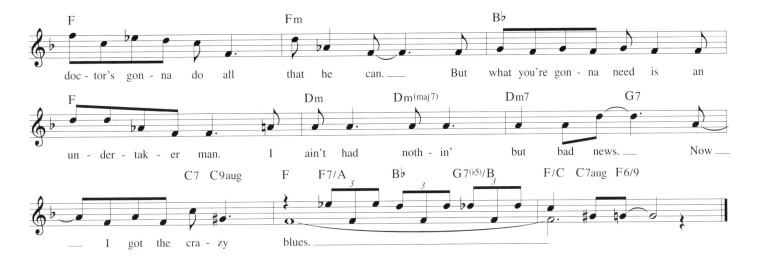

doc - tor's gon - na do all that he can. ___ But what you're gon - na need is an

un - der - tak - er man. I ain't had noth - in' but bad news. ___ Now

___ I got the cra - zy blues. ___

160. Cousins

By Angelo Badalamenti

161. The Call Of The Faraway Hills

Words by Mack David. Music by Victor Young

162. Christmas Island

Words & Music by Lyle Moraine

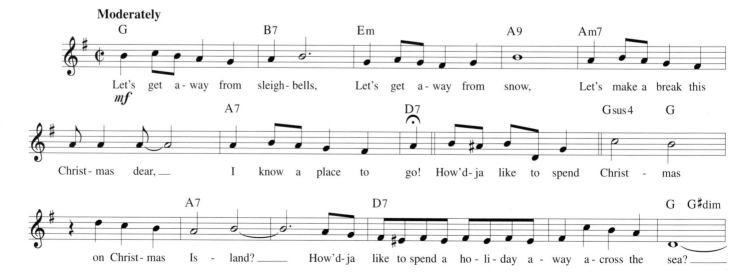

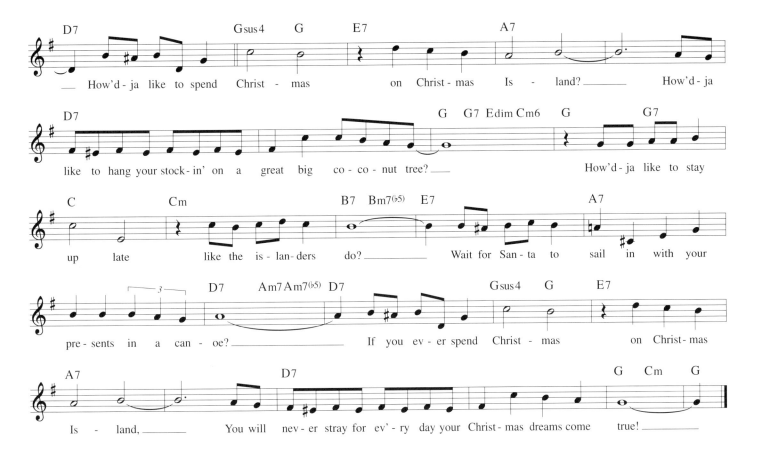

How'd-ja like to spend Christ-mas on Christ-mas Is - land? _____ How'd-ja like to hang your stock-in' on a great big co-co-nut tree? _____ How'd-ja like to stay up late like the is-lan-ders do? _____ Wait for San-ta to sail in with your pre-sents in a can-oe? _____ If you ev-er spend Christ-mas on Christ-mas Is - land, _____ You will nev-er stray for ev'-ry day your Christ-mas dreams come true!

163. Don't Ask Me Why

Words by Joe Young. Music by Robert Stolz

Moderately

mf

Don't ask me why I'm leav-ing, Don't ask me why. Don't ask me why I'm griev-ing, Don't ask me why. I on-ly want to tell you I'll miss you so, And love you for-ev-er, For-get you, nev-er. Tho' you may hear me sigh-ing, Don't ask me why. Just keep the mo-ments fly-ing, Till bye and bye. Then we will start a new love, You'll whis-per you're a true love, And no more you'll be ask-ing me why. _____

169

164. Could You Be Loved

Words & Music by Bob Marley

⊕ **Coda**

Stay a-live __ oh. Could you be loved __ and be loved?

1. **2.**

You ain't gon-na miss your wa - ter un -

- til your well __ runs dry. __ No mat - ter how __ you treat __ him, the man will

nev - er be sat - is - fied. Could you be, could you be, could you be loved?

Repeat to fade

Could you be, could you be loved? Say some - thin', say some - thin'.

165. **Ding Dong Merrily On High**

Traditional

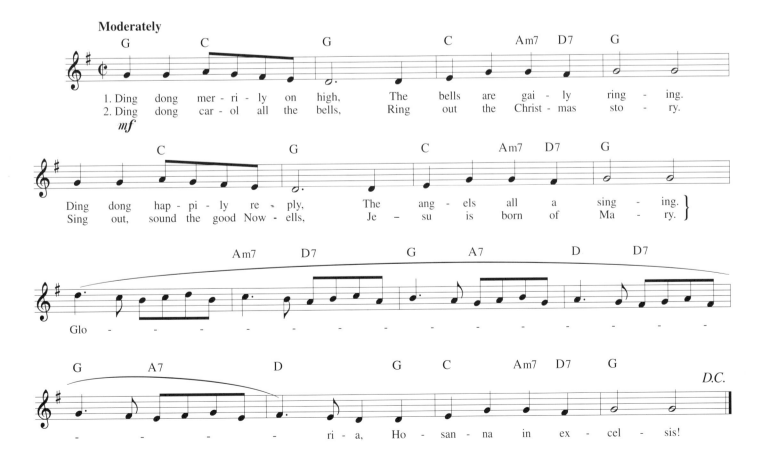

Moderately

1. Ding dong mer - ri - ly on high, The bells are gai - ly ring - ing.
2. Ding dong car - ol all the bells, Ring out the Christ - mas sto - ry.

mf

Ding dong hap - pi - ly re - ply, The ang - els all a sing - ing.
Sing out, sound the good Now - ells, Je - su is born of Ma - ry.

Glo - - - - - - - - -

- - - - - ri - a, Ho - san - na in ex - cel - sis!

D.C.

171

166. Cow-Cow Boogie

Words & Music by Don Raye, Gene De Paul & Benny Carter

172

-yip - it - tl - e - yi - ay." —   Tsk   tsk   tsk   tsk   yip pee e e e e...

167. **Doctor Robert**

Words & Music by John Lennon & Paul McCartney

Moderately

mf 1. Ring   my   friend,   I   said   you'd   call,   Doc - tor   Rob - ert.
2. If   you're   down,   he'll   pick   you   up,   Doc - tor   Rob - ert.
3. My   friend   works   for   the   Na - tional Health, Doc - tor   Rob - ert.

Day   or   night   he'll   be   there   an - y   time   at   all,   Doc - tor Rob - ert,   Doc - tor
Take   a   drink   from his   spec - ial   cup   Doc - tor   Rob - ert,   Doc - tor
Don't   pay   mon - ey just   to   see   your - self with   Doc - tor   Rob - ert,   Doc - tor

Rob - ert.   You're   a   new   and bet - ter   man,   He   helps   you,   to un - der-
Rob - ert.   He's   a   man   you must be - lieve,   Help - ing   ev - 'ry - one   in
Rob - ert.   You're   a   new   and bet - ter   man,   He   helps   you   to un - der-

1.

stand.   He   does   ev - 'ry - thing   he   can,   Doc - tor   Rob - ert.
need.   No   one   can   suc -
stand.   He   does   ev - 'ry - thing   he

2, 3.

ceed   like   Doc - tor   Rob - ert. }
can,   Doc - tor   Rob - ert. }

Well,   well,   well   you're

feel - ing   fine.   Well,   well,   well   he'll   make   you,   Doc - tor

To Coda ⊕   *D.C. al Coda*   ⊕ **Coda**

Rob - ert.

Repeat to fade

Ring   my   friend,   I   said   you'd   call,   Doc - tor   Rob - ert.

173

168. Could It Be Magic

Words & Music by Barry Manilow & Adrienne Anderson

169. Distant Drums

Words & Music by Cindy Walker

170. Crazy He Calls Me

Words & Music by Carl Sigman & Bub Russell

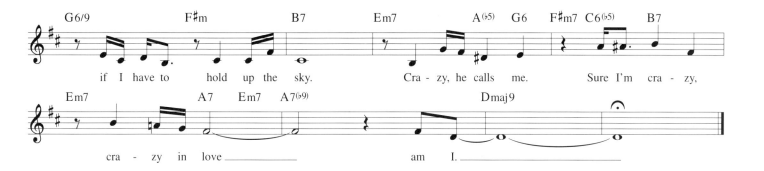

171. Devil May Care

Words & Music by Terrell P. Kirk Jr. & Robert Dorough

172. The Day We Find Love

Words & Music by Eliot Kennedy & Helen Boulding

as the on - ly one _ who set _ you free, _ may - be
time a - lone _ will make _ you see _ how deep _ our love _ could _ be, _
_ no it's nev - er too late. _ 'Cause I know _ this is - n't the first _
_ time, won't be the last _ time, I sur - ren - der my soul _ 'cause you're al - ways keep - ing me wait-
- ing, an - ti - ci - pa - ting, the day _ we find love _ once a- gain. _

2. I won't give up while there's a glimmer of a chance
    A dream that's never-ending, inviting love and a perfect romance
    A burning passion, oh baby, you're my destiny
    But the message I'm receiving is you're through with me but I'll be there
    Even though you tell me you don't care
    How could you forget the times we've shared?
    Don't throw our love away
    You know it's never too late.

173. Clarinet Concerto Theme

Composed by Wolfgang Amadeus Mozart

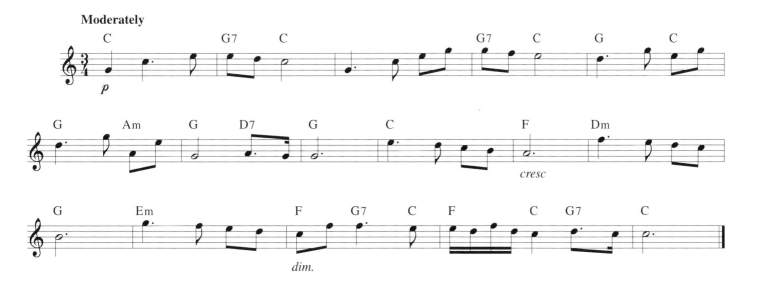

Moderately

174. Daddy's Home

Words & Music by James Sheppard & William Miller

175. Dance To The Bop

Words & Music by Floyd Edge

176. The Day We Caught The Train

Words & Music by Steve Cradock, Damon Minchella, Oscar Harrison & Simon Fowler

And you and I when we're com-ing down, __ we're on-ly get-ting back __ and you know __

Vocal tacet 1st

__ I feel __ no sor - row. Oh __ la la, __ oh __

__ la la. __ Oh __ la la, __ oh __ la. __

Play 4 times, then
D.%. and fade

__ When you find that things __ are get-ting wild, but don't __ you want days like these.

2. He sipped another rum and Coke and told a dirty joke
Walking like Groucho, sucking on a number 10
Rolling on the floor with the cigarette burns walked in
I'll miss the crush and I'm home again
Stepping through the door
With the night in store, whiling just an hour away
Step into the sky in the star bright feeling it's a brighter day.

177. Dance Of The Hours (from 'La Gioconda')

Composed by Amilcare Ponchielli

Moderately

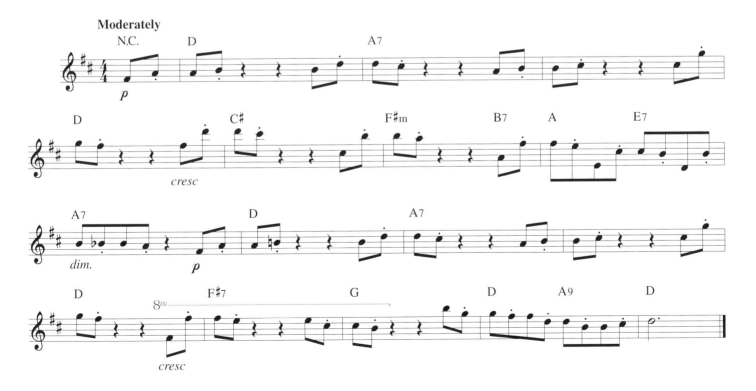

178. Daddy Won't You Please Come Home

Words & Music by Sam Coslow

Moderately

Night af-ter night, _____ I'm cry-in', "Dad-dy won't you please come home." _____

mf

Dad-dy won't you please come home, _____ I'm so lone-some. No one can fill _____ that

va-cant chair; _____ home is-n't home _____ when you're not there. _____ No need to knock _____

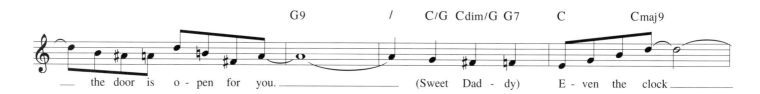

_____ the door is o-pen for you. _____ (Sweet Dad-dy) E-ven the clock _____

_____ keeps tick-in' "Dad-dy won't you please come home." _____ Dad-dy do you have to roam,

_____ so ver-y long. _____ There's lots of oth-er new sheiks who would

like to be sheik - in'. Have - n't slipped yet, but I'm lia - ble to weak - en.

Dad - dy, dad - dy won't you please come home. _____

184

179. Deep In Romance

By Mercer Ellington

180. Deadlier Than The Male

Words & Music by Scott Engel & John Franz

1. She whis-pers oh, such pret-ty lies.
(Verses 2 & 3 see block lyrics)

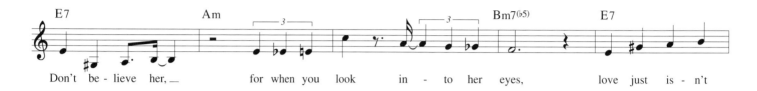

Don't be - lieve her, __ for when you look in - to her eyes, love just is - n't

there bro - ther be - ware, take care my bro - ther take care, for the fe - male of the spe - cies is

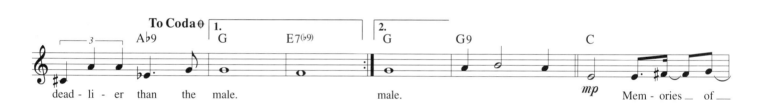

dead - li - er than the male. male. Mem - ories __ of

__ kiss - es on a sum - mer's __ day, __ that's all __ she left you __ when

she went a - way, __ now you pay. male. __

2. The smile that made a dream begin
   Clouds your vision
   It's just the shadow of our dream
   That you're living in
   She'd never dare
   Beware my brother beware
   For the female of the species
   Is deadlier than the male.

3. By walking streets you've never known
   When the night comes
   Sitting in places that you go
   Hoping she'll be there
   Brother beware
   Take care my brother take care
   For the female of the species
   Is deadlier than the male.

181. Do What You Do, Do Well

Words & Music by Ned Miller

Bright tempo

mf He could-n't move a moun - tain, Nor __ pull down a big oak
times he'd __ kiss my moth - er, And __ hold her ten - der -
he was a man of laugh - ter, But if tra - ge - dy came
day I __ still re - mem - ber, Just like __ yes - ter -

tree __ But my dad - dy be - came __ a might - y big man, __ With a
ly __ Then he'd look a - cross __ the top of her head, __ Then he'd
by __ The tears __ ran free __ and he'd say __ to me, __ "Nev - er
day 'Bout a might - y big man __ with a might - y big heart, And a

Chorus

sim - ple phil - os - o - phy. __ Do what you do, do well
wink and say to me. __
be __ a - fraid to cry" __
might - y few words to say. __

boy Do what you do, do well __ Give your love __ and

1, 2, 3.

all your heart __ And do what you do, do well. __

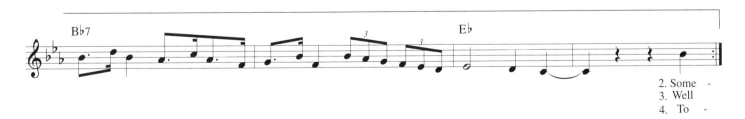

2. Some -
3. Well
4. To -

4.

well Do what you do, do well. __

187

182. Dear Prudence

Words & Music by John Lennon & Paul McCartney

183. Don't Say You're Sorry Again

Words & Music by Lee Pearl, Art Berman & Eugene West

184. Disco 2000

Music by Pulp. Lyrics by Jarvis Cocker

2. You were the first girl at school to get breasts
   Martyn said that yours were the best
   The boys all loved you but I was a mess
   I had to watch them trying to get you undressed
   We were friends but that was as far as it went
   I used to walk you home sometimes but
   It meant nothing to you
   'Cause you were so popular.

185. Double Trouble

Words & Music by Doc Pomus & Mort Shuman

Medium rock

186. Do U Still

Words & Music by Tony Mortimer

2. I know just like a rainbow, everything must end
Sometime, someway, somehow someday
But the bloom was immature, it ended premature
Two hearts broken, by soft words spoken
Well in the garden of beginning
Our flowers grew the same
I guess they grew apart, from the wind and the rain
Now I'm living in pain, will it remain?
Tell me.

187. Dolores

Music by Louis Alter. Words by Frank Loesser

188. Day By Day

Words & Music by Sammy Cahn, Axel Stordahl & Paul Weston

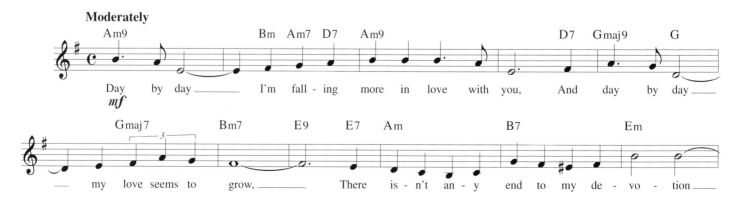

189. Drop Me Off In Harlem

Words by Nick Kenny. Music by Duke Ellington

190. Don't Bother Me

Words & Music by George Harrison

191. Dream On Little Dreamer

Words & Music by Fred B. Burch & Jan Crutchfield

192. Don't Be A Stranger

Words & Music by Coral Gordon & Geoff Gurd

2. You're on my mind all of the time
   I really shouldn't stay with you tonight
   But the more and more I think of it, the more it seems just right
   That's why I shouldn't be here tonight
   Now I find I don't know who I really am, I'm lost without a trace
   So take me high, take me low, anyhow you know, and help me if you can.

193. Don't Be Cruel

Words & Music by Otis Blackwell & Elvis Presley

200

194. Don't Go Home (My Little Darlin')

Words & Music by Stanley Lebowsky & Johnny Lehmann

195. Don't Let Go (Love)

Words & Music by Ivan Matias, Andrea Martin, Marqueze Etheridge & Organized Noise

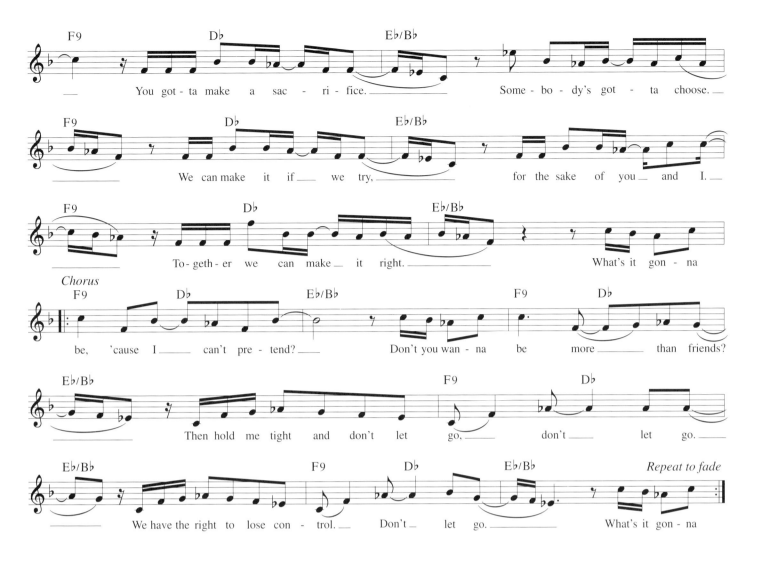

You got-ta make a sac-ri-fice. ___ Some-bo-dy's got-ta choose. ___

We can make it if ___ we try, ___ for the sake of you ___ and I. ___

To-geth-er we can make ___ it right. ___ What's it gon-na

Chorus

be, 'cause I ___ can't pre-tend? ___ Don't you wan-na be more ___ than friends?

Then hold me tight and don't let go, ___ don't ___ let go.

Repeat to fade

We have the right to lose con-trol. ___ Don't ___ let go. ___ What's it gon-na

196. **Drum Boogie**

Words & Music by Gene Krupa & Roy Eldridge

Moderate

mf

Boo-gie, You hear the rhy-thm

romp-in', ___ Boo-gie, You see the drum-mer stomp-in' ___ Drum

Boo-gie, Drum Boo-gie, It real-ly is a kill-er, Drum

Boo-gie, Drum Boo-gie, The Drum Boo-gie woo-gie! ___

197. Don't Let Me Down, Gently

Words & Music by Malcolm Treece, Martin Gilks, Robert Jones & Miles Hunt

how could I ____ ex - plain ____ the pleas - ure in ____ the pain, ____ they're

call - ing us ____ in - sane, ____ oh, the knives, the blood, ____ the bad, the good ____ d'ya think you could ____

do do do do you? ____

Don't let me down, _____ if you have to let me down ____ at all, ____ don't let me down.

____ If you have to let me down ____ at all, ____ don't let me down. ____

If you have to let me down ____ at all, ____ don't let me down, ____ if you have to

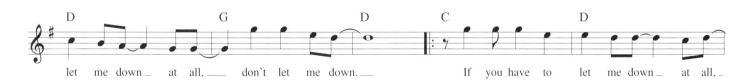
let me down ____ at all, ____ don't let me down. ____ If you have to let me down ____ at all, ____

____ don't let me down. ____ ____ don't let me down, ____ don't let me down, ____ don't let me down,

____ no no.

198. Don't

Words & Music by Jerry Leiber & Mike Stoller

199. Down In The Boondocks

Words & Music by Joe South

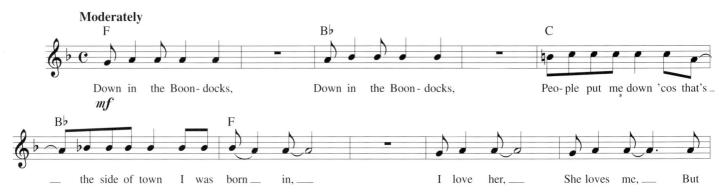

I don't fit ___ her so - ci - e - ty; ___ Lord have mer - cy on a boy from down in the
Boon - docks. ___ Ev - 'ry night ___ I watch the light ___ of the house up - on the hill. ___
___ I love a lit - tle girl that lives up there, ___ and I guess I al - ways will. ___
But I don't dare knock on her door, ___ 'cos her dad is my boss - man, ___ So
I'll just have to be con - tent ___ to see her when - ev - er I can. ___

Fine

D.C. al Fine

200. Eternal Father, Strong To Save

Music by John Bacchus Dykes. Words by William Whiting

Moderately

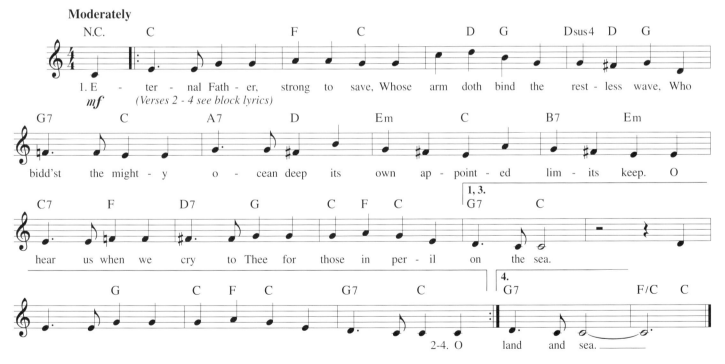

1. E - ter - nal Fath - er, strong to save, Whose arm doth bind the rest - less wave, Who
(Verses 2 - 4 see block lyrics)
bidd'st the might - y o - cean deep its own ap - point - ed lim - its keep. O
hear us when we cry to Thee for those in per - il on the sea.
2-4. O land and sea. ___

2. O Saviour whose almighty word
   The winds and waves submissive heard
   Who walkedst on the foaming deep
   And calm amid its rage did sleep
   O hear us when we cry to Thee
   For those in peril on the sea.

3. O sacred Spirit who didst brood
   Upon the waters dark and rude
   And bid their angy tumult cease
   And give, for wild confusion, peace
   O hear us when we cry to Thee
   For those in peril on the sea.

4. O Trinity of love and power
   Our brethren shield in danger's hour
   From rock and tempest, fire and foe
   Protect them wheresoe'er they go
   And ever let there rise to Thee
   Glad hymns of praise from land and sea.

201. Dreamlover

Words & Music by Mariah Carey, Dave Hall & David Porter

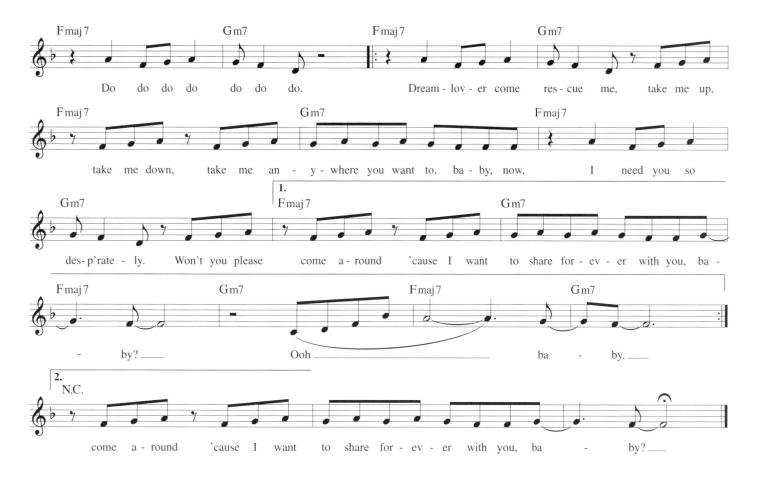

Do do do do do do do. Dream-lov-er come res-cue me, take me up, take me down, take me an-y-where you want to, ba-by, now, I need you so des-p'rate-ly. Won't you please come a-round 'cause I want to share for-ev-er with you, ba-by? Ooh ba-by. come a-round 'cause I want to share for-ev-er with you, ba-by?

202. Eight Bells

Traditional

With a swing

1. My mat-ey's a sau-cy fore-top-man, A chum of the cook, don't you
mf *(Verses 2 - 4 see block lyrics)*
know, he stuck his head down the fun-nel, and bel-lowed come up from be-low! *Chorus* Eight bells, eight bells Rouse up then the watch from be-low Eight bells, eight bells, Rouse up then the watch from be-low.

2. My matey once shipped on a whaler
   That sailed in the far northern seas
   He was a good bold hearted sailor
   And cared not for ice, sea, nor breeze.

3. My matey's no longer a sailor
   And often he wakes in the night
   And thinking he's still on the whaler
   Cries out in the greatest delight.

4. At the end of each watch, though, his fancy
   Was to get to his bunk quickly, O
   For he wanted to dream of his Nancy
   So he called to the watch "Hi, below!"

209

203. Dream Of You

Words & Music by Sy Oliver

204. Easy Living

Words & Music by Leo Robin & Ralph Rainger

205. Ezekiel Saw The Wheel

Traditional

'Ze - kiel saw the wheel, 'Way up in the mid - dle of the air, 'Ze - kiel saw the wheel, 'Way in the mid - dle of the air, The big wheel run by faith, Lit - tle wheel run by the grace of God. Wheel with - in a wheel, 'Way in the mid - dle of the air. Wheel, wheel, wheel, Wheel in the mid - dle of the air, Wheel, wheel, wheel, Wheel in the mid - dle of the air.

206. Don't Laugh At Me (Just Because You See Me Cryin')

Words & Music by George Weiss & Bennie Benjamin

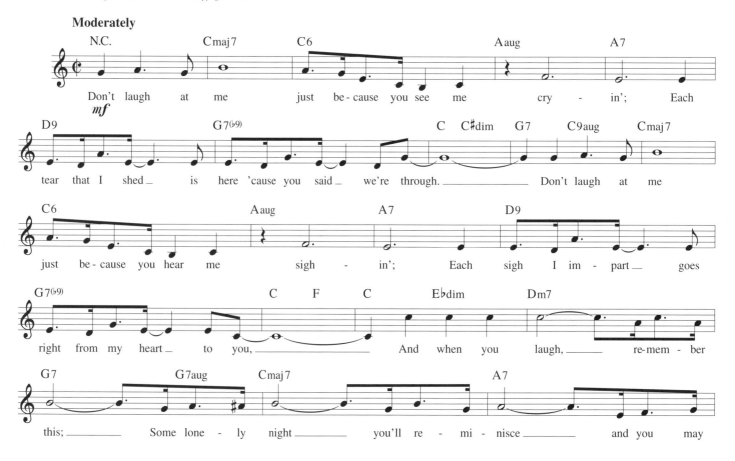

Don't laugh at me just be - cause you see me cry - in'; Each tear that I shed __ is here 'cause you said __ we're through. __ Don't laugh at me just be - cause you hear me sigh - in'; Each sigh I im - part __ goes right from my heart __ to you, And when you laugh, __ re - mem - ber this; __ Some lone - ly night __ you'll re - mi - nisce __ and you may

207. Early One Morning

Traditional

Moderately

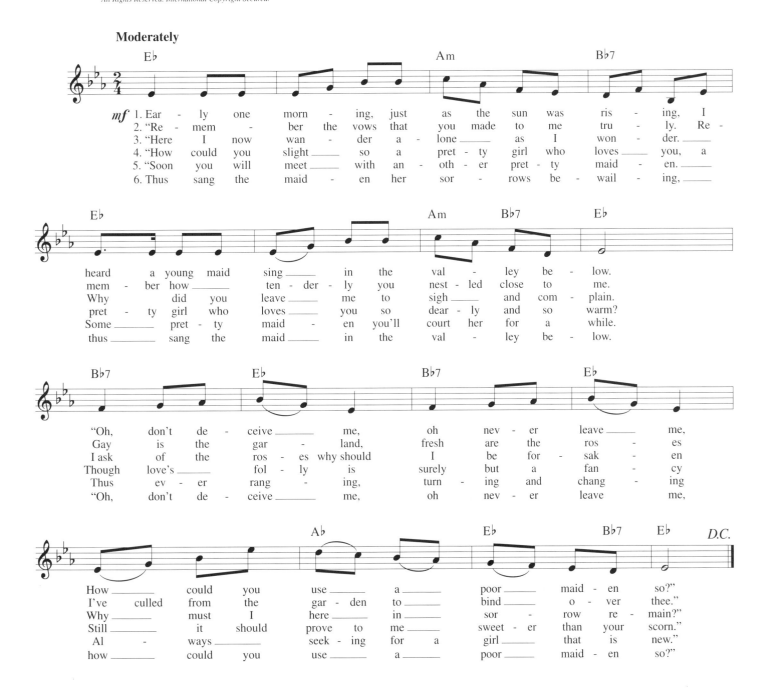

1. Ear - ly one morn - ing, just as the sun was ris - ing, I
2. "Re - mem - ber the vows that you made to me tru - ly. Re -
3. "Here I now wan - der a - lone as I won - der.
4. "How could you slight so a pret - ty girl who loves you, a
5. "Soon you will meet with an - oth - er pret - ty maid - en.
6. Thus sang the maid - en her sor - rows be - wail - ing,

heard a young maid sing in the val - ley be - low.
mem - ber how ten - der - ly you nest - led close to me.
Why did you leave me to sigh and com - plain.
pret - ty girl who loves you so dear - ly and so warm?
Some pret - ty maid - en you'll court her for a while.
thus sang the maid in the val - ley be - low.

"Oh, don't de - ceive me, oh nev - er leave me,
Gay is the gar - land, fresh are the ros - es
I ask of the ros - es why should I be for - sak - en
Though love's fol - ly is surely but a fan - cy
Thus ev - er rang - ing, turn - ing and chang - ing
"Oh, don't de - ceive me, oh nev - er leave me,

How could you use a poor maid - en so?"
I've culled from the gar - den to bind o - ver thee."
Why must I here in sor - row re - main?
Still it should prove to me sweet - er than your scorn."
Al - ways seek - ing for a girl that is new."
how could you use a poor maid - en so?"

208. Enlightenment

Words & Music by Van Morrison

2. I'm in the here and now
And I'm meditating
And still I'm suffering, but that's my problem
Enlightenment, don't know what it is.
(Wake up!)
Instrumental 8 bars
Enlightenment says the world is nothing
Nothing but a dream
Everything's an illusion
And nothing is real.

3. Good or bad baby
You can change it any way you want
You can rearrange it
Enlightenment, don't know what it is.

Chop that wood
And carry water
What's the sound of one hand clapping
Enlightenment, don't know what it is.

D.C. All around baby
You can see
You're making your own reality
everyday because
Enlightenment, don't know what it is.
(One more time)

Instrumental 8 bars.

209. Every Little Thing

Words & Music by John Lennon & Paul McCartney

210. Emotions

Music by Mariah Carey, David Cole & Robert Clivilles. Words by Mariah Carey

211. End Of The Road

Words & Music by Kenny Edmonds, Antonio Reid & Daryl Simmons

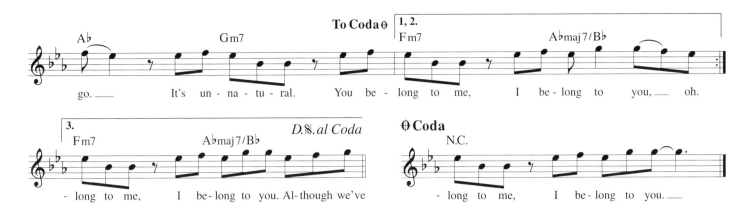

3. *(Spoken:)*
Girl, I'm here for you
All those times at night when you just hurt me
And just ran out with that other fellow
baby, I knew about it
I just didn't care
You just don't understand how much I love you, do you?
I'm here for you
I'm not out to go out there and cheat all night just like you did, baby
But that's alright, huh, I love you anyway
And I'm still gonna be here for you 'til my dyin' day, baby
Right now, I'm just in so much pain, baby
'Cause you just won't come back to me, will you?
Just come back to me.

Yes, baby, my heart is lonely
My heart hurts, baby, yes, I feel pain too
Baby please...

212. Everyday

Words & Music by Charles Hardin & Norman Petty

213. Even Better Than The Real Thing

Words & Music by U2

214. Evil Hearted You

Words & Music by Graham Gouldman

spread a-round a-gainst me, a-bout me   What would you   do with-out me

Smi - lin' be - gui - lin'   you lead me on   till all hope is gone.

215. Etude No.3

Composed by Frédéric Chopin

216. Everybody (Backstreet's Back)

Words & Music by Denniz Pop & Max Martin

So ev-'ry-bo-dy ev-'ry-where ___ don't
be a-fraid __ don't have no fear. _____ I'm gon-na tell the world, _ make it un-der-stand, _
as long as there'll be mu-sic we'll be com-ing back a-gain. ___
Ev-'ry-bo-dy ___
(Yeah.) ___ rock your bo-dy. ___ (Yeah.) ___ Ev-'ry-bo-dy ___
rock your bo-dy right. ___ Back-street's back. Ev-'ry Back-street's back al-right!

2. Now throw your hands up in the air
   And wave 'em around like you just don't care
   If you wanna party let me hear you yell
   'Cos we got it going on again.

   Am I original...

217. Ein Prosit Der Gemütlichkeit (To All Good Cheer)

German Traditional

Moderately

Ein pro - sit, ein pro - sit der ge - müt - lich -
A toast now, a toast now, and to all good

keit, Ein pro - sit, ein pro - sit der ge - müt - lich - keit.
cheer. A toast now, a toast now, and to all good cheer.

218. Exodus

Words & Music by Bob Marley

219. España

By Emmanuel Chabrier

220. Fame And Fortune

Music by Ben Weisman. Words by Fred Wise

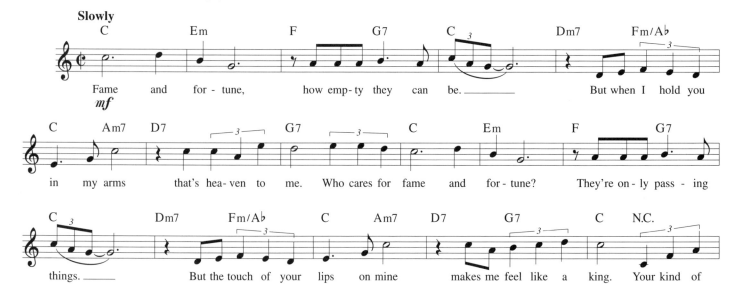

221. Full Moon And Empty Arms

Music by Sergei Rachmaninov. Words & Arrangement by Buddy Kaye & Ted Mossman

222. Falling Into You

Words & Music by Rick Nowles, Marie-Claire D'Ubalio & Billy Steinberg

So close your eyes and let me kiss you,
and while you sleep, I will miss you. Oh I'm fall-ing in-to
you, this dream could come true and it feels so good
fall-ing in-to you. Fall-ing like a leaf, fall-ing like a star,
find-ing a be-lief, fall-ing where
you are. Fall-ing in-to you,
fall-ing in-to you, fall-ing in-to you,
hey.,

223. Theme From Far And Away

By John Williams

Sweetly

224. Fantasie Impromptu Op.66 Theme

Composed by Frédéric Chopin

225. Theme From Fatal Attraction

By Maurice Jarre

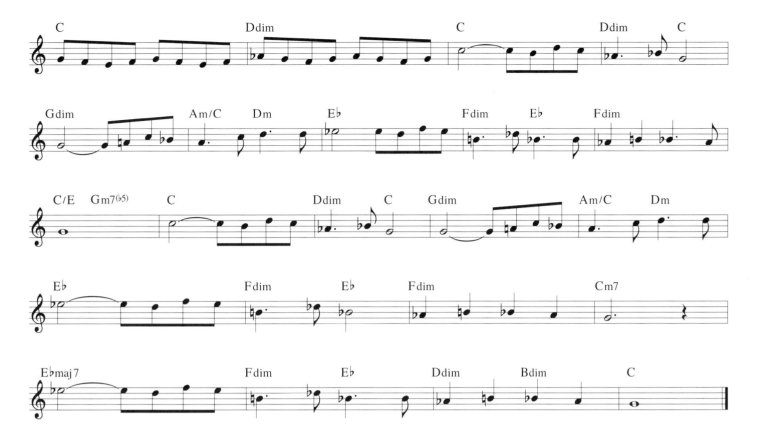

226. Foggy Foggy Dew

Traditional

Moderately

mf 1. When I was a bach-e-lor I lived all a-lone, I worked at the wea-ver's
(Verses 2 & 3 see block lyrics)

trade, And the on-ly on-ly thing I did that was wrong was to woo a fair young maid. I

wooed her in the win-ter-time, and in the sum-mer too,_____ And the

on-ly on-ly thing I did that was wrong was to keep her from the fog-gy fog-gy dew.

2. One night she knelt close by my side
   When I was fast asleep
   She threw her arms around my neck
   And then began to weep.
   She wept, she cried, she damn near died
   And cried what can I do?
   So all night long I held her in my arms
   Just to keep her from the foggy foggy dew.

3. Now I am a bachelor, I live with my son
   We work at the weaver's trade
   And every single time I look into his eyes
   He reminds me of the fair young maid.
   He reminds me of the wintertime
   And of the summer too
   And the many many times that I held her in my arms
   Just to keep her from the foggy foggy dew.

227. Fascination

Music by F. D. Marchetti. English Lyric by Dick Manning

228. First Love Never Dies

Words & Music by Bob Morris & Jimmy Seals

2. Whenever I feel lonely
   I'm thinking of you only
   One last kiss and then we said goodbye.
   The love I left behind me
   Comes back to remind me
   That you were my first love
   And first love never ever dies.

3. And if you're thinking of me
   And you find you still love me
   There's no use to go on living lies.
   Let's hurry to each other
   For there could be no other
   Yes you were my first love
   And first love never ever dies.

235

229. Fields Of Gold

Words & Music by Sting

230. Fraulein

Words & Music by Lawton Williams

Moderate country waltz

231. 5th Season

Words & Music by Paul Weller

1. A storm is rag - ing in - side my head, ___ the wind is howl-
(Verses 2 - 4 see block lyrics)

-ing such thoughts of death. ___ Why am I so lost ___ and con-

fused? Can't ___ find the rea - son for feel-ing blue. There's ___ so much

___ I can't ___ ex - plain ___ hope this sea - son chan - ges soon.

2. 4. The light- ning strikes ___

3. The ser - pent tang ___

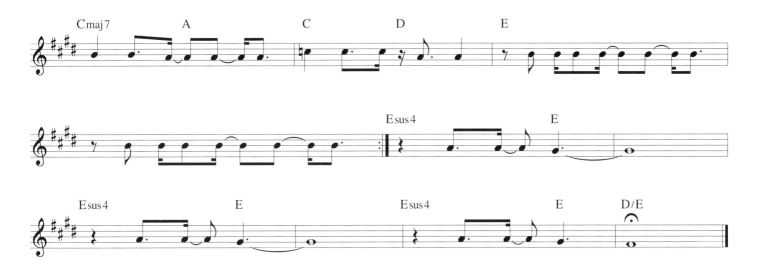

2 & 4. The lightning strikes and the mountains fall
        The sea's come crashing against it all
        Hang on tight in the tides of change
        And get your bearings from those still sane
        There's so much I've yet to feel
        Hope the seasons change me too.

3. The serpent tangles in the lion's claw
    A cloud of darkness hangs over all
    As fires soar in search of sky
    So blow embers like fireflies
    Hoping love is where they'll lie
    And the season changes us too.

232. From A Window

Words & Music by John Lennon & Paul McCartney

233. Five Brothers

By Gerry Mulligan

234. Feel So Bad

Words & Music by Chuck Willis

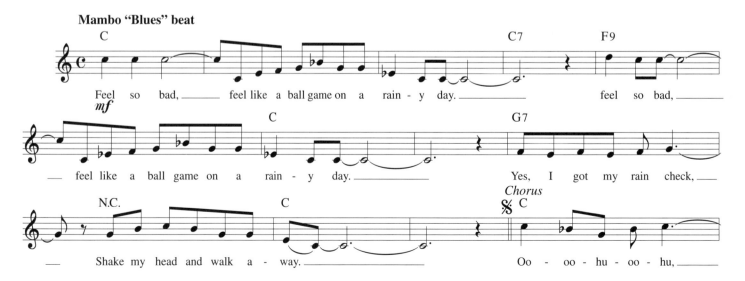

240

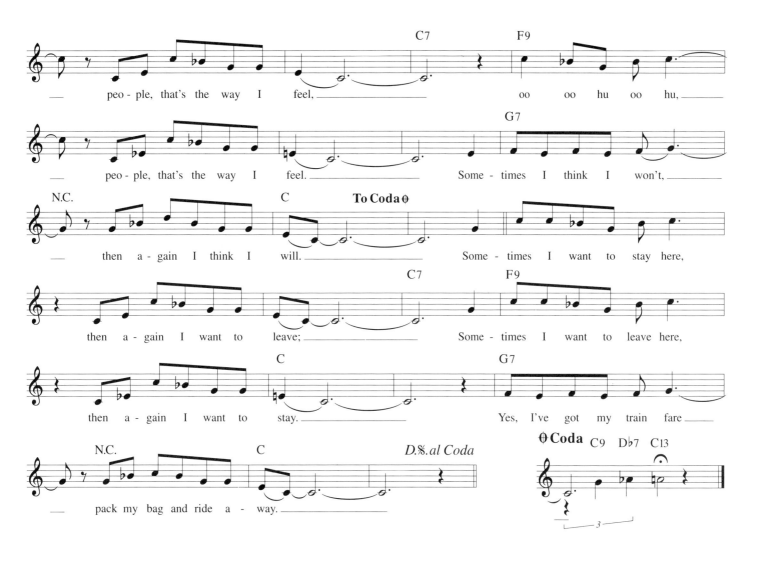

people, that's the way I feel,_____ oo oo hu oo hu,_____ people, that's the way I feel._____ Some - times I think I won't,_____

N.C.

then a - gain I think I will._____ Some - times I want to stay here,

To Coda ⊕

then a - gain I want to leave;_____ Some - times I want to leave here,

then a - gain I want to stay._____ Yes, I've got my train fare_____

N.C.   C   D.%.al Coda   ⊕ Coda C9 D♭7 C13

pack my bag and ride a - way._____

3

235. The First Time I Saw You

Words by Allie Wrubel. Music by Nathaniel Shilkret

Moderately

The first time I saw you I knew at a glance I was meant to be
I stood be - fore you My heart seem'd to dance, And I prayed you would

yours, yours a - lone._____ As   When I look in your eyes I am thrilled to the
call me your own.

skies, And I feel like a {king / queen} on a throne,_____ The first time I

saw you I knew at a glance, I was meant to be yours, yours a - lone._____

236. Forrest Gump Suite

By Alan Silvestri

237. Fortuosity

Words & Music by Richard M. Sherman & Robert B. Sherman

For-tu-os-i-ty, That's me by word. For-tu-os-i-ty, me
For-tu-os-i-ty, That's me own word. For-tu-os-i-ty, me

twin-kle in the eye word. Some-times cas-tles fall to the ground, ___ but
nev-er feel a-lone word. 'Round a cor-ner un-der a tree, ____ good

that's where four-leaf clo-vers are found. ___ For-tu-os-i-ty, luck-y
for-tune's wait-in' just wait and see. ___ For-tu-os-i-ty, luck-y

chanc-es. For-tu-i-tous lit-tle hap-py hap-pen-stan-ces. I don't wor-ry 'cause
chanc-es. For-tu-i-tous lit-tle hap-py hap-pen-stan-ces. I keep smil-in' 'cause

ev-'ry-where I see that ev-'ry bit of life is lit by for-tu-os-i-ty!
my phil-os-o-phy is "Do your best and leave the rest to for-tu-os-i-ty!"

238. Four Weddings And A Funeral/Funeral Blues

Composed & Arranged by Richard Rodney Bennett

239. Frenesi

English Words by Ray Charles & S. K. Russell. Music by Alberto Dominguez

240. Fragile

Words & Music by Sting

241. The Fleet's In

Music by Victor Schertzinger. Words by Johnny Mercer

Fast and spirited

242. Footloose

Words & Music by Kenny Loggins & Dean Pitchford

Fast rock 'n' roll

mf 1. I been work - in' ___ so hard; I'm punch - in' my ___ card.
(Verses 2 & 3 see block lyrics)

Eight hours, ___ for what? Oh, tell me what I got. I've got this

feel - in' ___ that time's just hold - in' me down. ___ I'll hit the ceil - in', ___

Or else I'll tear up this town. ___ *(instrumental)*

To - night I got - ta cut loose, Foot - loose, Kick off your Sun - day shoes.

Please, Lou - ise, Pull me off ___ of my knees. Jack, get back,

Come on be - fore we crack. Lose your blues, Ev - 'ry - bo - dy cut foot - loose. *D.C.*

2. You're playin' so cool
Obeying every rule
Dig way down in your heart
You're burnin', yearnin', for some...
Somebody to tell you
That life ain't a-passin' you by
I'm tryin' to tell you
It will if you don't even try
You can fly if you'd only cut...

3. Loose, footloose
Kick off your Sunday shoes
Ooh-ee, Marie
Shake it, shake it for me
Whoa, Milo
Come on, come on, let's go!
lose your blues
Everybody cut footloose.

248

243. A Four Legged Friend

Words & Music by Jack Brooks

Moderately

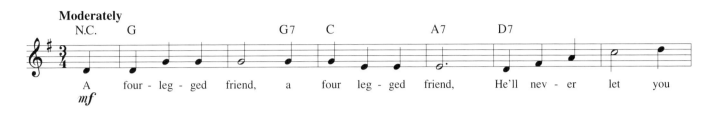

A four-leg-ged friend, a four leg-ged friend, He'll nev-er let you

down. _____ He's hon-est and faith-ful right up to the end, That won-der-ful

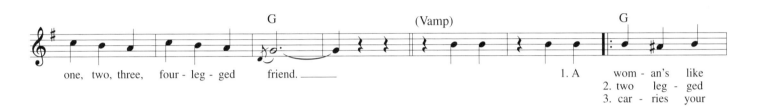

one, two, three, four-leg-ged friend. _____
1. A wom-an's like
2. two leg-ged
3. car-ries your

cac-tus and cac-tus can hurt; 'Cause she's just a tight-waist-ed wink-y-eyed flirt. _____ She'll
hom-bre is worth-less as sand. He'll smile like a saint with a gun in his hand _____ He'll
bur-den, who car-ries your load on tum-ble-weed land or a long dust-y road? _____ Who

soon have your land and your pride and your gold and bur-y you deep long be-fore you grow old. _____
prom-ise to stick by your side all your life but he al-so prom-ised the same to your wife. _____
asks you no ques-tions and tells you no lies? That four leg-ged friend with the two hon-est eyes. _____

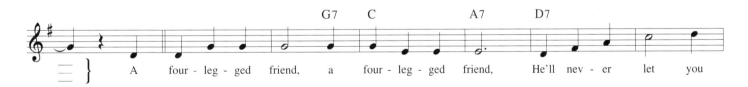

A four-leg-ged friend, a four leg-ged friend, He'll nev-er let you

down. _____ He's hon-est and faith-ful right up to the end, That won-der-ful

1, 2.   **3.**

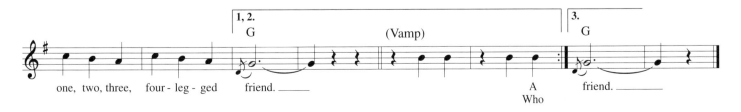

one, two, three, four-leg-ged friend. _____   friend. _____
A
Who

244. Follow That Dream

Music by Ben Weisman. Words by Fred Wise

245. Fun In Acapulco

Words & Music by Ben Weisman & Sid Wayne

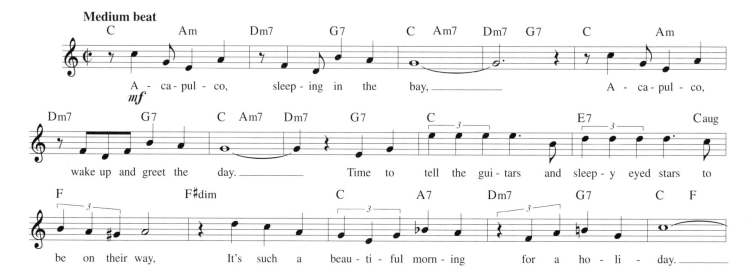

Hey now, come on, you old sleep-y head, See the sky turn-ing red and you're still in bed. It's fun in A-ca-pul-co. A-ca-pul-co, look, here come the sun, A-ca-pul-co, it's a day for fun. I can't wait till I meet your sweet se-ño-ri-tas, kiss ev-'ry-one. This is no time for si-es-ta, This is time for fun. fun.

246. Give Me That Old Time Religion

Traditional

Moderately

Give me that old time re-li-gion, Give me that old time re-li-gion, Give me that old time re-li-gion; It's good e-nough for me.

It was
It will
It was

good for the He-brew chil-dren, It was good for the He-brew chil-dren, It was
bring you out of bond-age, It will bring you out of bon-dage, It will
good for my dear old moth-er, It was good for my dear old moth-er, It was

good for the He-brew chil-dren, And it's good e-nough for me. Give me that
bring you out of bond-age, And it's good e-nough for me. Give me that
good for my dear old moth-er, And it's good e-nough for me.

247. Frankfort Special

Words & Music by Sherman Edwards & Sid Wayne

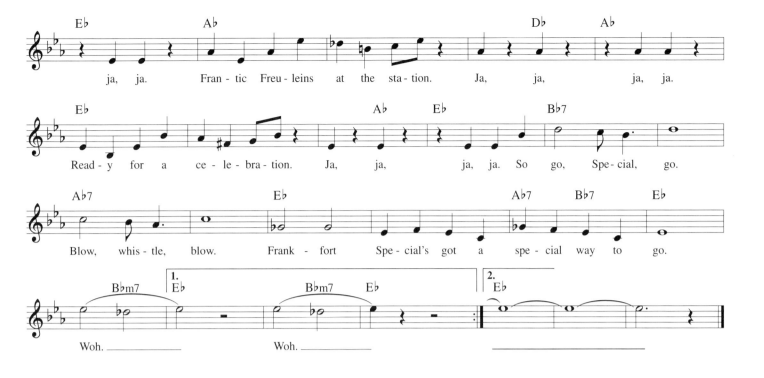

ja, ja.   Fran - tic Freu - leins at the sta - tion.   Ja,   ja,   ja, ja.

Read - y for a ce - le - bra - tion. Ja,   ja,   ja, ja. So go, Spe - cial, go.

Blow,   whis - tle,   blow.   Frank - fort   Spe - cial's got a   spe - cial way to go.

Woh. _____   Woh. _____

248. Go Tell It On The Mountain

Traditional

© Copyright 1999 Dorsey Brothers Music Limited, 8/9 Frith Street, London W1.
All Rights Reserved. International Copyright Secured.

With movement

mf Go   tell   it   on   the   moun - tain,   Ov - er   the   hills   and   ev - 'ry - where,

Go   tell   it   on   the   moun - tain,   Our   Je - sus   Christ ___ is   born.

1. When   I   was   a   learn - er,   I   sought   both   night   and   day,   I
2. He   made   me   a   watch - man,   Up - on   the   cit - y   wall,   An'

ask   the   Lord   to   aid   me,   An'   He   show   me   the   way. _____
if   I   am   a   Christ - ian,   I   am   the   least   of   all. _____

Go   tell   it   on   the   moun - tain,   Ov - er   the   hills   an'   ev - 'ry - where,

Go   tell   it   on   the   moun - tain,   Our   Je - sus   Christ ___ is   born.   born.

253

249. G.I. Blues

Words & Music by Roy Bennett & Sid Tepper

Groove march

They give us a room with a view of the beau-ti-ful Rhine. They
get has-sen-fef-fer and black pump-er-nick-el for chow. We
like to be he-roes, but all that we do here is march. We'd
Frau-leins are pret-ty as flow'rs, but we can't make a pass. The

give us a room with a view of the beau-ti-ful Rhine. Gim-me a
get has-sen-fef-fer and black pump-er-nick-el for chow. I'd blow my
like to be he-roes, but all that we do here is march. And they
Frau-leins are pret-ty as flow'rs, but we can't make a pass. 'Cause they're

mud-dy old creek in Tex-as an-y old time. I've got those hup, two, three, four,
next month's pay for a slice of Tex-as cow.
don't give the Pur-ple Heart for a fall-en arch.
all wearin' signs sayin', "Keepen Sie off the grass!"

oc-cu-pa-tion G. I. blues. From my G. I. hair to the heels of my G. I. shoes.

1-3. | **4.**

And if I don't go state-side soon, I'm gon-na blow my fuse. We fuse.
We'd
The

250. Globe Trotter

By Joe Meek

Brightly

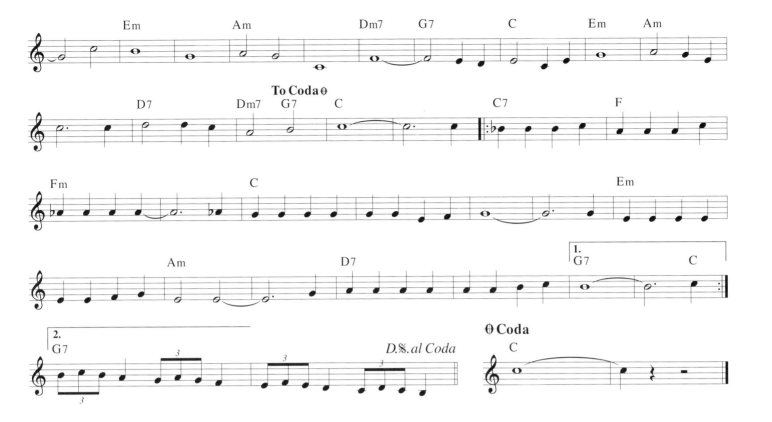

251. The Golden Years

Words & Music by Jay Livingstone & Ray Evans

252. Ghost

By Maurice Jarre

253. A Girl Like You

Music by Burt Bacharach. Words by Anne Croswell

254. A Girl Like You

Words & Music by Edwyn Collins

2. You give me just a taste so I want more
   Now my hands are bleeding and my knees are raw
   Now you've got me crawlin', crawlin' on the floor
   And I've never known a girl like you before.

255. Go Down Moses

Traditional

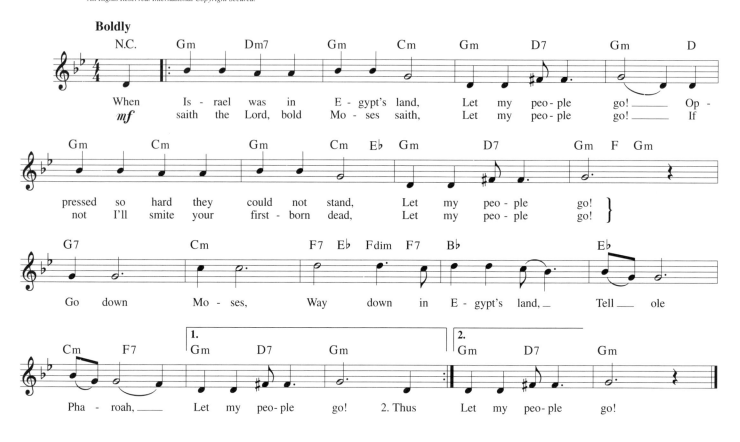

256. Games People Play

Words & Music by Joe South

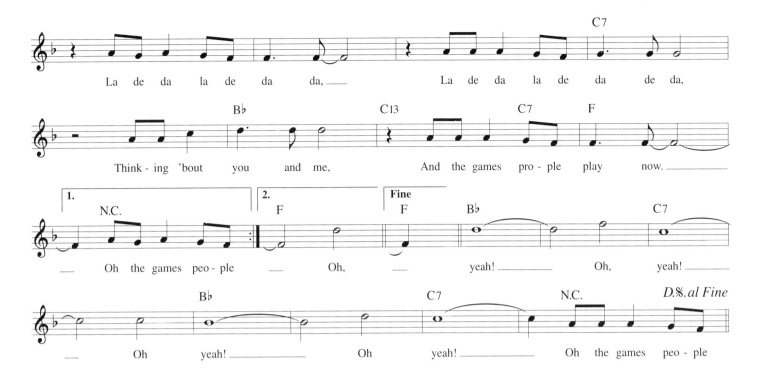

257. Gone Is My Love

Words & Music by Paul Vance & Leon Carr

© Copyright 1988 Paul J. Vance Publishing Corporation, USA.
Campbell Connelly & Company Limited, 8/9 Frith Street, London W1.
All Rights Reserved. International Copyright Secured.

258. Gentle On My Mind

Words & Music by John Hartford

2. It's not clinging to the rocks and ivy planted on their columns now that binds me
   Or something that somebody said because they thought we fit together walkin'
   It's just knowing that the world will not be cursing or forgiving
   When I walk along some rail-road track and find
   That you're moving on the back-roads by the rivers of my mem'ry
   And for hours you're just gentle on my mind.

3. Though the wheat-fields and the clothes lines and the junk-yards and the highways come between us
   And some other woman crying to her mother 'cause she turned and I was gone
   I still might run in silence, tears of joy might stain my face
   And a summer sun might burn me 'til I'm blind
   But not to where I cannot see you walkin' on the back-roads
   By the rivers flowing gentle on my mind.

4. I dip my cup of soup back from the gurglin' cracklin' cauldron in some train yard
   My beard a roughing coal pile and a dirty hat pulled low across my face
   Through cupped hands 'round a tin can I pretend
   I hold you to my breast and find
   That you're waving from the back-roads by the rivers of my mem'ry
   Ever smilin', ever gentle on my mind.

259. Girl Happy

Words & Music by Doc Pomus & Norman Meade

263

260. Ghost Riders In The Sky

Words & Music by Stan Jones

3. Their faces guant, their eyes were blurred and shirts all soaked with sweat
   They're ridin' hard to catch that herd but they ain't caught them yet
   'Cause they've got to ride forever on that range up in the sky
4. On horses snortin' fire as they ride on, hear their cry
   Yi-pi-yi-ay, yi-pi-yi-o, the ghost riders in the sky.

As the riders loped on by him he heard one call his name
"If you want to save your soul from hell a ridin' on our range
The cowboy change your ways today or with us you will ride
A-try'n to catch the devil's herd across these endless skies."
Yi-pi-yi-ay, yi-pi-yi-o, the ghost herd in the sky.
Ghost riders in the sky.

261. The Girl In The Little Green Hat

Words & Music by Jack Scoll, Bradford Browne & Max Rich

262. Girl Talk

Words & Music by Neal Hefti & Bobby Troup

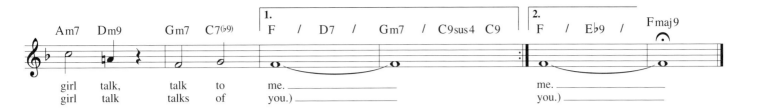

263. Go Away Blues

Words & Music by Duke Ellington

264. Girls! Girls! Girls!

Words & Music by Jerry Leiber & Mike Stoller

think - in' a - bout. girls, girls, girls, girls. girls, girls.

265. The Girl In The Wood (Remember Me)

Words & Music by Neal Stuart & Terry Gilkyson

Moderately slow

1. Oh, when I was a young ___ boy and drove my Mo - ther wild, I met a maid - en
2. Her eyes were green as grass - y pools ___ look - ing right at me, Her hair was red and

in the woods and she ___ said ___ "Child, look deep in - to my green eyes and at my au - tumn
grown with leaves just like an au - tumn tree; She moved her ti - ny hands and she made a lit - tle

hair, When you're a man, you'll nev - er see a girl ___ quite as fair." "Re - mem - ber me ___
turn, She swayed ___ in the wind just ___ like a grace - ful fern. *mf*

___ re - mem - ber me ___ re - mem - ber for the rest of your life."

3. I swore ___ as she van - ished that when I was full grown, I'd ___ have a girl just
wished a hun - dred times that she'd nev - er looked at me, With the first ___ wild ___

like ___ her to be my ver - y own. And ___ now I am a man ___ and I'd mar - ry if I
beau - ty ___ that on - ly youth can see; For a man ___ can - not find it when he's look - ing for a

could, But I can't lose the mem - 'ry of the girl ___ in the wood. "Re - mem - ber me ___
wife, And he'll end up in bach - 'lor - hood the rest ___ of his life. *mf*

3. Dm Gm Dm   4. Dm Gm7 Dm

___ re - mem - ber me ___ re - mem - ber for the rest of your life." ___ 4. I've ___ life."

269

266. The Girl Who Used To Be Me

Music by Marvin Hamlisch. Words by Alan & Marilyn Bergman

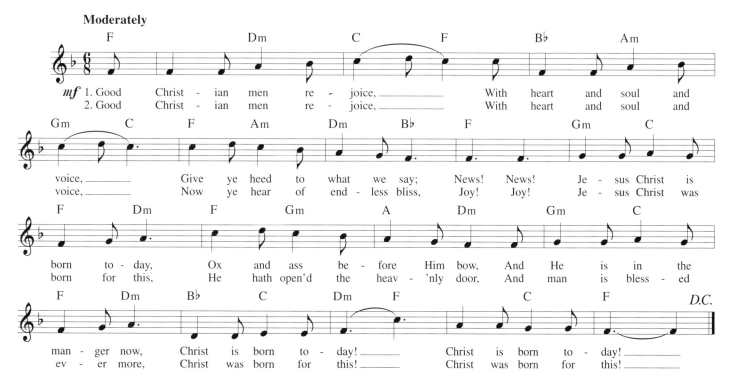

used to — go danc - ing

{ She's — been gone such a long, long
And — I feel she's been gone too

while.

D.%.al Coda

She ——

⊕ **Coda**

long. ____ I'd like the ___ chance to be the girl who used to be

me.

267. Good Christian Men Rejoice

Traditional Christmas Song

Moderately

mf
1. Good Christ - ian men re - joice, ____ With heart and soul and
2. Good Christ - ian men re - joice, ____ With heart and soul and

voice, ____ Give ye heed to what we say; News! News! Je - sus Christ is
voice, ____ Now ye hear of end - less bliss, Joy! Joy! Je - sus Christ was

born to - day, Ox and ass be - fore Him bow, And He is in the
born for this, He hath open'd the heav - 'nly door, And man is bless - ed

man - ger now, Christ is born to - day! ____ Christ is born to - day! ____
ev - er more, Christ was born for this! ____ Christ was born for this! ____

D.C.

3. Good Christian Men rejoice
With heart and soul and voice
Now ye need not fear the grave
Peace! Peace!
Jesus Christ was born to save
Calls you one and calls you all
To gain His everlasting hall
Christ was born to save!
Christ was born to save!

268. Girls And Boys

Words & Music by Damon Albarn, Graham Coxon, Alex James & David Rowntree

2. Avoiding all work
   Because there's none available
   Like battery thinkers
   Count their thoughts on 1 2 3 4 5 fingers
   nothing is wasted
   Only reproduced
   You get nasty blisters
   Du bist sehr schön
   But we haven't been introduced.

269. Good Morning Blues

Traditional

Moderately

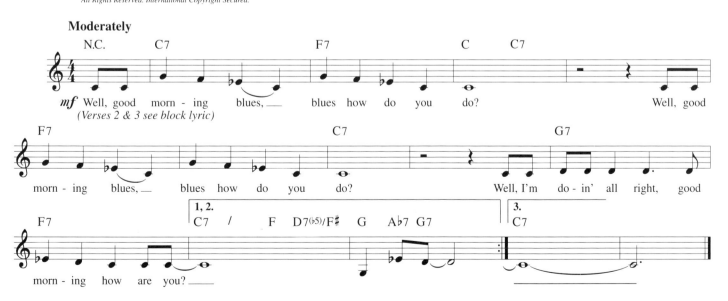

2. I got up this morning, blues walkin' 'round my bed
   I got up this morning, blues walkin' 'round my bed
   Went to eat my breakfast, blues was in my bread.

3. I sent for you yesterday, here you come today
   I sent for you yesterday, here you come today
   You got your mouth wide open, you don't know what to say.

273

270. Give Me Just A Little More Time

Words & Music by R. Dunbar & E. Wayne

2. You're young and you're in a hurry
You're eager for love but don't you worry
We both want the sweetness in life
'Cause these things don't come overnight
Don't give up 'cause love's been slow
Boy we're gonna succeed with another blow.

3. Love is that mountain we must climb
Let's climb it together your hand in mine
We haven't known each other too long
But that feeling I have is oh so strong
I know we can make is, there's no doubt
We owe it to ourselves to find it out.

271. Golden Earrings

Music by Victor Young. Words by Jay Livingston & Ray Evans

272. Git On Board, Little Children

Traditional

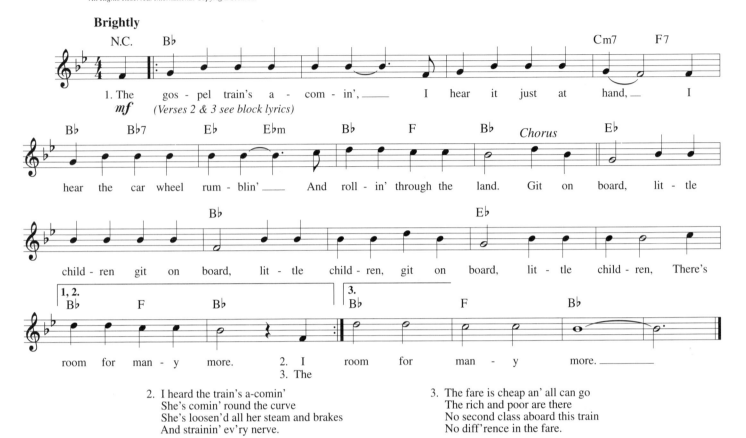

2. I heard the train's a-comin'
   She's comin' round the curve
   She's loosen'd all her steam and brakes
   And strainin' ev'ry nerve.

3. The fare is cheap an' all can go
   The rich and poor are there
   No second class aboard this train
   No diff'rence in the fare.

273. The Girl Of My Best Friend

Words & Music by Beverly Ross & Sam Bobrick

What if she got real mad and told him so, I could nev-er face ei-ther one a-gain.

The way they kiss, Their hap-pi-ness. Will my ach-ing heart ev-er mend, Or will I al-ways be in love With the girl of my best friend? friend?

274. Goober Peas

Traditional

Brightly

Sit-tin' by the road-side on a sum-mer's day,

Chat-tin' with my mess-mates, pass-in' time a-way.

Ly-in' in the shad-ows un-der-neath the trees,

Good-ness how de-li-cious, Eat-in' goob-er peas.

Chorus

Peas, peas, peas, peas, Eat-in' goob-er peas,

Good-ness how de-li-cious, Eat-in' goob-er peas.

277

275. Gladiators

By Muff Murfin

1. Do you feel the pow - er of the gla - di - a - tors? _____ Can you face the chal - lenge of the cham - pi - ons? Do you have the cou - rage of a he - ro? Do you have the will and the skill? _____ Do you have the speed, the strength, the heart to be a win - ner? _____ It's not for be - gin - ners, _____ deep down in your soul _____ are you a gla - di - a - tor?

(Verse 2 see block lyric)

(instrumental) Got - ta move like a street - fight fight - er; got - ta breathe fi - re, a ti - ger; got - ta give your all to win; _____ rea - dy or not let the chal - lenge be - gin. _____ *(instrumental)*

Show the stuff you're made of, can you seal the fate of the

gla - di - a - tors? Can you chal - lenge the gla - di - a - tors? Will you take on the

gla - di - a - tors? Will you be the new cham - pion?

The gla - di - a - tors.

2. Can you match the strength of the gladiators?
Do you have the fire within you?
Do you have the heart of a lion?
Do you have the power in your soul?
Now it's time to race, it's face to face
Get on track now
Your future's on the line
Are you a gladiator?

Got to move at frightening speed
Skill and strengh are what you need
Got to take it on the chin
Got to love it, love to fight and win.

276. Granada

Music by Agustin Lara. English Lyric by Dorothy Dodd

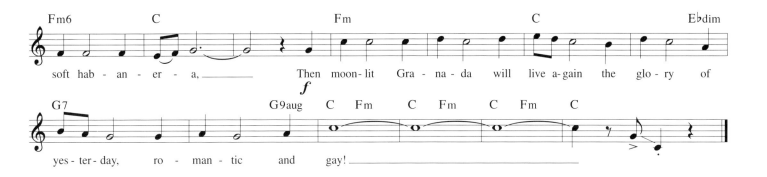

soft hab- an- er- a, ___ Then moon- lit Gran- a- da will live a- gain the glo- ry of
yes- ter- day, ro- man- tic and gay! ___

277. Gonna Get Along Without You Now

Words & Music by Milton Kellem

Got a- long with- out ___ ya be- fore I met ___ ya, gon- na get a- long with- out ya now. ___

Gon- na find some- bo- dy twice as cute, ___ 'cause ya did- n't love me an- y- how. ___

1. You
2. I

ran a- round ___ with ev- 'ry {girl/boy} in town ___ and ya nev- er cared ___ if it got me down. ___ You
lost my mon- ey and I lost my pride, ___ did- n't have much mon- ey but I real- ly tried. ___ It

had me wor- ried, al- ways on my guard, ___ but ya laughed at me ___ 'cause I
made you hap- py when you made me cry, ___ and ya broke my heart ___ so I

tried too hard. } Boom- boom, boom- boom, gon- na get a- long with- out ya now. ___
said good- bye. }

Boom- boom, boom- boom, gon- na get a- long with- out ya now. ___

D.%.al Coda

___ Gon- na

Coda

- boom, boom- boom, gon- na get a- long with- out ya now. ___ Boom-

281

278. Goodnight Girl

Words & Music by Graeme Clark, Tom Cunningham, Neil Mitchell & Marti Pellow

279. The Green Cockatoo

Words & Music by Don Rellegro

280. A Groovy Kind Of Love

Words & Music by Toni Wine & Carole Bayer Sager

We got a groo-vy kind of love.

281. (Got-ta Have) Something In The Bank, Frank

Words by Bob Hilliard. Music by Mort Garson.

Moderately bright

(Boy) 1. I say ba - by I love you but ev - 'ry time I say I do,
(Boy) 2. Ev - 'ry time we park the car un - der - neath a lov - ing star,
3. night you called me on the phone and told me with a heart of stone,

you come back with words so true, you
you set all my dreams a - jar with your   got - ta have some - thing in the bank, Frank!
we can't live on love a - lone, you

(Girl) Got - ta have some - thing in the bank, Frank! You got - ta have some - thing to start. When

you get some - thing in the bank, Frank, I'll give you my heart.

Fine heart.   heart.   (Everybody) Hey there Frank - y you

got - ta pay the rent. No, no Frank - y we can't live in a tent. We need a stove to
We need a house, we

cook the food and a big re - fri - ger - at - or. They'll come from the
need a car, with lots of gad - gets on it. You need lots of

D.% al Fine

fac - to - ry an' we'll make the pay - ments la - ter.
steaks and chops and the ba - by needs a bon - net.   (Boy) 3. Last

282. Good Luck Charm

Words & Music by Aaron Schroeder & Wally Gold

2. Don't want a silver dollar
   Rabbit's foot on a string
   The happiness in your warm caress
   No rabbit's foot can bring.
   Come one and *(etc.)*

3. I found a lucky penny
   Toss it across the bay
   Your love is worth all the gold on earth
   No wonder that I say.
   Come one and *(etc.)*

286

283. Goodbye Sam, Hello Samantha

Words & Music by Mitch Murray, Peter Callander & Geoff Stephens

284. Goodbye

Words & Music by Gordon Jenkins

285. The Green Door

Music by Bob Davie. Words by Marvin Moore

289

286. Go Where You Wanna Go

Words & Music by John Phillips

287. A Good Idea, Son

Words & Music by Leslie Bricusse

288. Go Away!

Music by Danny Williams. Words by Gil King

289. Grandfather's Clock

Words & Music by Henry Clay Work

2. In watching its pendulum swing to and fro
Many hours had he spent while a boy
And in childhood and manhood, the clock seemed to know
And to share both his grief and his joy
For it struck twenty-four when he entered at the door
With blooming and beautiful bride
But it stopped short, never to go again
When the old man died.

3. My grandfather said that of those he could hire
Not a servant so faithful he found
For it wasted no time, and had but one desire
At the close of each week, to be wound
And it kept in its place, not a frown upon its face
And its hands never hung by its side
But it stopped short, never to go again
When the old man died.

4. It rang an alarm in the dead of the night
An alarm that, for years, had been dumb
And we knew that his spirit was pluming its flight
That the hour of departure had come
Still the clock kept the time, with a soft and muffled chime
As we silently stood by his side
But it stopped short, never to go again
When the old man died.

290. GoldenEye (Theme from the James Bond Film)

Words & Music by Bono & The Edge

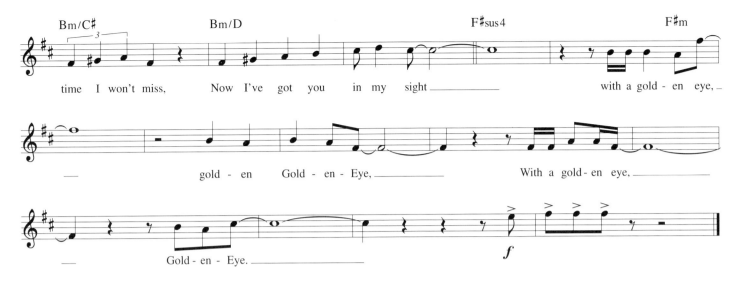

time I won't miss, Now I've got you in my sight _____ with a gold-en eye, ___

___ gold-en Gold-en-Eye, _____ With a gold-en eye, _____

___ Gold-en-Eye. _____

f

2. See him move through smoke and mirrors
   Feel his presence in the crowd
   Other girls, they gather round him
   If I had him I wouldn't let him out
   Goldeneye, my lace for leather
   Golden chain break him to the spot
   Goldeneye, I'll show him forever
   It'll take forever to see what I've got.

   You'll never know how I watched you from the shadows as a child
   You'll never know how it feels to get so close and be denied.

291. House Of The Rising Sun

Traditional

Moderately

There is a house in New Or - leans, They

mp *(Verses 2 - 6 see block lyrics)*

call the Ris - ing ___ Sun; _____ It's

been the ru - in of man - y a poor ___ boy, And

God, I know I'm ___ one.

2. My mother was a tailor
   She sewed my new blue jeans
   My father was a gambling man
   Way down in New Orleans.

3. The only thing a gambler needs
   Is a suitcase and a trunk
   And the only time he's satisfied
   Is when he's on a drunk.

4. Oh, mother's, tell your children
   Not to do what I have done
   To live in sin and misery
   In the House of the Rising Sun.

5. One foot on the platform
   The other's on the train
   I'm going down to New Orleans
   To wear that ball and chain.

6. Going back to New Orleans
   My race is almost run
   I'm going to spend the rest of my life
   Beneath that Rising Sun.

292. Goodnight, Wherever You Are

Words & Music by Dick Robertson, Al Hoffman & Frank Weldon

293. The Greatest Show On Earth

Words & Music by Victor Young & Ned Washington

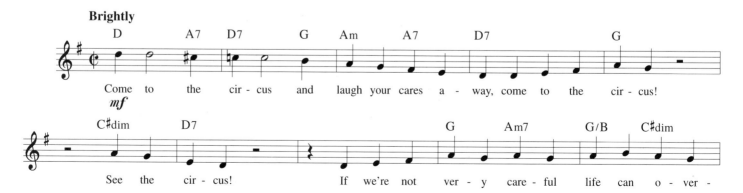

work us. So take to-day and make it gay. For there are too man-y tears a-long the way! So, come to the cir-cus, It's cir-cus day to-day! Come see the bark-ers and the gawk-ers, the bare-back rid-ers and the fear-less tight-rope walk-ers. The fun-ny bears do their rou-tine. The great-est ex-trav-a-gan-za the world has e-ver seen.

294. Heartbreaker

Words & Music by Monty Berk, Max C. Freedman & Frank Campano

Moderately

Heart-break-er, the cu-test gal in town, you heart-break-er, boys fol-low you a-round, you think that you are hav-ing your fling, mak-ing hearts dance just like pup-pets on a string. You heart-break-er, you'll be the lone-ly one when all your fun is through, so be care-ful what you do, when you break a heart in two, for that heart may be-long to you. you.

295. Guess Who I Saw Today

Words & Music by Murray Grand & Elisse Boyd

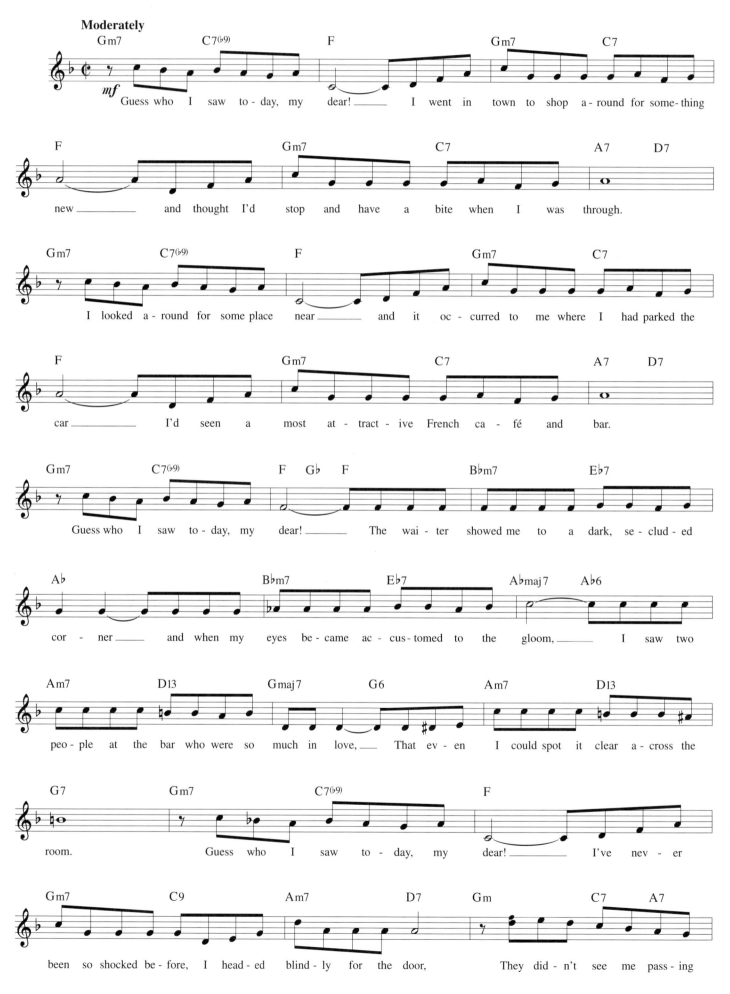

Moderately

Guess who I saw to-day, my dear! ___ I went in town to shop a-round for some-thing new ___ and thought I'd stop and have a bite when I was through. I looked a-round for some place near ___ and it oc-curred to me where I had parked the car ___ I'd seen a most at-tract-ive French ca-fé and bar. Guess who I saw to-day, my dear! ___ The wai-ter showed me to a dark, se-clud-ed cor - ner ___ and when my eyes be-came ac-cus-tomed to the gloom, ___ I saw two peo - ple at the bar who were so much in love, ___ That ev-en I could spot it clear a-cross the room. Guess who I saw to-day, my dear! ___ I've nev - er been so shocked be-fore, I head-ed blind-ly for the door, They did - n't see me pass-ing

through. _____ Guess who I saw to-day I saw you! you!

296. A Guy What Takes His Time

Words & Music by Ralph Rainger

Moderately slow

A guy what takes his time, I'll go for an-y time. _____ I'm _____ a fast mov-in' gal who likes 'em slow.
guy what takes his time, I'll go for an-y time. _____ A hast-y job real-ly spoils the mas-ter's touch.

_____ Got _____ no use for fan-cy driv-in', want to see a guy ar-riv-in' in low. _____
_____ I _____ don't like a big com-mo-tion, I'm a de-mon for slow mo-tion or such. _____

_____ I'd _____ be sat-is-fied, e-lec-tri-fied to
_____ Why _____ should I de-ny that I would die to

know a guy what takes _____ his time. _____ A hur-ry-up af-fair, I
know a guy what takes _____ his time. _____ There is -n't an-y fun in

al-ways give the air. Would -n't give an-y rush-in' gent a smile. _____ I _____ could
get-tin' some-thin' done _ if _____ you're rushed when you have to make the grade. _____ I _____ can

go for an-y sing-er who would con-de-scend to lin-ger a while. _____
spot an am-a-teur, ap-pre-ci-ate a con-nois-seur at his trade. _____

_____ What a lul-la-by would be sup-plied to have a guy what takes _____ his time. _____
_____ Who _____ would qual-i-fy, no al-i-bi, to be the guy what takes _____ his time. _____

A

297. Guns Of Navarone

Music by Dimitri Tiomkin. Words by Paul Francis Webster

298. The Glory Of Love

Words & Music by Billy Hill

299. Humoresque

Composed by Antonín Dvořák

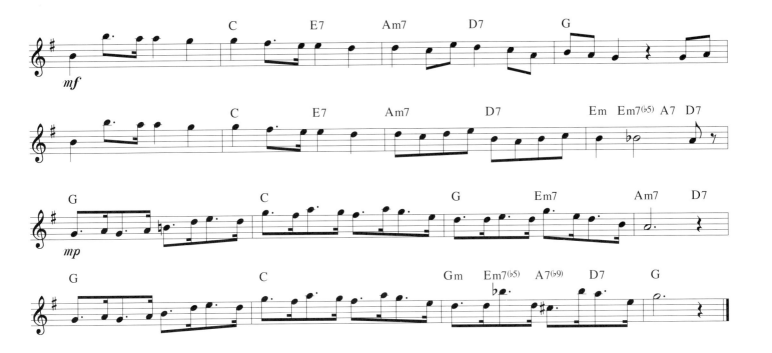

300. Hey Lawdy Mama

Words & Music by Cleve Reed

2. Now the man I love, the man I long to see
Hey Lawdy Mama, little pretty Mama
The man I love, the man I long to see
He's in Cincinatti and he won't write to me.

3. Now the man I love got his feet right on the ground
Hey Lawdy Mama, little pretty Mama
The man I love got his feet right on the ground
He's tailor made, he ain't no hand me down.

4. I'm down and out, ain't got a friend in the world
Hey Lawdy Mama, hey pretty Mama
I'm down and out, ain't got a friend in the world
I know I've been a fool for being someone else's girl.

5. When I had money, I had money to spend
Hey Lawdy Mama, little pretty mama
When I had money, I had money to spend
Every time I left home, I had a brand new friend.

6. Soon this morning, about a quarter to four
Hey Lawdy Mama, little pretty Mama
Soon this morning, about a quarter to four
You brought your new girl right up to my door.

303

301. Theme From Godfather II

By Nino Rota

302. Good Mornin' Life

Music by Joseph Meyer. Words by R.I. Allen

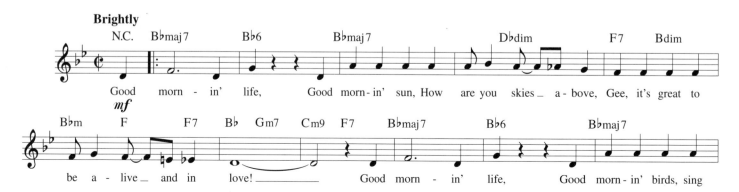

Good morn-in' life, Good morn-in' sun, How are you skies _ a-bove, Gee, it's great to

be a-live _ and in love! _____ Good morn-in' life, Good morn-in' birds, sing

out your hap - py tune, Feel so good 'cause I'll be see-in' {her} {him} soon! _____ Last

night {she} {he} said {she} {he} loved me What a pi - ty to part _____ I slept with

both eyes op - en Wait-in' for to - day to start. _____ Good morn - in' life, Good

morn - in' world, How are you hap - pi - ness, All at once I know what liv - in' can be. _____

It's light, it's free it's some - one wait - in' for me _____ Who'll some-day {be my} {call me}

wife, Good morn - in' life. _____ Good life. _____

303. Hearts Of Oak

English Traditional Song

Rhythmically

mf
1. Come, cheer up my lads! 'tis to glor - y we steer, To add some - thing more to this
2. We ne'er see our foes but we wish - 'em to stay, They nev - er see us but they
3. They swear they'll in - vade us, these ter - ri - ble foes, They fright - en our wom - en, our

won - der - ful year; To _____ hon - our we call you, not press you like slaves, For
wish us a - way; If they run, why, we fol - low and run 'em a - shore, For
child - ren and beaux; But _____ should their flat bot - toms in dark - ness get o'er, Still

who are so free as the sons of the waves? } Hearts of oak are our ships, Hearts of oak are our men; We
if they won't fight us, we can - not do more. } *f*
Brit - ons they'll find to re - ceive them on shore.

al - ways are read - y; stead - y, boys, stead - y We'll fight _____ and we'll con - quer a - gain and a - gain.

304. Home Sweet Home

Traditional

'Mid pleas-ures and pal-a-ces though we may roam, Be it
ev-er so hum-ble there's no place like home. A
charm from the skies seems to hal-low us there, Which
seek thro' the world, is ne'er met with else-where. Home, home,
Sweet, sweet home, There's no place like home, There's no place like home!

305. Golden Slumbers

Words & Music by John Lennon & Paul McCartney

Once, there was a way to get back home-ward;
Once, there was a way to get back home. Sleep, pret-ty dar-ling, do not
cry, And I will sing a lul-la-by. Gold-en slum-
-bers fill your eyes. Smiles a-wake you when you rise;

306. The Huron Carol

Traditional

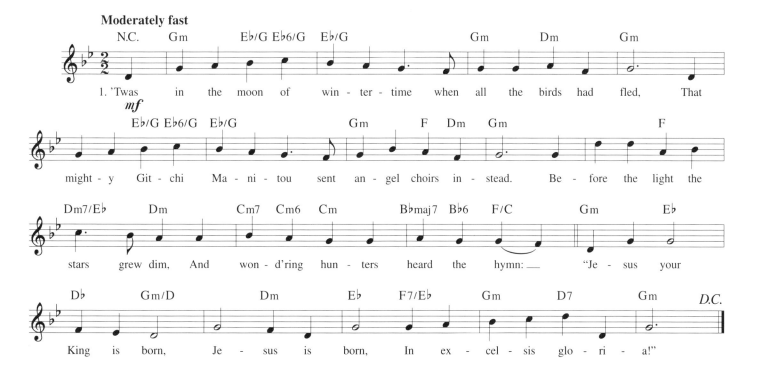

2. Within a lodge of broken bark the tender Babe was found
A ragged robe of rabbit skin enwrapped His beauty round
And as the hunter braves drew nigh the angel song rang loud and high
"Jesus your King is born, Jesus is born, In excelsis gloria!"

3. The earliest moon of wintertime is not so round and fair
As was the ring of glory on the helpless Infant there
The chiefs from far before him knelt with gifts of fox and beaver pelt
"Jesus your King is born, Jesus is born, In excelsis gloria!"

4. O children of the forest free, O sons of Manitou
The holy Child of earth and heaven is born today for you
Come kneel before the radiant Boy who brings you beauty, peace and joy
"Jesus your King is born, Jesus is born, In excelsis gloria!"

307. Hands Up (Give Me Your Heart)

Words & Music by Jean Kluger, Daniel Vangarde & Nelly Byl

308. Happy Days

Music by Charles Fox. Words by Norman Gimbel

309. Hand In My Pocket

Words & Music by Alanis Morrissette & Glenn Ballard

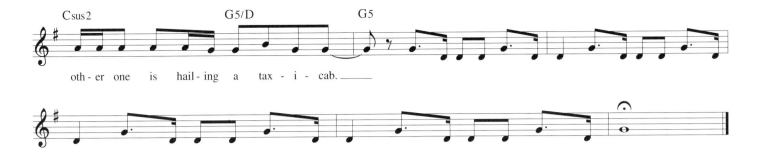

oth - er one is hail - ing a tax - i - cab.

310. Half Of My Heart

Words & Music by Ned Washington & George Duning

Half of my heart tells me love's the on - ly thing,
half of my heart says to walk a - lone. One half is cold, it
longs for fame and gold, the oth - er half would much pre - fer a dream to have and to
hold. If we just live for our - selves, life can be a lone - ly thing.
Miss - ing the love that we might have known. I see your
face and then I know I'd be a fool to lis - ten to
half of my heart when all of my heart loves you.
all of my heart loves you.

311. Happiness Is A Warm Gun

Words & Music by John Lennon & Paul McCartney

312. Hannukah Song

Jewish Traditional Song

313. Has My Fire Really Gone Out?

Words & Music by Paul Weller

one clear voice in the wil - der - ness. _____

Has my fi - re real - ly gone out? _____

And put an end _____ to all _____ your doubts, _____

D.C. al Coda

has my fi - re real - ly real - ly gone out. _____

Coda

Some - thing real is what I'm seek - ing,
(Vocal 1st time only)

1.
one clear voice in the wil - der - ness. _____

2.

Repeat ad lib. x 3

314. Hail To The Chief

Music by James Sanderson. Words by Sir Walter Scott

2. Ours is no sapling, chance-sown by the fountain
   Blooming at Beltane, in winter to fade
   When the whirlwind has stripp'd ev'ry leaf on the mountain
   The more shall Clan-Alpine exult in her shade
   Ours is no sapling, chance-sown by the fountain
   Blooming at Beltane, in winter to fade
   When the whirlwind has stripp'd ev'ry leaf on the mountain
   The more shall Clan-Alpine exult in her shade
   Moor'd in the rifted rock, proof to the tempest shock
   Firmer he roots him, the ruder it blow
   Menteith and Breadalbane, then, echo his praise again
   "Roderigh Vich Alpine dhu, ho! ieroe!"

3. Row, vassals, row for the pride of the Highlands!
   Stretch to your oars for the evergreen pine!
   Oh, that the rosebud that graces yon islands
   Were wreath'd in a garland around him to twine!
   Row, vassals, row for the pride of the Highlands!
   Stretch to your oars for the evergreen pine!
   Oh, that the rosebud that graces yon islands
   Were wreath'd in a garland around him to twine!
   O, that some seedling gem, worthy such noble stem
   Honor'd and bless'd in their shadow might grow!
   Loud should Clan-Alpine then, ring from her deepmost glen
   "Roderigh Vich Alpine dhu, ho! ieroe!"

315. Heaven Can Wait

By Dave Grusin

316. Happy New Year

Music by Francis Lai. English Lyric by Hal Shaper

317. Here Comes The Rain Again

Words & Music by A. Lennox & D. A. Stewart

318. The Heat Is On

Words & Music by Keith Forsey & Harold Faltermeyer

319. Hi Ho Silver Lining

Words & Music by Scott English & Lawrence Weiss

You're ev-'ry-where and no-where ba - by _____ That's where you're at _____
Rol - ling down a bum-py hill - side _____ In your hip-py hat _____
Fly - ing a-cross the coun-try And get-ting fat _____ Say-ing ev-'ry-thing is groo-
-vy When your ty-res are flat _____ And it's hi - ho sil - ver lin - ing
And a-way you go _____ now ba - by I see the sun ain't shin - ing
But I won't make a fuss _____ Though it's ob - vi - ous. _____

320. Happy Ending

Words & Music by Sid Wayne & Ben Weisman

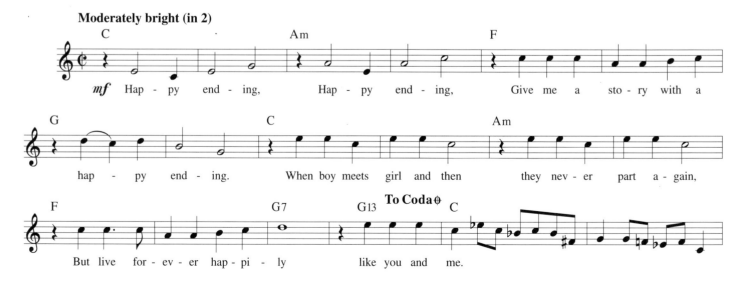

Hap - py end - ing, Hap - py end - ing, Give me a sto - ry with a
hap - py end - ing. When boy meets girl and then they nev - er part a - gain,
But live for - ev - er hap - pi - ly like you and me.

Dm   Em

1. Hard luck sto - ries   get me so up - set,
2. Nev - er thought that   I would stand a chance,

Dm   C   Dm   Em   C   Am

Like Ro - me - o   and Ju - li - et.   I'm not smart e -
that you'd give me   a sec - ond glance.   On - ly think I

E7   Am   D7   G7   *D.C. al Coda*

- nough to fig - ure why   some folks en - joy   a real good cry.
fake and play a part   and give a guy   a hap - py heart.

Coda
C

me. (You and me,   You and me.)

321. Hungarian Dance No.4

Composed by Johannes Brahms

322. Heavy Soul (Pt. 1)

Words & Music by Paul Weller

2. Tuesday's dressed in shearling
Anchored on belief
In the sunlight on the water
Or rain upon a leaf
And I'm touched by its beauty
And I hope to touch you too
'Cause I still seek the same things
That I once sought to be true.

And you know
That's where the wind blows
Though I wouldn't be lying
When I tell you that I
Got a heavy soul.

3. We're words upon a window
Written there in steam
In the heat of a moment
Everything is what it seems
Vapours passing nearly
So I'm touched by the thought
That I can't be beaten
And I can't be bought.

And you'll know
It's a joy to know
I don't think I'd be lying
When I tell you that I
Got a heavy soul.

323. He's A Tramp

Words & Music by Peggy Lee & Sonny Burke

324. Here Comes The Sun

Words & Music by George Harrison

Moderately

Here comes the sun, doo da doo doo, Here comes the sun,

and I say "It's all right."

1. Lit-tle dar-ling, it's been a long, cold, lone-ly win-ter;
2. Lit-tle dar-ling, the smiles re-turn-ing to their fac-es;
3. Lit-tle dar-ling, I feel that ice is slow-ly melt-ing;

Lit-tle dar-ling, it feels like years since it's been here.
Lit-tle dar-ling, it seems like years since it's been here.
Lit-tle dar-ling, it seems like years since it's been clear.

Here comes the sun, Here comes the sun, and I say

"It's all right."

Sun, sun, sun, here it comes.

Here comes the sun, Here comes the sun,

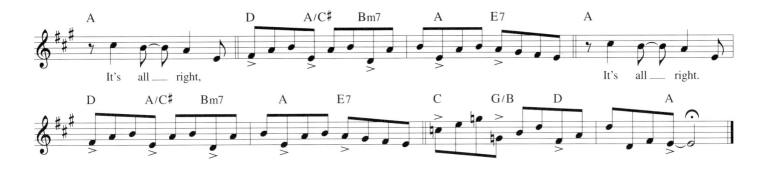

325. Heart And Soul

Music by Hoagy Carmichael. Words by Frank Loesser

326. Hey Mister Christmas

Words & Music by Malcolm J. Allured, David F Bartram, Al James,
R. A. Challenger, R. S. Deas, J. J. Field, W. G. Gask & T. L. Oakes

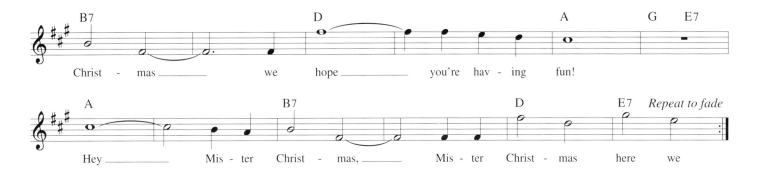

327. Hello Little Girl

Words & Music by John Lennon & Paul McCartney

328. He Makes Me Believe He's Mine

Words & Music by Duke Ellington & John Latouche

329. Hold Me In Your Arms

Words & Music by Ray Heindorf, Don Pippin & Charles Henderson

330. He Who Would Valiant Be

English Traditional Hymn

With vigour

1. He ____ who would val-i-ant be 'gainst all dis-as-ter, Let ____ him in
(Verses 2 & 3 see block lyrics)

con-stan-cy fol-low the Mas-ter. There's no dis-cou-rage-ment ____ shall make _ him

once re-lent ____ His first a-vowed _ in-tent to be a pil-grim. pil-grim.

2. Who so beset him round
   With dismal stories,
   Do but themselves confound:
   His strength the more is.
   No foes shall stay his might,
   Though he with giants fight
   He will make good his right
   To be a pilgrim.

3. Since, Lord, Thou dost defend
   Us with Thy Spirit,
   We know we at the end
   Shall life inherit.
   Then fancies flee away,
   I'll fear not what men say,
   I'll labour night and day
   To be a pilgrim.

331. Home Is Where The Heart Is

Words & Music by Sherman Edwards & Hal David

Moderately slow

Home is where the heart is, And my heart is

an-y-where you are. An-y-where you _ are is home. ____

I don't need a man-sion on a hill that o-ver-looks the sea, An-y-where you're with

me is home. ____ May-be I'm a roll-ing stone

332. Hurting Each Other

Words by Peter Udell. Music by Gary Geld.

333. Here I Go Again

Words & Music by David Coverdale & Bernie Marsden

334

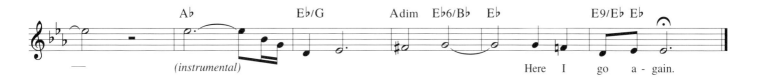

334. Home Lovin' Man

Words & Music by Tony Macauley, Roger Greeneway & Roger Cook

335. Hero

Words & Music by Walter Afanasieff & Mariah Carey

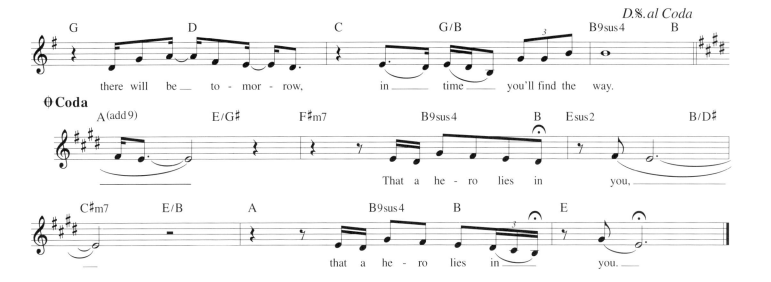

⊕ Coda

there will be — to-mor-row, in time you'll find the way.

That a he-ro lies in you, —

that a he-ro lies in — you. —

336. Hot Diggity (Dog Ziggity Boom)

Words & Music Al Hoffman & Dick Manning

Moderately bright

Hot dig-gi-ty, dog zig-gi-ty boom! What you do to me! It's so new to me,
(Verse 3 see block lyric)

what you do to me. Hot dig-gi-ty, dog zig-gi-ty boom! What you do to me! When you're

hold-ing me tight!
1. Nev-er dreamed an-y-bo-dy could kiss that-a-way,
2. Nev-er knew that my heart could go "Zing!" that-a-way,

Bring me bliss that-a-way, With a kiss that-a-way. — What a won-der-ful feel-ing to
Ting-a-ling that-a-way, Make me sing that-a-way. — Said "Good-bye" to my trou-bles, they

feel that-a-way! Tell me where have you been all my life? Oh! Oh!
went that-a-way, Ev-er since you came in-to my life! Oh.

⊕ Coda

How my fu-ture will shine — from the mo-ment you're mine!

3. There's a cute little cottage for two that-a-way
Skies are blue that-a-way
Dreams come true that-a-way
If you say I can share it with you that-a-way
I'll be happy the rest of my life! Oh!
(Chorus)

337. Hey Rock And Roll

Words & Music by Malcolm Allured, Dave Bartram, Geoffrey Betts, James Field,
Romeo Challenger, Roderick Deas, Buddy Gask & Trevor Oakes

2. Rockin' to the band in a rocket machine
Susie Handjive she's a rock and roll queen
Johnny sings a love song he sings it right from the ha-ha-ha-heart
Whenever Mickey's dancing with the girl in blue
Over to the band and a song for you
Everybody's shouting to the world's greatest rock and roll band.

338. Hold Me Tight

Words & Music by John Lennon & Paul McCartney

339. High

Music by Paul Tucker & Tunde Baiyewu. Words by Paul Tucker

2. Don't you think it's time you started
   Doing what we always wanted
   One day we're gonna get so high
   'Cause even the impossible
   Is easy when we got each other
   One day we're gonna get so high

340. The Huntsmen's Chorus

Composed by Carl Maria Von Weber

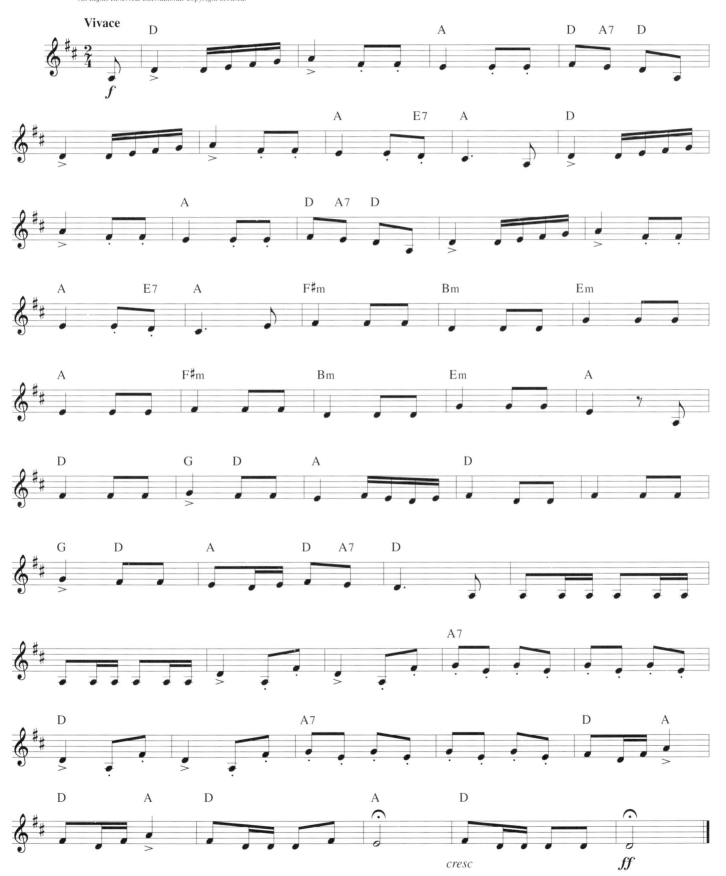

341. Hit The Road To Dreamland

Music by Harold Arlen. Words Johnny Mercer

Bye, bye, ba - by   Time to hit the road to dream - land   You're my ba - by

Dig you in the land of Nod.   Hold tight ba - by   We'll be swing - ing up in dream - land

All   night ba - by   where the lit - tle Cher - ubs trod.   Look   at that knocked out

moon, ___ Been a - blow - in' his top ___ in the blue ___   Nev - er saw the likes of

you; ___   What an An - gel,   Bye,   bye,   ba - by   Time   to   hit   the   road   to

dream - land.   Don't   cry   ba - by   It   was di - vine but the roost - er has fin - 'lly crowed

1.   Time to hit the   road. ___   **2.**   road. ___

342. Heartbeat

Words & Music by Jerry Stevens

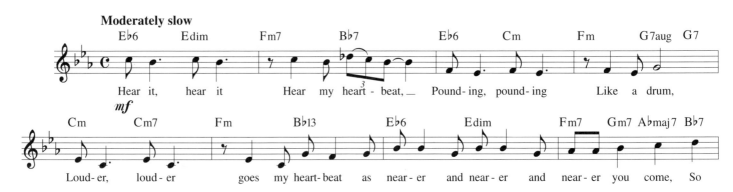

Hear it,   hear it   Hear my heart - beat, ___ Pound - ing, pound - ing   Like a drum,

Loud - er,   loud - er   goes my heart - beat   as near - er   and near - er   and near - er you come,   So

"Hur-ry! Hur-ry!" says my heart-beat _ "Take me, touch me, make me thrill" Fast-er, fast-er

goes my heart-beat, I try, but I can't keep it still. They say when a heart beats too wild-ly _____ That it

breaks like a toy bal-loon, But dar-ling that's put-ting it mild-ly, _____ Com-

-pared to what will hap-pen to mine If some-thing does - n't hap-pen soon List-en, list-en,

to my heart-beat, _ Cry-ing, sigh-ing breath-less-ly, Tell it, tell it, Tell my heart-beat, That

1.
your heart beats for me.

2.
your heart beats for me. _____

343. Holy, Holy, Holy

Music by John Bacchus Dykes. Words by Reginald Heber.

Moderately

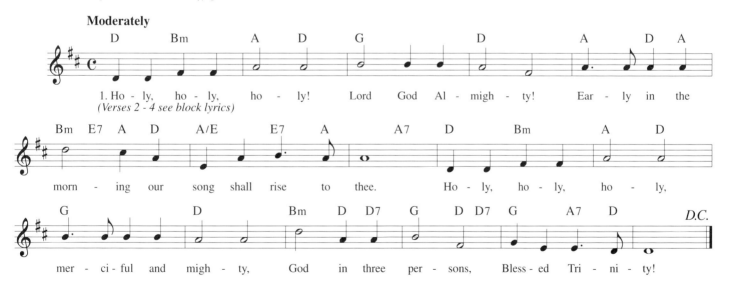

1. Ho - ly, ho - ly, ho - ly! Lord God Al - migh - ty! Ear - ly in the
(Verses 2 - 4 see block lyrics)

morn - ing our song shall rise to thee. Ho - ly, ho - ly, ho - ly,

mer - ci - ful and migh - ty, God in three per - sons, Bless - ed Tri - ni - ty!

D.C.

2. Holy, holy, holy! All the saints adore Thee
   Casting down their golden crowns around the glassy sea
   Cherubim and Seraphim falling down before Thee
   Who wert, and art, and evermore shall be.

3. Holy, holy, holy! Though the darkness hides Thee
   Though the eye of sinful man Thy glory may not see
   Only Thou art holy; there is none beside Thee
   Perfect in power, in love, and purity.

4. Holy, holy, holy! Lord God Almighty!
   All Thy works shall praise Thy name in earth and sky and sea
   Holy, holy, holy! Merciful and mighty
   God in three persons, blessed Trinity!

344. Home And Away

Words & Music by Mike Perjanik

D.%. al Coda

sud - den - ly clear ___ I will al - ways need you here. ___

Coda

F(add 9)   Dm

You know we be - long to - ge - ther, You and I for - ev - er and ev - er,

F(add 9)   rall.   B♭   B♭m6   F

You know we be - long to - ge - ther.   *(instrumental)*

345. Hymn To Red October

By Basil Poledouris

Slowly

mf Wok - tya - breh.   Wok - tya - breh   rah - par   tu - ium miy na - she - pa   bi - e - diy.   Wok - tya -
In October   we report out   victories   to   you,   our Revolution   and   to   the heritage

- breh,   Wok - tya - breh,   no - vie mee - ir dah - li num - nash - y   deh - i - diy.   Tiy - pliy - vee   pliy - vee be-
left by   you   for us.   Sail   on   fearlessly,

- stra shna, ___ got - dest seh   vier - nykh ma - rieye, ___ Re - vo - luy - tzi - ye na-
Pride   of   the Northern seas.   Hope   of   the   Revolution,

- dezh - dah   sgoo - stk vier - if sekh luy - deye.   Sa - lute - a - tsam   e - na - shem
you are the   burst of faith of   the people.   Hail   to   our fathers   and   forefathers.

de - durn   zah - vie - tum eekh   fsig d - ah - vier - ney.   Tie - pierre nich - toh   ni - a - sta
We are   faithful to   the covenant made with the past.   No one   can stop our   victorious march,

noe - vit,   pa - biad - ney sha - rk rad noy - stra - ney.   Wok - tya - breh,   Wok - tya - breh,
our Motherland's victorious   march.   In   October,

rah - par   tu - ium miy na - she - pa   bi - e - diy.   Wok - tya - breh.   nuh - viy - dienye.
we report our   victories   to you, our Revolution and to the heritage   left by you for us.

346. Hungarian Dance No.5

Composed by Johannes Brahms

347. Hungarian March

Composed by Hector Berlioz

348. Hole In The Ground

Music by Ted Dicks. Words by Myles Rudge

349. Home Cookin'

Words & Music by Jay Livingston & Ray Evans

350. A House Is Not A Home

Music by Burt Bacharach. Words by Hal David

351. How Would You Like To Be

Words & Music by Mark Barkan & Ben Raleigh

352. Hornpipe (from 'The Water Music')

Composed by George Frideric Handel

353. Hey There, Lonely Girl

Music by Leon Carr. Words by Earl Shuman

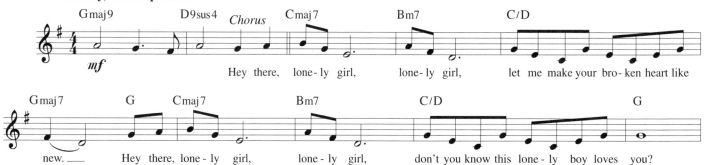

1. Ev - er since he broke your heart, _____ you seem so lost _____ each time you pass my way,
lips _____ can kiss your lips _____ and make your heart stand still.

Oh, how I long to take your hand _____ and say, "Don't cry, _____ I'll kiss your
But once you're in my arms you'll see _____ no one can kiss _____ your lips the

Chorus

tears a - way." _____ Hey there, lone - ly girl, lone - ly girl, let me make your bro - ken heart like
way I will. _____

new. _____ Hey there, lone - ly girl, lone - ly girl, don't you know this lone - ly boy loves

1.
you?

2.
2. You think that on - ly his two you. Hey there, lone - ly girl,

lone - ly girl, don't you know this lone - ly boy loves you? _____

354. **The Harmonious Blacksmith**

Composed by George Frideric Handel

Andante

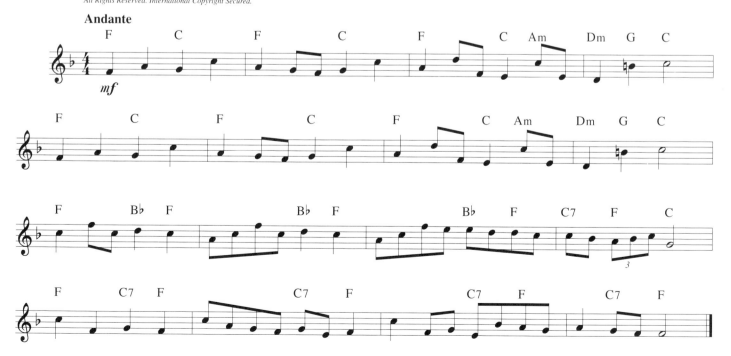

355. I Am The Monarch Of The Sea

By W. S. Gilbert & Sir Arthur Sullivan

Moderately fast

356. How Cute Can You Be?

Music by Carl Fischer. Words by Bill Carey

Moderately slow

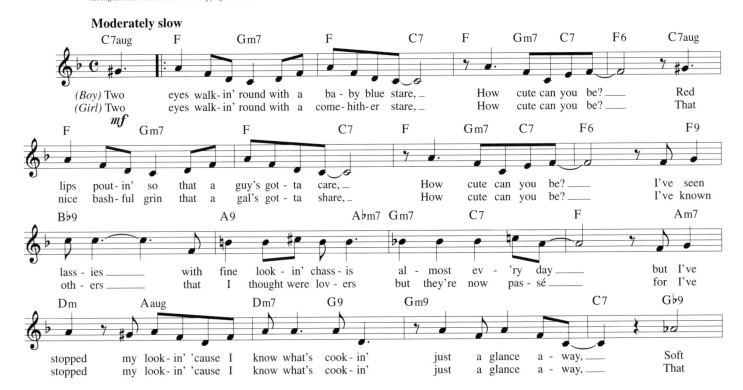

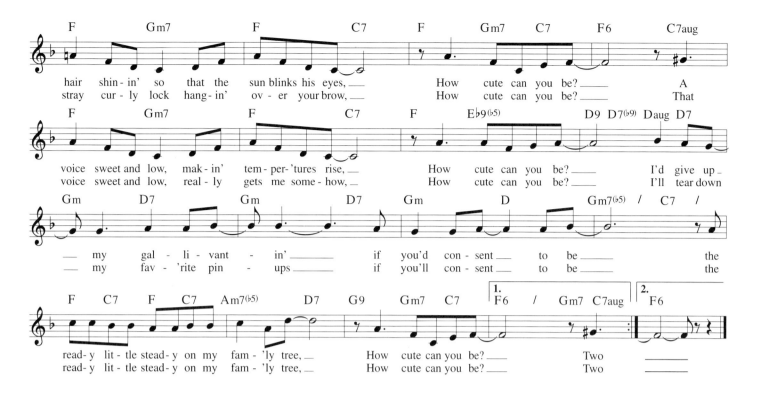

357. I Have Eyes

Words & Music by Leo Robin & Ralph Rainger

358. I Am Blessed

Words & Music by Marsha Malamet & Mark Mueller

life, I re-al-ise you have gi-ven me such peace and hap-pi-ness, in this world where some have more and some have less, I have love and I am blessed.

2. So many changes
    This world can put you through
    Sometimes it's hard to find a way
    A heart can get confused
    But then I hold you and it all falls into place
    You give me what's right and I cannot erase
    So when I'm feeling down
    I feel sorry for myself
    I look around and it's easy to tell.

359. I Need Your Love Tonight

Words & Music by Sid Wayne & Bix Reichner

Medium bright rock

Oh, oh! I love you so. Uh, uh, can't let you go. Ooh, ooh, don't tell me no. I need your love to-night. Oh, gee, the way you kiss. Swee-dee, too good to miss. Wow-whee, want more of this. I need your love to-night. I've been wait-in' just for to-night to do some lov-in' and hold you tight. Don't tell me, ba-by, you got-ta go; I got the hi-fi high and the lights down low. Hey, now, hear what I say, Ooh-wow, you bet-ter stay. Pow-pow, don't run a-way. I need your love to-night. Oh,

360. I Didn't Believe In Santa Claus ('Til The Day He Gave Me You)

Words & Music by Dick Charles

361. I Wonder Why

Words & Music by Curtis Stigers & Glen Ballard

Verse 2.   Though I'm no angel
With my selfish pride
But I love you more
Every day
Love is an anger
That builds up inside
As the tears of frustration
Roll down my face
Why does love always have to turn out
This way?

Chorus 2.   And I wonder why we hold on
With tears in our eyes
And I wonder why we have to break down
To just make things right
And I wonder why I can't seem
To tell you goodbye
Oh I wonder why.

362. I Didn't Mean To Hurt You

Words & Music by Paul Weller

2. Whatever they tell you
There's more I could say
Lending motion to the wheel
How you built me up
When I was falling down down
Who knows you might just find

You might just find that I'm just your kind
And I really didn't mean to hurt you.

Oh darling, I didn't mean to hurt you
Deep down inside I never meant to hurt you
Oh child, didn't mean to hurt you girl.

363. I Don't Want To Walk Without You

Music by Jule Styne. Words by Frank Loesser

364. I Laugh To Keep From Crying

Words & Music by Nacio Porter Brown & Leon Pober

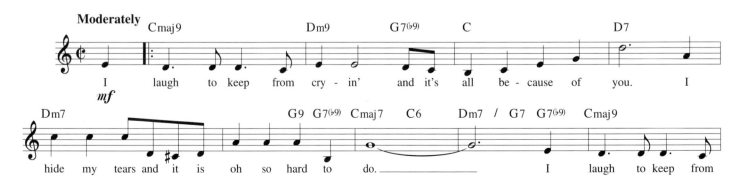

365. Inamorata

Music by Harry Warren. Words by Jack Brooks

366. I Don't Want To Put A Hold On You

Words & Music by Mike & Bernie Flint

Moderately

If you wan-na leave ___ me, well, that's all right.

Come the morn-in', ___ find you're gone, ___ well, well I won't mind.

It's not that I don't love ___ you, ba-by, you know I do, ___

but I don't want to put no hold ___ on you. Such a love-ly

feel-ing, dar-ling, hav-ing you ___ so near. Gee, it's good to

know that you're ___ a-round. ___ But should you ev-er ___ go a-way ___ then

let me make ___ it clear, I won't ev-er try ___ to tie ___ you down.

And if you should get

rest-less, well, that's all right, find that you're in ___ need of a change, ___ well,

364

367. I Get Along Without You Very Well

Words & Music by Hoagy Carmichael

368. I Like It

Words & Music by Mitch Murray

369. I Hear Music

Music by Burton Lane. Words by Frank Loesser

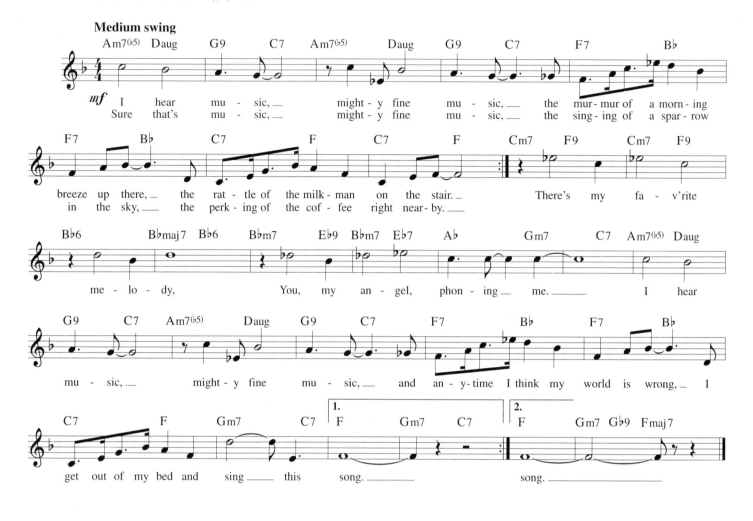

I hear mu - sic, __ might - y fine mu - sic, __ the mur - mur of a morn - ing
Sure that's mu - sic, __ might - y fine mu - sic, __ the sing - ing of a spar - row

breeze up there, __ the rat - tle of the milk - man on the stair. __ There's my fa - v'rite
in the sky, __ the perk - ing of the cof - fee right near - by. __

me - lo - dy, You, my an - gel, phon - ing __ me. __ I hear

mu - sic, __ might - y fine mu - sic, __ and an - y - time I think my world is wrong, __ I

get out of my bed and sing __ this song. song.

370. I Believe In Father Christmas

Words by Peter Sinfield. Music by Greg Lake

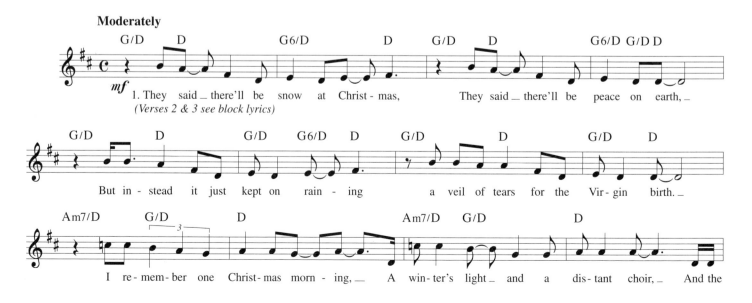

1. They said __ there'll be snow at Christ - mas, They said __ there'll be peace on earth, __
(Verses 2 & 3 see block lyrics)

But in - stead it just kept on rain - ing a veil of tears for the Vir - gin birth.

I re - mem - ber one Christ - mas morn - ing, __ A win - ter's light __ and a dis - tant choir, __ And the

peal of a bell and that Christ-mas tree smell, ___ And their eyes full of tin-sel and fire. ___

2. They sold me a dream of Christmas
They sold me a silent night
And they told me a fairy story
Till I believed in the Israelite
And I believed in Father Christmas
And I looked to the sky with excited eyes
Till I woke with a yawn in the first light of dawn
And I saw him and through his disguise.

3. I wish you a hopeful Christmas
I wish you a brave New Year
All anguish, pain and sadness
Leave your heart and let your road be clear
They said there'd be snow at Christmas
They said there'd be peace on earth
Hallelujah Noel be it heaven or hell
The Christmas we get we deserve.

371. It's A Small World

Words & Music by Richard M. Sherman & Robert B. Sherman

Moderate march

It's a world of laugh-ter, a world of tears; it's a world of hopes and a
just one moon and one gold-en sun and a smile means friend-ship to

world of fears, There's so much that we share that it's time we're a - ware. It's a
ev - 'ry one, Though the moun - tains di - vide and the o - ceans are wide, It's a

small world af - ter all. ___
small world af - ter all. ___

It's a small world

af - ter all, It's a small world af - ter all. It's a

small world af - ter all. It's a small, small world. ___ There is

372. I Remember You

Music by Victor Schertzinger. Words by Johnny Mercer

373. I Wish I Didn't Love You So

Words & Music by Frank Loesser

smil-ing by now ____ with some new ____ ten-der friend, ____ smil-ing by now ____
with my heart ____ on the mend. ____ But when I try, some-thing in that heart says
"No," _____ you're still there. I wish I did-n't love you so. ____

374. I Want To Walk You Home

Words & Music by Antoine Domino

Moderate slow rock

I want to walk you home, ____ Please let me walk you home, ____ I want to
hold your hand, ____ Please let me hold your hand, ____ I want to

walk you home, ____ Please let me walk you home, ____ You look so good to me,
hold your hand, ____ Please let me hold your hand, ____ You look so good to me,

Oh ooh - ee, ____ I wish I was the luc-ky guy ____ who could walk you right on down the aisle, I love the

way you walk, ____ I love to hear you talk, ____ I love the

way you walk, ____ I love to hear you talk, ____ I'm not try-in' to be smart, I'm

not try-in' to break your heart, But if I ask you for a date, ____ Will you tell me that I'm not too late? I want to

⊕ Coda

Oh ooh - ee, ____ I saw you walk-in' all al - one, ____ That's why I want to walk ____ you home.

371

375. I Said No

Words & Music by Jule Styne & Frank Loesser

I said "No" He said, "Please" I said, "No" He said, "Please" I said, "No" He said, "Please pret - ty ba - by" _____ I said, "No" He said, "Why?" I said, "No" He said, "Why?" I said "No" He said, "Try" I said, "May - be." _____ He said, "Now" I said, "Well" He said, "Ah, This is swell," "And you'll nev - er know how much it will mean!" ___ So at last I con - fess I said "Yes, yes - yes - yes - yes." That's how I sub - scribed to Lib - er - ty Mag - a - zine. _____

376. I Don't Care If The Sun Don't Shine

Words & Music by Mack David

I don't care _ if the sun don't shine, _ I get my lov - in' in the eve - nin' time, _ When I'm with my ba - by, _____ It's no fun _ with the sun a - roun', _ But I get go - in' when the sun goes down, _ And I meet my ba - by. _____ ___ That's when we kiss, _ and kiss, _ and kiss, _ And then ___ we kiss _ some more,

377. I Only Saw Him (You) Once

Words & Music by Joan Whitney & Alex Kramer

Moderately slow

378. I Wonder Where Our Love Has Gone

Words & Music by Woodrow Buddy Johnson

379. I'll Be Back

Words & Music by John Lennon & Paul McCartney

380. I'll Never Break Your Heart

Words & Music by Eugene Wilde & Albert Manno

(Spoken): Baby, I know you are hurting; right now you feel like you could never love again. Now all I ask is for a chance

to prove that I love you. (1.) From the first day that I saw your smil-ing face, ho-ney, I

(Verse 2 see block lyric)

knew that we would be to-geth-er for-ev-er. Ooh, when I asked you out, you said

no, but I found out, dar-ling that you'd been hurt, you felt that you'd nev-er

love a-gain. I de-serve a try ho-ney, just once,

give me a chance and I'll prove this all wrong. You walked in, you were so quick to judge, but

1st time only
2nd time only

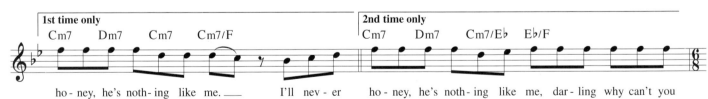

ho-ney, he's noth-ing like me. I'll nev-er ho-ney, he's noth-ing like me, dar-ling why can't you

see? I'll nev-er break your heart, I'll nev-er make you cry. I'd rath-er

die than live with-out you, I'll give you all of me, ho-ney that's no lie. I'll nev-er

376

break your _____ heart, _____ I'll nev - er make you _____ cry. _____ I'd rath - er

die than live with - out you, I'll give you all of me, ho - ney that's no lie.

No way, no how, I _____ swear, no way, no how,

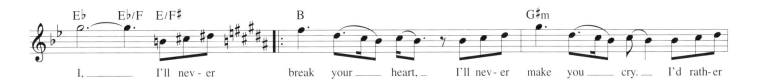

I, _____ I'll nev - er break your _____ heart, _____ I'll nev - er make you _____ cry. _____ I'd rath - er

die than live with - out you, I'll give you all of me, ho - ney that's no lie. I'll nev - er

break your _____ heart, _____ I'll nev - er make you _____ cry. _____ I'd rath - er

Repeat to fade

die than live with - out you, I'll give you all of me, ho - ney that's no lie, I'll nev - er

2. As I walked by you,
Will you get to know me
A little more better?
Girl, that's the way love goes
And I know you're afraid
To let your feelings show
And I understand
But girl it's time to let go.

I deserve a try, honey
Just once
Give me a chance
And I'll prove this all wrong
You walked in
You were so quick to judge
But honey he's nothing like me
Darling why can't you see?

381. I'll Never Fall In Love Again

Words by Hal David. Music by Burt Bacharach.

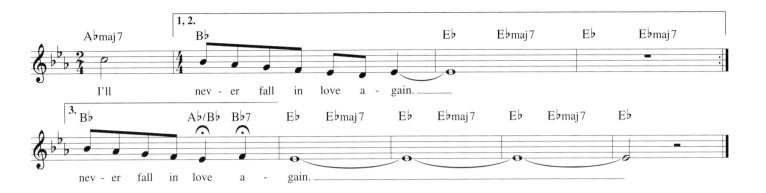

382. I Think Of You

Words & Music by Jack Elliott & Don Marcotte

383. I'm A Little Christmas Cracker

Words & Music by Cosy Lee

384. I'm Gonna Make It All The Way

Words & Music by Floyd Huddleston

2. You hurt me and abused me
Took advantage of and used me
I swear it almost made a wreck of me
When I needed your devotion
You were never in the notion
You were colder than an iceberg in the sea
Love to you had lost its splendor
My pride went out the window
When you left me I kept beggin' you to stay
But now me heart is healin'
I've got a real good feelin'
I think I'm gonna make it all the way.

3. My troubles came in bunches
I kept rollin' with the punches
You'd shoot me down, I'd get back up again
I tried to be your lover
In no time I discovered
Your lovin' cup was not for me to win
Your kisses weren't the same
But I kept tryin' to fan the flame
'Til I just couldn't face another day
You can't blame me for tryin'
Now that I've stopped cryin'
I think I'm gonna make it all the way.

4. I tried my best to fake it
But a smilin' face don't make it
'Cause in my heart I knew there was no hope
Each place reminded me of
The memories of your love
I'd come right to the end of my rope
That's when I met my new friend
She's just a passing-through friend
But she treats me like love is here to stay
It's workin' out real well now
And you can go to hell now
This time I'm gonna make it all the way
Oh yes! I'm gonna make it all the way.

385. I'm Late

Words by Bob Hilliard. Music by Sammy Fain

Brightly

I'm late, I'm late for a ver-y im-por-tant date. No time to say hel-lo, good-bye, I'm late, I'm late, I'm late, I'm late and when I wave, I lose the time I save. My fuz-zy ears and whis-kers took me too much time to shave. I run and then I hop, hop, hop, I wish that I could fly. There's dan-ger if I dare to stop and here's the rea-son why, (you see) I'm o - ver-due, I'm in a rab-bit stew, Can't e-ven say good-bye, hel-lo, I'm late, I'm late, I'm late.

386. I Won't Cry Anymore

Words by Fred Wise. Music by Al Frisch

Moderately slow

I won't cry an-y-more ___ now that you've left me, ___ I won't cry an-y-more ___ now that you're gone. ___ I've shed a mil-lion tears since we're a-part But tears can nev-er mend a bro-ken heart. I won't sigh an-y-more, ___

387. I Only Have Eyes For You

Words by Al Dubin. Music by Harry Warren

388. I'm Not The Marrying Kind

Words & Music by Mack David & Sherman Edwards

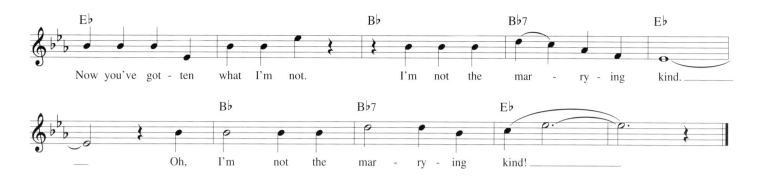

389. I'm Popeye The Sailor Man

Words & Music by Sammy Lerner

© Copyright 1934 Famous Music Corporation, USA.
All Rights Reserved. International Copyright Secured.

390. I'm Only Sleeping

Words & Music by John Lennon & Paul McCartney

391. I Say A Little Prayer

Words by Hal David. Music by Burt Bacharach

392. If I Ever Lose My Faith In You

Words & Music by Sting

first: ___ If I ev-er lose ___ my faith ___ in you, ___

if I ev-er lose ___ my faith ___ in you, there'd be no-thing left ___ for me ___ to do,

there'd be no-thing left ___ for me ___ to do. If I ev-er lose ___

___ my faith, ___ if I ev-er lose ___ my faith, ___ if I ev-er lose ___

___ my faith, ___ if I ev-er lose ___ my faith ___ in you...

Repeat to fade

393. I Saw Three Ships

Traditional Christmas Carol

Moderately

1. I saw three ships come sail-ing in on Christ-mas day, On Christ-mas day, I

saw three ships come sail-ing in, On Christ-mas day in the morn-ing.

2. And what was in those ships all three
On Christmas day, on Christmas day
And what was in those ships all three
On Christmas day in the morning?

3. The Virgin Mary and Christ were there
On Christmas day, on Christmas day
The Virgin Mary and Christ were there
On Christmas day in the morning.

4. Pray, whither sailed those ships all three
On Christmas day, on Christmas day
Pray, whither sailed those ships all three
On Christmas day in the morning?

5. O they sailed into Bethlehem
On Christmas day, on Christmas day
O they sailed into Bethlehem
On Christmas day in the morning.

6. And all the bells on earth shall ring
On Christmas day, on Christmas day
And all the bells on earth shall ring
On Christmas day in the morning.

7. And all the angels in heaven shall sing
On Christmas day, on Christmas day
And all the angels in heaven shall sing
On Christmas day in the morning.

8. And all the souls on earth shall sing
On Christmas day, on Christmas day
And all the souls on earth shall sing
On Christmas day in the morning.

9. Then let us all rejoice again
On Christmas day, on Christmas day
Then let us all rejoice again
On Christmas day in the morning.

394. If I Loved You

Words by Oscar Hammerstein II. Music by Richard Rodgers

395. If You Are But A Dream

Words by Moe Jaffe & Jack Fulton. Music by Nat Bonx

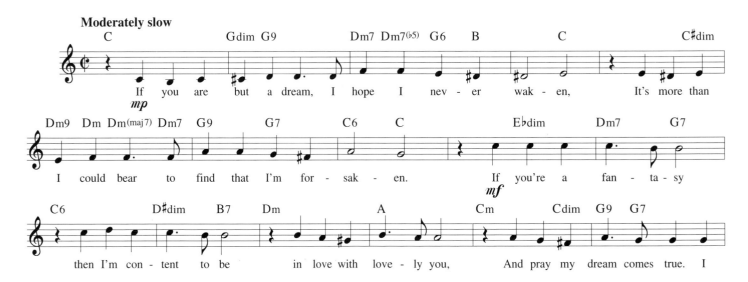

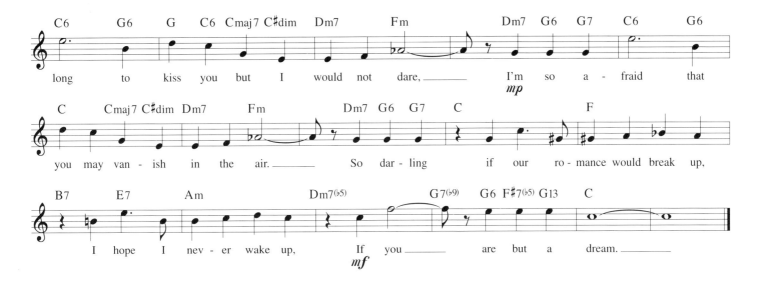

long to kiss you but I would not dare, ___ I'm so a - fraid that
you may van - ish in the air. ___ So dar - ling if our ro - mance would break up,
I hope I nev - er wake up, If you ___ are but a dream. ___

396. I've Got The World On A String

Music by Ted Koehler. Words by Harold Arlen

Easy swing

I've got the world on a string, ___ sit - tin' on a rain - bow,
song that I sing, ___ I can make the rain go,

Got the string a - round my fin - ger, What a world, what a ___ life, ___ I'm in
an - y time I move my fin - ger, Luck - y me, can't you ___ see, ___ I'm in

1. love! I've got a
2. love? ___ Life is a beau - ti - ful thing, ___

as long as I hold the string, ___ I'd be a sil - ly so and so,

if I should ev - er let go. ___ I've got the world on a string, ___

sit - tin' on a rain - bow, Got the string a - round my fin - ger,

What a world, what a ___ life, I'm in love. ___

391

397. If I Said You Have A Beautiful Body Would You Hold It Against Me

Words & Music by David M. Bellamy

Moderately

If I said ___ you have a beau-ti-ful bo - dy, would you hold it a-gainst ___ me? ___

If I swore ___ you were an an - gel, would you treat me like the dev - il to-night? ___

If I was dy - ing of thirst, ___ would your flow-ing love ___ come quench ___ me? ___

If I said ___ you have a beau-ti-ful bo - dy, would you hold it a-gainst

___ me? ___

Verse

Now, we could talk all night ___ a - bout the weath-er;
Now, rain can fall so soft ___ a-gainst the win - dow;

could tell you 'bout my friends ___ out on the coast.
the sun can shine so bright ___ up in the sky.

I could ask a lot ___ of cra - zy ques - tions, ___
But dad-dy al - ways told ___ me, don't ___ make small ___ talk;

he said or ask you ___ what I real - ly ___ want to know.
"Come on out ___ and ___ say ___ what's on your mind."

1.
If I said

2.
D.%. and fade on Chorus
So, if I said ___

398. It's A Most Unusual Day

Music by Jimmy McHugh. Words by Harold Adamson.

399. If You Please

Music by Jimmy Van Heusen. Words by Johnny Burke

400. I Slipped, I Stumbled, I Fell

Words by Fred Wise. Music by Ben Weisman

cake of ice.__ You skate a - long, but then you nev - er can tell.__ I slipped, I

stum - bled, I fell.__ I nev - er thought I'd get tricked - a by your sweet talk - in' lies.__

You've got a bag__ of tricks. __ And when you got bu - sy I got daz - zled and diz - zy. I

fell like a ton of bricks. My knees are weak; my head is spin - ning a - round._ I guess that

love has turned me up - side down. Thought I'd get hurt, but, gee, it's turn - ing out swell.__ I

slipped, I stum - bled, I fell. __ I look at stum - bled, I fell. __

401. I'm Falling In Love With Someone

Words by Rida Johnson Young. Music by Victor Herbert

Moderately

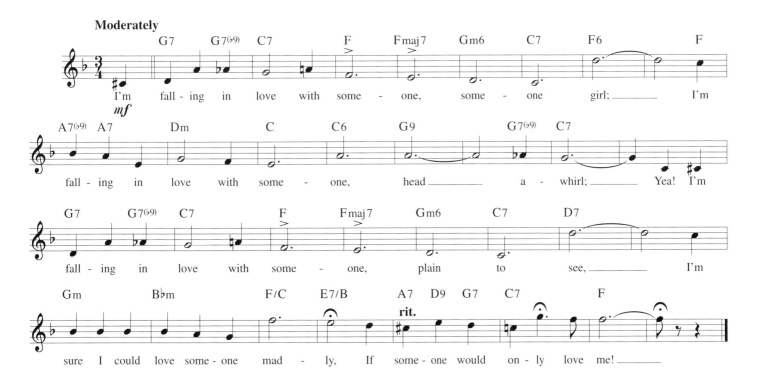

I'm fall - ing in love with some - one, some - one girl;_____ I'm

fall - ing in love with some - one, head _____ a - whirl; _____ Yea! I'm

fall - ing in love with some - one, plain to see, _____ I'm

sure I could love some - one mad - ly, If some - one would on - ly love me! _____

402. In Old New York

Music by Victor Herbert. Words by Henry Blossom

403. I Was Telling Her About You

Music by Mark Charlap. Words by Don George.

404. In Old Lisbon (Lisboa Antigua)

Music by Paul Portela, J Galhardo & A. do Vale. English Lyric by Henry Dupree.

Moderate beguine

I gave my heart _____ to you in old Lis-bon that night, _____

Un-der the spell of your charms, _____ I felt your arms _____ hold me so tight; _____ 'Twas

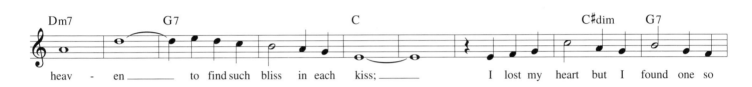

heav - en _____ to find such bliss in each kiss; _____ I lost my heart but I found one so

true, _____ in old Lis - bon with you. _____ I gave my you. _____

you. _____ It hap-pened one night in Por - tu - gal _____ Lis-bon was

gay in the moon - light, _____ The stars were shin - ing a - bove _____ when I

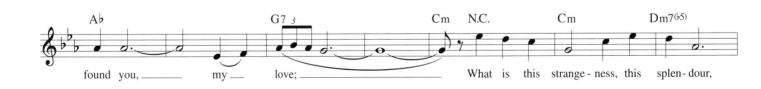

found you, _____ my ____ love; _____ What is this strange - ness, this splen - dour,

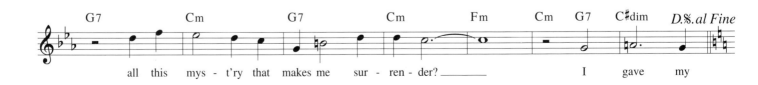

all this mys - t'ry that makes me sur - ren - der? _____ I gave my

398

405. It's Christmas Once Again

Words & Music by Evelyn Blackman, Elaine Blackman & Leona Blackman

406. In The Middle Of A Kiss

Words & Music by Sam Coslow

In the mid-dle of a kiss _____ Sud-den-ly it dawned _ on me _____ In the mid-dle of a kiss _____ I knew _ you were mine _____ In the mid-dle of a sweet _ em-brace _____ That you at first re-sent-ed _____ Re-mem-ber, how sur-prised we were _ To find we real-ly meant it? In the mid-dle of a sigh _____ We stum-bled in-to Par- -a-dise _____ In the twin-kle of an eye _____ We lost _ it a-gain _____ For we did-n't com-pre-hend _____ That our dream of love would end _____ Just the way it be-gan _____ In the mid-dle of a kiss.

407. In The Cool, Cool, Cool Of The Evening

Music by Hoagy Carmichael. Words by Johnny Mercer

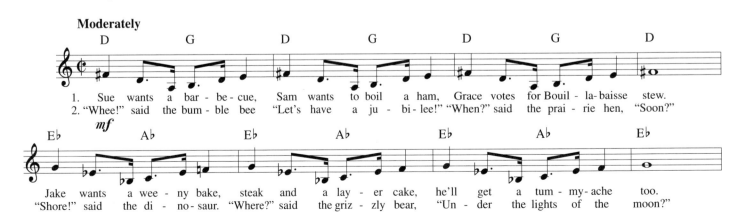

1. Sue wants a bar-be-cue, Sam wants to boil a ham, Grace votes for Bouil-la-baisse stew.
2. "Whee!" said the bum-ble bee "Let's have a ju-bi-lee!" "When?" said the prai-rie hen, "Soon?"

Jake wants a wee-ny bake, steak and a lay-er cake, he'll get a tum-my-ache too.
"Shore!" said the di-no-saur. "Where?" said the griz-zly bear, "Un-der the lights of the moon?"

We'll rent a tent or tee - pee, Let the town cri - er cry.____ And if it's R. S.
"How 'bout ya, broth - er jack - ass?" Ev - 'ry - one gai - ly cried,____ "You com - in' to the

V. P. this is what I'll re - ply. In the cool, cool, cool of the eve - nin',
fra - cas?" Ov - er his specks he sighed; In the cool, cool, cool of the eve - nin',

tell 'em I'll be there.____ In the cool, cool, cool of the eve - nin', bet - ter save a chair.____
tell 'em I'll be there.____ In the cool, cool, cool of the eve - nin', slick - um on my hair.____

____ When the par - ty's get - tin' a glow_____ on, 'n' sing - in' fills the air,____ In the
____ When the par - ty's get - tin' a glow_____ on, 'n' sing - in' fills the air,____ If I

shank o' the night, when the do - in's are right, _ you can tell 'em I'll be there. ____
ain't in the clink, and there's sump - in' to drink, _ you can tell 'em I'll be there.

408. Johnny And Mary

Words & Music by Robert Palmer

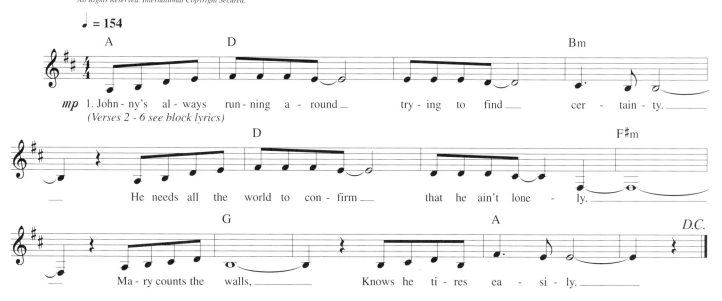

♩ = 154

mp 1. John - ny's al - ways run - ning a - round ___ try - ing to find ___ cer - tain - ty. ___
(Verses 2 - 6 see block lyrics)

___ He needs all the world to con - firm ___ that he ain't lone - ly.

Ma - ry counts the walls, _____ Knows he ti - res ea - si - ly. _____

2. Johnny thinks the world would be right
If he could buy the truth from you
Mary says he changes his mind
More than a woman
But she made her bed
Even when chances were slim.

3. Johnny says he's willing to learn
When he decides he's a fool
Johnny says he'll live anywhere
Any old time at all
Mary combs her hair
Says she should be used to it.

4. Mary always hedges her bets
She never knows what to think
She says that he still acts
Loke he's being discovered
Scared that he'll be caught
Without a second thought.

5. Johnny feels he's wasting his breath
Trying to talk sense to her
Mary says he's lacking a real
Sense of proportion
So she combs her hair
Knows he tires easily.

6. Johnny's always running around
Trying to find certainty
He needs all the world to confirm
That he ain't lonely
Mary counts the walls
Says she should be used to it.

409. In These Arms

Words & Music by Jon Bon Jovi, Richie Sambora & David Bryan

403

410. Into Each Life Some Rain Must Fall

Words & Music by Allan Roberts & Doris Fisher

411. It Looks Like Rain In Cherry Blossom Lane

Words & Music by Edgar Leslie & Joe Burke

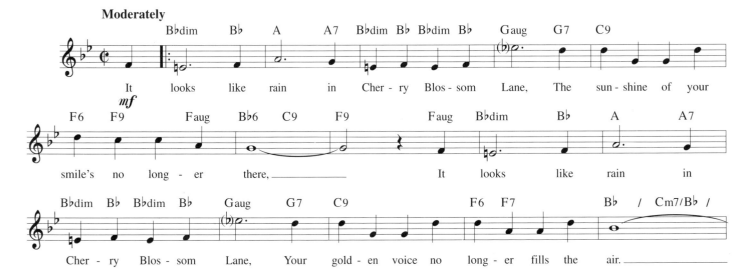

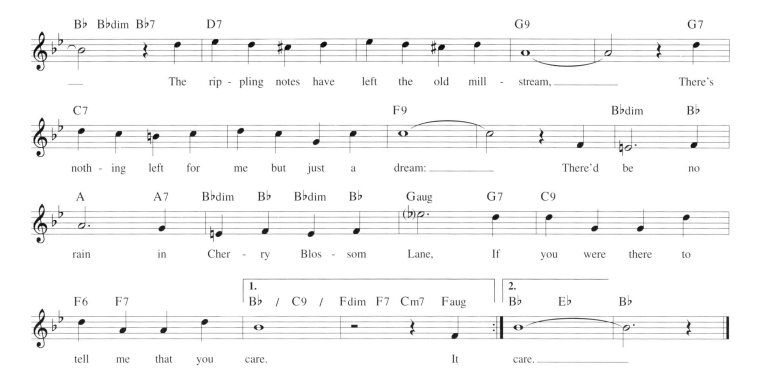

The rip - pling notes have left the old mill - stream, There's
noth - ing left for me but just a dream: There'd be no
rain in Cher - ry Blos - som Lane, If you were there to
tell me that you care. It care.

412. It's All Over But The Memories

Words & Music by Irving Kahal, Sammy Fain & Rudy Vallee

Moderately slow

It's all o - ver but the mem - o - ries It's all
o - ver but the tears Your face be - fore my sight
Your kiss to haunt me through the night. It's all o - ver but the
emp - ty years What more can I look for - ward to? It's
all o - ver but the mem - o - ries of you,
just you. It's just you.

413. Iron Lion Zion

Words & Music by Bob Marley

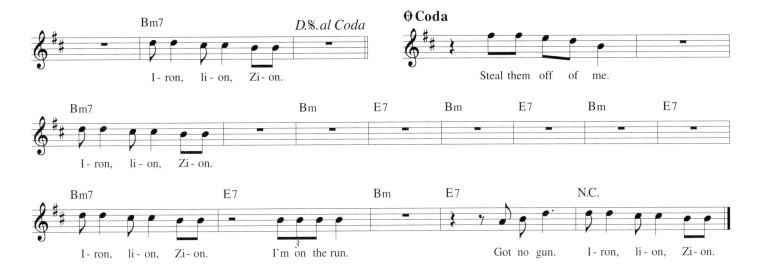

I- ron, li - on, Zi - on.

Steal them off of me.

I- ron, li - on, Zi - on.

I- ron, li - on, Zi - on. I'm on the run. Got no gun. I- ron, li - on, Zi - on.

414. I'm Walkin'

Words & Music by Antoine Domino & Dave Bartholomew

Moderate rock

I'm walk- in', ___ yes in - deed, ___ and I'm talk- in' ___ 'bout you and me, ___ I'm

hop- in' ___ that you'll come back to me, Yes, ___ I'm lone- ly ___ as

I can be, ___ I'm wait- in' ___ for your com - pa - ny, ___ I'm hop- in' ___ that

you'll come back to me. ___ What ya gon- na do when the well runs dry?

You're gon- na run a - way and hide, I'm gon- na run right by your side, For

you pret- ty ba - by I'll ev - en die. I'm walk- in', ___ yes in - deed, I'm talk- in' ___ 'bout

you and me, ___ I'm hop- in' that you'll come back to me. ___

415. Isn't It Romantic

Music by Richard Rodgers. Words by Lorenz Hart

416. It's The Talk Of The Town

Words & Music by Marty Symes, Al J. Neiburg & Jerry Levinson

Ev-'ry time we meet, My heart skips a beat, We don't stop to speak, Tho' it's just a week,

Ev-'ry-bo-dy knows you left me, It's the talk of the town. _____ We

sent out in-vi-ta-tions, To friends and re-la-tions, An-nounc-ing our wed-ding day,

Friends and our re-la-tions, Gave con-gra-tu-la-tions, How can you face them? What can you say?

Let's make up sweet-heart, We can't stay a-part, Don't let fool-ish pride, Keep you from my side,

How can love like ours be en-ded? It's the talk of the town. _____

417. Jolly Old Saint Nicholas

Words & Music by Vaughn Horton

Moderately

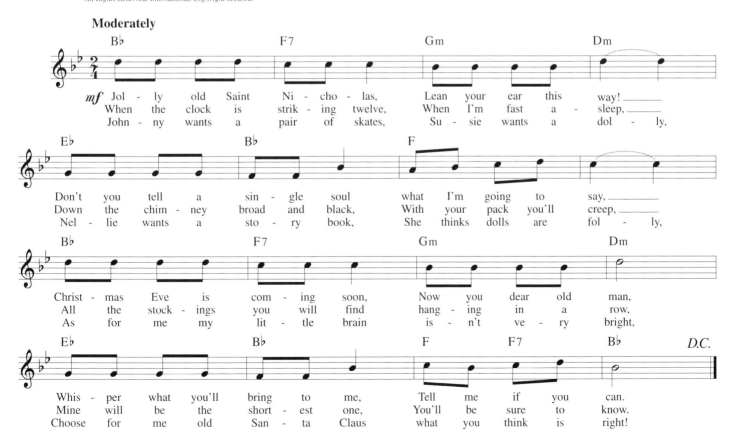

Jol - ly old Saint Ni - cho - las, Lean your ear this way! _____
When the clock is strik - ing twelve, When I'm fast a - sleep, _____
John - ny wants a pair of skates, Su - sie wants a dol - ly,

Don't you tell a sin - gle soul what I'm going to say, _____
Down the chim - ney broad and black, With your pack you'll creep, _____
Nel - lie wants a sto - ry book, She thinks dolls are fol - ly,

Christ - mas Eve is com - ing soon, Now you dear old man,
All the stock - ings you will find hang - ing in a row,
As for me my lit - tle brain is - n't ver - y bright,

Whis - per what you'll bring to me, Tell me if you can.
Mine will be the short - est one, You'll be sure to know.
Choose for me old San - ta Claus what you think is right!

418. It Was Almost Like A Song

Words & Music by Hal David & Archie Jordan

419. I'm Just A Lucky So And So

Words & Music by Mack David & Duke Ellington

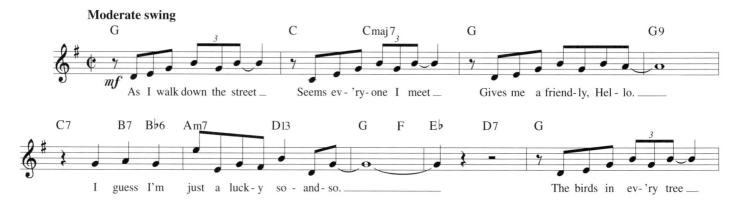

Are all so neigh-bor-ly ___ They sing wher-ev-er I go. ___ I guess I'm

just a luck-y so- and-so. ___ If you should ask me the a-mount

In my bank ac-count, I'd have to con-fess ___ that I'm slip-pin' ___ But that don't wor-ry me,

con-fi-den-tial-ly, I've got a dream that's a pip-pin'. ___

And when the day is through ___ Each night I hur-ry to ___ a home where love waits, I know. ___

I guess I'm just a luck-y so- and -so. ___

420. In The Hall Of The Mountain King

Music by Edvard Grieg

Moderate march

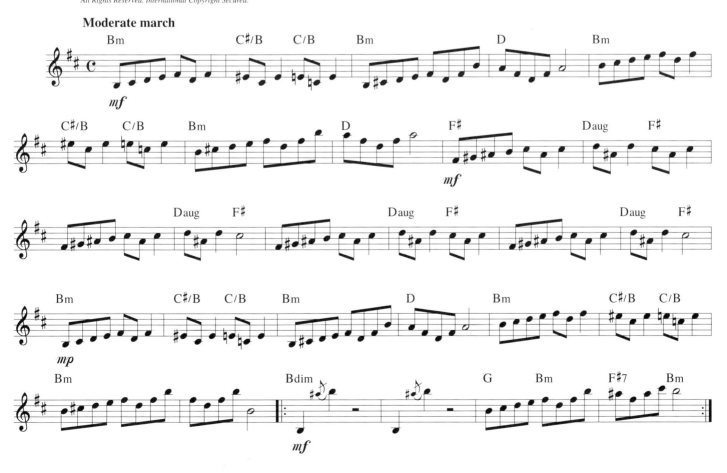

421. It's A Long Road

Music by Jerry Goldsmith. Words by Hal Shaper

live. _____ It's a real war _____ Right out-side your front door I tell ya _____

Out where they'll kill ya _____ you could use a friend _____ Cause _____

the road is long, yeah _____ Each step is on-ly a be-gin-ning _____

No breaks, just heart - aches _ Oh man, is an-y-bo-dy win-ning? _____

It's a long road, _____ It's a long road. _____

422. It Could Happen To You

Music by Jimmy Van Heusen. Words by Johnny Burke

Moderately slow

Hide your heart from sight, lock your dreams at night. It could hap-pen to

you. _____ Don't count stars or you might stum - ble, Some - one

drops a sigh, and down you tum - ble. Keep an eye on Spring, run when church bells ring.

It could hap-pen to you. _____ All I did was won-der how your arms would

be and it hap-pened to me! me!

423. It's Alright (Baby's Coming Back)

Words & Music by A. Lennox & D. A. Stewart

Lyrics under staves (top section):

— your ease). — I will be __ your storm __ at seas. And I'll be (your sharp in - take __

— of breath). __ And I'll be (your work; I'll take __ no rest). __ And

D.C. to fade

when the world __ falls to _____ de - cline __ I'll be your __ and you'll __ be mine. _____

424. I Wan'na Be Like You (The Monkey Song)

Words & Music by Richard M. Sherman & Robert B. Sherman

Brightly

Lyrics under staves (song section):

Now I'm the king of the swing-ers. the jun - gle V. I. P. I've
try to kid __ me, man - cub, and don't get in a stew what

reached the top and had to stop and that's what's both - er - in' me. I wan-na be a man
I de - sire is man's red fire, so I can be __ like you. Give me __ the __ sec - ret

man - cub, And stroll right in - to town, and be just like the oth - er men, I'm
man - cub, Just clue me what to do, give me the pow'r of man's red flow'r, and

tired of mon - key - in' 'round! } Oh Ooh, ooh, oh! (Ee - ee) I wan - na be like
make my dream come true! } I wan - na be like

you, ooh, ooh! (Ee - ee) I wan - na walk like you, talk like you, too ooh, ooh. (Ee -

ee) You'll see it's true, ooh, ooh! (Ee - ee) An ape like me, ee, ee (ooh - ooh) Can learn to be

1.
Hu - ooh - ooh - man, __ too, Ooh - ooh. (Ee - ee)

2.
Don't too, Ooh - ooh. (Ee - ee)

415

425. It's Delightful Down In Chile

Music by Jule Styne. Lyrics by Leo Robin

426. It Must Be Him

Music by Gilbert Becaud. English Lyric by Mack David.
Original French Lyric by Maurice Vidalin

427. It's Easy To Remember

Words by Lorenz Hart. Music by Richard Rodgers

Your sweet ex - pres - sion, the smile you gave me, the way you looked when we met. It's ea - sy to re - mem - ber but so hard to for - get. I hear you whis - per, "I'll al - ways love you." I know it's ov - er and yet, it's ea - sy to re - mem - ber but so hard to for - get. So I must dream to have your hand ca - ress me, fin - gers press me tight. I'd rath - er dream than have that lone - ly feel - ing steal - ing through the night. Each lit - tle mo - ment is clear be - fore me, and though it brings me re - gret, it's ea - sy to re - mem - ber and so hard to for - get. Your sweet ex - so hard to for - get.

428. It's Now Or Never

Words & Music by G. Capurro & E. Di Capua.
English Lyric by Aaron Schroeder & Wally Gold

It's now or nev - er; come hold me tight. Kiss me, my dar - lin', be mine to - night. To - mor - row will be too late. It's now or

never;_____ my love won't wait. When I first saw you_____ with your smile so
Just like a wil-low_____ we would cry an

ten-der, my heart was cap-tured,_____ my soul sur-ren-dered. I've spent a
o-cean if we lost true love_____ and sweet de-vo-tion. Your lips ex-

life-time_____ wait-ing for the right time. Now that you're
-cite me;_____ let your arms in-vite me, for who knows

near the time is here at last._____ It's now or
when we'll meet a-gain this

way._____ It's now or

_____ my love won't wait._____

429. Jerusalem

Music by Hubert Parry. Words by William Blake

1. And did those feet in an-cient__ time Walk up-on Eng-land's moun-tains
(Verse 2 see block lyric)

green? And was the ho-ly Lamb of __ God On Eng-land's pleas-ant pas-tures

seen? And did the coun-te-nance di-vine Shine forth up-on our cloud-ed

hills? And was Je-ru-sa-lem build-ed here A-mong those dark sa-tan-ic mills?

2. Bring me my bow of burning gold!
Bring me my arrows of desire!
Bring me my spear! O clouds, unfold!
Bring me my chariot of fire!
I will not cease from mental fight
Nor shall my sword sleep in my hand
Till we have built Jerusalem
In England's green and pleasant land.

430. It's Gonna Be A Cold Cold Christmas

Words & Music by Roger Greenaway & Geoff Stephens

431. I Still Haven't Found What I'm Looking For

Words & Music by U2

2. I have run I have crawled
   I have scaled
   These city walls
   These city walls
   Only to be with you.

3. I have kissed honey lips
   Felt the healing in her fingertips
   It burned like fire
   This burning desire.

4. I have spoke with the tongue of angels
   I have held the hand of a devil
   It was warm in the night
   I was cold as a stone.

5. I believe in the Kingdom Come
   Then all the colours will
   Bleed into one
   Bleed into one
   But yes I'm still running

6. You broke the bonds
   You loosed the chains
   You carried the cross
   And my shame
   And my shame
   You know I believe it.

432. It's Impossible (Somos Novios)

Words by Sid Wayne. Music by A. Manzanero

433. It's The Same Old Shillelagh

Words & Music by Pat White

434. It's A Hap-Hap-Happy Day

Words & Music by Al J. Neiburg, Winston Sharples & Sammy Timberg

435. It's Carnival Time

Words & Music by Sid Wayne & Ben Weisman

436. It Only Takes A Minute

Words & Music by Russ Morgan & Nelson Ingham

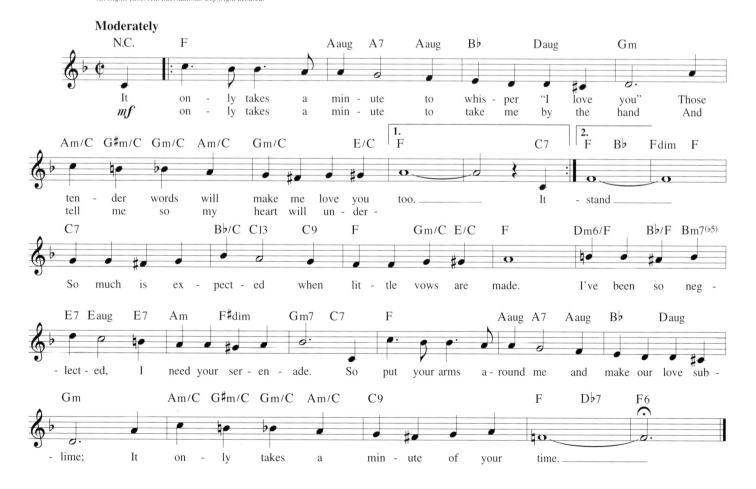

437. It's Always You

Music by Jimmy van Heusen. Words by Johnny Burke

438. It's Christmas All Over The World

Words by Terry O'Brien. Music by Terry O'Brien & Les Johnson

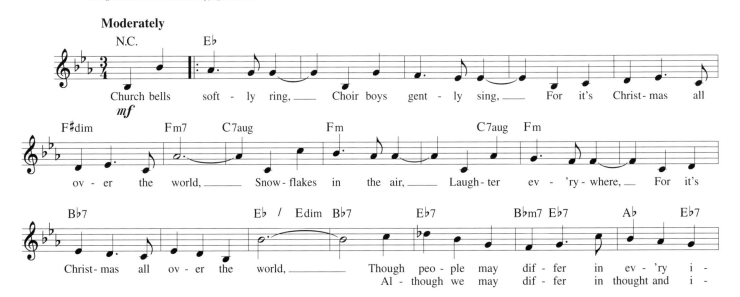

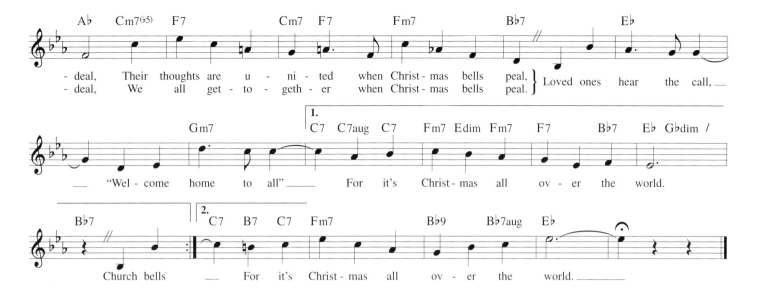

- -deal, Their thoughts are u - ni - ted when Christ - mas bells peal.
- -deal, We all get - to - geth - er when Christ - mas bells peal. } Loved ones hear the call, __

__ "Wel - come home to all" _____ For it's Christ - mas all ov - er the world.

Church bells ___ For it's Christ - mas all ov - er the world. ___

439. In The Summertime

Words & Music by Ray Dorset

Moderately fast

(instrumental)

1. In the sum - mer - time when the
(Verses 2 - 4 see block lyrics)

wea - ther is high, __ You can stretch right __ up an' __ touch __ the sky, __ When the

wea - ther's _ fine, you got wo - men, you got wo - men on your mind. *(instrumental)* Have a

drink, have a drink, go out an' see what you can find. *(instrumental)*
2. If her
3. We're not
4. When the

2. If her daddy's rich
Take her out for a meal
If her daddy's poor
Just do as you feel
Speed along the lane
Do a ton, or a ton an' twenty-five
When the sun goes down
You can make it, make it good in a lay-by.

3. We're not grey people
We're not dirty, we're not mean
We love everybody
But we do as we please
When the weather's fine
We go fishing or go swimming in the sea
We're always happy
Life's for living, yeah! That's our philosophy.

4. When the winter's here
Yeah! It's party time
Bring a bottle, wear your bright clothes
It'll soon be summertime
And we'll sing again
We'll go driving, or maybe we'll settle down
If she's rich, if she's nice
Bring your friends, an' we'll all go into town.
(al Fine)

440. Jenifer Juniper

Words & Music by Donovan Leitch

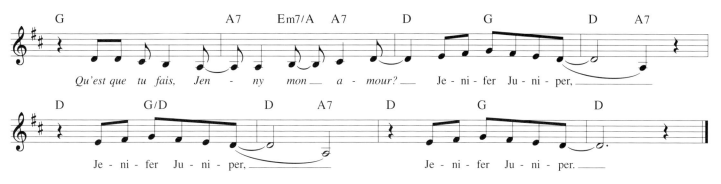

2. Jenifer Juniper, rides a dappled mare
   Jenifer Juniper, lilacs in her hair
   Is she dreaming? Yes, I think so
   Is she pretty? Yes, ever so
   Watcha doin', Jenifer, my love.

3. Jenifer Juniper, hair of golden flax
   Jenifer Juniper, longs for what she lacks
   Do you like her? Yes, I do sir
   Would you love her? Yes, I would sir
   Watcha doin', Jenifer, my love.

441. The Irish Wedding Song

Words & Music by Ian Betteridge

442. Julia Says

Words & Music by Wet Wet Wet

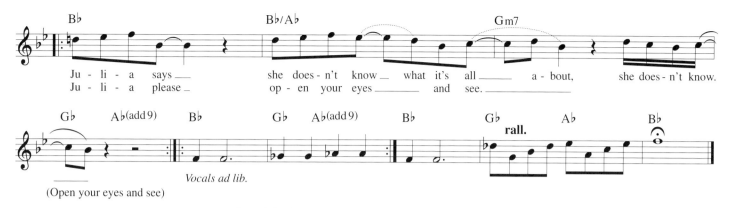

2. I won't be fooled again looking for the dream I couldn't find
The dream for me was left behind
I'm sorry now it's funny how
I don't feel the love, I just hear the words.

443. If You Never Come To Me (Inutil Paisagem)

Music & Original Words by Antonio Carlos Jobim. English Lyric by Ray Gilbert

444. Jumps, Giggles & Shouts

Words & Music by Gene Vincent & Sheriff 'Tex' Davis

Oh, I got a gal and her name is Jane, — All the kids call her pud-din' and tane, —
I got a gal and her name is Liz-zie, Man, that wo-man sure is diz-zy,

Al - ways bop-pin round the town, — Ev - 'ry bit of all her pounds, She
Bop-pin' to the juke ma-chine, — Cra-zi-est cat you ev - er seen, She

Jumps, Gig-gles and Shouts, *Go!* Jumps, Gig-gles and Shouts, *Go!*

Jumps, Gig-gles and Shouts, *Go!* Jumps, Gig-gles and Shouts, *Go!*

1.
Jumps, Gig-gles and Shouts, *Go!* Jump! Jump! Jump! Jump! Oh,

2.
Jump! Jump! Jump! Jump!

445. I'm Yours

Music by John Green. Lyrics by E. Y. Harburg

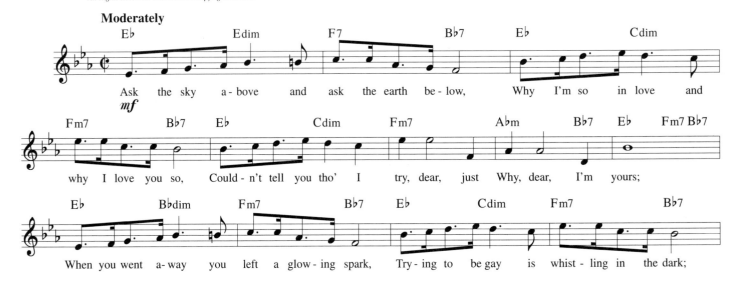

Ask the sky a-bove and ask the earth be-low, Why I'm so in love and

why I love you so, Could - n't tell you tho' I try, dear, just Why, dear, I'm yours;

When you went a-way you left a glow-ing spark, Try-ing to be gay is whist-ling in the dark;

I am on-ly what you make me, Come take me, I'm yours. How hap-py
I would be to beg and bor-row, or sor-row with you,
Ev-en tho' I knew to-mor-row You'd say we were through;
If we drift a-part, then I'll be lost a-lone. Though you use my heart just for a step-ping stone,
How can I help dream-ing of you? I love you, I'm yours. yours.

446. June In January

Words & Music by Leo Robin & Ralph Rainger

Moderately

It's June in Jan-u-a-ry be-cause I'm in love; It al-ways is
Spring in my heart, with you in my arms. _____ The snow is just white blos-soms
that fall from a-bove, and here is the rea-son my dear, your ma-gi-cal charms. _____
The night is cold, the trees are bare, but I can feel the scent of
ros-es in the air. It's June in Jan-u-a-ry be-cause I'm in love,
but on-ly be-cause I'm in love with you. _____ It's you. _____

447. Java

By Freddy Friday, Allen Toussaint & Alvin Tyler

448. Jailhouse Rock

Words & Music by Jerry Leiber & Mike Stoller

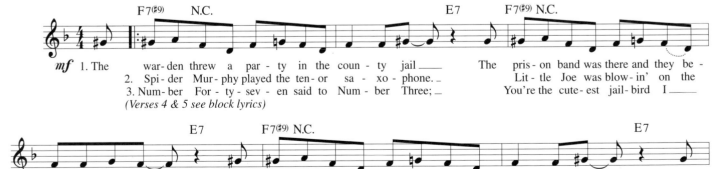

434

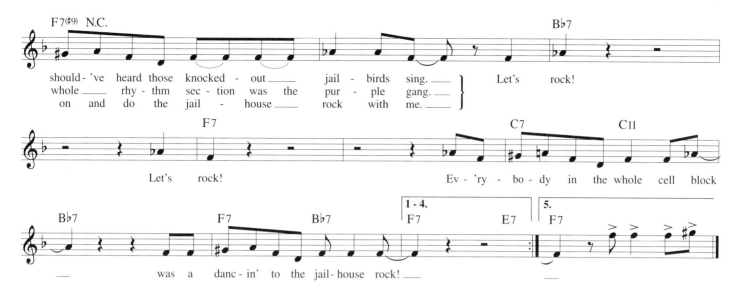

4. The sad sack was a-sittin' on a block of stone
   Way over in the corner weeping all alone
   The warden said: Hey, buddy, don't you be no square
   If you can't find a partner, use a wooden chair!
   Let's rock, etc.

5. Shifty Henry said to Bugs; For heaven's sake
   No one's lookin'; now's our chance to make a break
   Bugsy turned to Shifty and he said: Nix, nix
   I wanna stick aroound a while and get my kicks
   Let's rock, etc.

449. The Kiss In Your Eyes

Music by Richard Heuberger. Words by Johnny Burke

450. Jingle, Jangle, Jingle

Words by Frank Loesser. Music by Joseph J. Lilley

451. June Is Bustin' Out All Over

Music by Richard Rodgers. Words by Oscar Hammerstein II

452. Johnny Remember Me

Words & Music by Geoffrey Goddard

wind blow-ing in the tree - tops 'way a - bove me.

"John - ny re - mem - ber me". Yes, I'll al -

ways re - mem - ber, Till the day I die I'll

hear her cry "Oh John - ny re - mem - ber me."

Repeat to fade

453. Joey

Words & Music by Herb Wiener,
James J. Kriegsmann, Bertrand Salmirs & Stan Bernstein

Moderately slow

Jim - my kissed me in the spring-time, Tom - my kissed me in the fall, But I re-mem-ber

on - ly Jo - ey, Jo - ey kissed me not at all. Jim - my sang the sweet - est love songs,

Tom - my watched me hope-ful - ly, But I re-mem - ber on - ly Jo - ey, Jo - ey stole my

heart from me. Ev - 'ry now and then Jo - ey wan-dered by And I wished that he would

stay; Then I breathed a sigh And I won-dered why he nev-er ev-en looked my way.

Jim - my al - ways sent me flow - ers, Tom - my of - ten did the same; But I re-mem - ber

on - ly Jo - ey Jo - ey made me change my name. name.

454. Johnny Zero

Words by Mack David. Music by Vee Lawnhurst.

455. Julia

Words & Music by John Lennon & Paul McCartney

456. Jungle Drums (Canto Karabali)

Music by Ernesto Lecuona. English Lyrics by Carmen Lombardo & Charles O'Flynn

457. Jurame (Promise, Love)

Music & Original Spanish Words by Maria Grever. English Words by Frederick H. Martens

458. The Jolly Old Man In The Bright Red Suit

Words & Music by Sunny Skylar

Did you know that San - ta Claus has a face with the nic - est grin, He's the

He brings toys for girls and boys who've been good as they should have been, He's the

jol - ly old man in the bright red suit and the whis - kers on his chin. chin. He

jol - ly old man in the bright red suit and the whis - kers on his

keeps a page on ev - 'ry one, And he knows who's mis - be - haved, But for those who are good the

whole year 'round, You should see the gifts he's saved! So if you want a pret - ty doll or a

top that will hop and spin, Or if you want a sew - ing set or a wag - gon to ride

in, Make sure you're good as you can be, And these love - ly things you'll

win, From the jol - ly old man in the bright red suit and the whis - kers on his chin.

459. Just One More Chance

Music by Arthur Johnston. Words by Sam Coslow

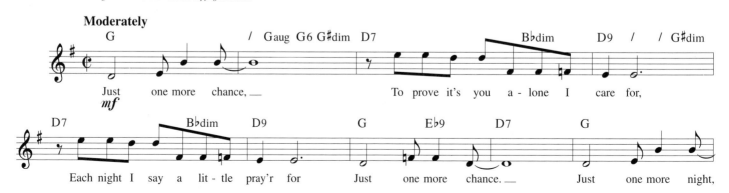

Just one more chance, __ To prove it's you a - lone I care for,

Each night I say a lit - tle pray'r for Just one more chance. __ Just one more night,

460. The Kerry Dance

By J. L. Molloy

461. Just Tell Her Jim Said Hello

Words & Music by Jerry Leiber & Mike Stoller

462. Just Another Star

Words & Music by Karl Jenkins & Carol Barratt

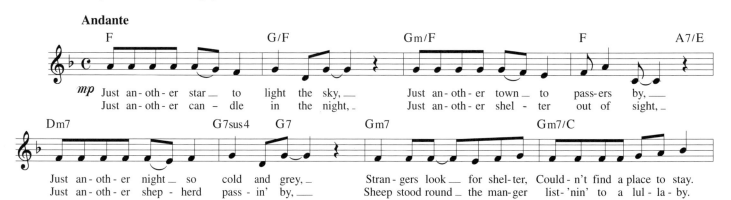

Just an-oth-er don-key warm and brown, Just an-oth-er jour-ney
It was such a spec-ial place to stay, ___ It was such a hap-py

thro' the town. ___ Just an-oth-er search foe some-where warm. ___ Found a ti-ny sta-ble
Christ-mas Day. ___ It was such a glow-ing star that shone, ___ Up a-bove ___ the sta-ble

just be-fore a child was born. Love is-n't ev-er far, ___ look up from
where the Ho-ly Child was born. ___

where you are, ___ Look for an-oth-er star, ___ Shin-in' like ___ it shone

1, 3. down on Beth - le - hem. **2.** down on Beth - le - hem. **4.** down on Beth - le - hem.

Shin-in' like ___ it shone down in Beth - le - hem. _____

463. Kay's Theme (from 'The Godfather II')

By Nino Rota

464. Kissin' Cousins

Words & Music by Fred Wise & Randy Starr

kiss - in' cous - ins. and that - 'll make __ it all right, __ all right, all right, all right. __ all right, all right, all right. We'll be kiss - in' cous - ins and that - 'll make __ it all right, __ all right, all right, all right. We'll be

Repeat to fade

465. Just For A Thrill

Words & Music by Lil Armstrong & Don Raye

Moderately slow

Just for a thrill __ you made me think you could care, __ just for a thrill, you changed the sun - shine to rain, __ just for a

thrill, you spoiled my first af - fair, __ the thought of you __ gave thrill, you filled my heart with pain, __ to me you were __ my

my heart wings, __ but to you it was one of those things, __ a ro - mance pride and joy, __ but to you I was mere - ly a toy, __ a play - thing

you could take or leave at will. __ Just for a thrill __ you pulled the sun from the you could toss a - round at will. __ Just for a thrill __ you made my life one sad

skies, __ just for a thrill you put rain in my eyes. __ I held your song, __ just for a thrill you just led me a - long. __ Al - though you're

heart for just a day __ but when you laughed __ and snatched it a - way __ you made my free and hav - ing fun __ to me, you're still __ the on - ly one __ you made my

heart stand still __ just for a thrill. __ just for a thrill. __ heart stand still __ just for a

449

466. Keep On Running

Words & Music by Jackie Edwards

467. Killer

Words & Music by A. Tinley & Seal

468. Keep The Faith

Words & Music by Jon Bon Jovi, Richie Sambora & Desmond Child

2. Tell me baby when I hurt you
Do you keep it all inside?
Do you tell me all's forgiven
And just hide behind your pride?

Everybody needs somebody to love
Everybody needs somebody to hate
Everybody's bleeding 'cause the times are tough
Well it's hard to be strong when there's no-one to dream on.

Faith
You know you're gonna live through the rain
Lord, you got to keep faith
Faith
Now you know it's never too late
Right now we got to keep the faith
Faith
Don't you let your love turn to hate
Lord, we got to keep the faith.

3. *(D.%.)* Mother, father, there's things I've done I can't erase
Every night we fall from grace
It's hard with the world in your face
Trying to hold on, trying to hold on.

Chorus as first time

Sung with third time verse
(Everybody needs somebody to love
Everybody needs somebody to hate
Everybody's bitching 'cause they can't get enough
Everybody needs. . . . . everybody needs.)

469. Key To My Life

Words & Music by Martin Brannigan, Stephen Gately, Ronan Keating, Michael Graham & Ray Hedges

454

2. Year after year I was blaming myself
   For what I'd done just thought of myself
   I know that you'll understand this was all my fault
   Dont go away.

470. Killing Me Softly With His Song

Words by Norman Gimbel. Music by Charles Fox

2. I felt all flushed with fever
Embarrassed by the crowd
I felt he found my letters
And read each one out loud
I prayed that he would finish
But he just kept right on…

471. Kingston Town

Words & Music by Randolph Patrick Kenrick

472. Kiss The Boys Goodbye

Music by Victor Schertzinger. Words by Frank Loesser

473. Kiss From A Rose

Words & Music by Seal

474. Kiss The Girl

Words by Howard Ashman. Music by Alan Menken

Now's your mo - ment, __ float - ing in a blue la - goon, __

Boy, you bet - ter do it soon, __ no time will be bet - ter, __ She don't

say a word, __ And she won't __ say a word un - til you kiss the girl. *(instrumental)*

Sha la la la la la, Don't be scared, You got the mood pre - pared, __ Go on and kiss the girl.
Sha la la la la la, Float a - long __ and lis - ten to the song, __ The song say kiss the girl.

Sha la la la la la, Don't stop now, __ Don't try to hide it now, __ You wan - na
Sha la la la la the mus - ic play, __ Do what the mus - ic say, __ You got - ta

1.
F

2.
F

kiss the girl. kiss the girl. You've got to kiss the girl. You wan - na kiss the girl,

You've got to kiss the girl, Go on and kiss the girl. *(instrumental)*

475. Let Us With A Gladsome Mind

Music by John Antes. Words by John Milton

Moderately

Let us with a glad - some __ mind praise the Lord for He is kind;
(Verses 2 - 6 see block lyrics)

Chorus

For His __ mer - cies shall en - dure, ev - er __ faith - ful, ev - er sure.

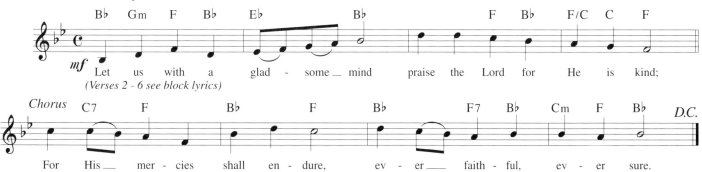

2. He, with all commanding might,
   Filled the new-made world with light:

3. All things living He doth feed,
   His full hand supplies their need:

4. He, His chosen race did bless
   In the wasteland wilderness:

5. He hath, with a piteous eye
   Looked upon our misery:

6. Let us then with gladsome mind
   Praise the Lord for He is kind!

476. Kites

Music by Lee Pockriss. Words by Hal Hackaday

Moderately

I will fly a yel-low pa-per sun in your sky___ When the wind is high,___
I will scat-ter rice___ pa-per stars in your hea-ven If there are no stars,___

___ when the wind is high.___ I will float a silk-en sil-ver moon near your
___ if there are no stars.___ All of these and sev-en won-ders more will I

win- dow. If your night is dark,___ if your night is dark.
fly. When the wind is high,___ when the wind is high.

In let- ters of gold on a snow - white kite I will

write, "I love you", ___ And send it soar- ing high a - bove you

1.
2.

___ for God to read. ___ **rall.**

477. Kids!

Music by Charles Strouse. Words by Lee Adams

Charleston tempo

Kids! I don't know what's wrong___ with these kids to - day! Kids! 1. 2. Who can
3. Ev - en

un - der - stand ___ an - y - thing they say? Kids! They are di - so - be - di - ent,
I don't un - der - stand what they say! Kids! They are so ri - di - cu - lous

dis - re - spect - ful oafs! ___ Noi - sy cra - zy slop - py la - zy loaf - ers! ___
and so im - ma - ture! ___ I don't see why an - y - bo - dy wants 'em!

464

While we're on the subject: Kids! You can talk and talk till your
Why are they so dread - ful? Kids! They are just im - pos - si - ble
Why are they so dread - ful? Kids! What the dev - il's wrong with these

face is blue! Kids! But they still do just what they
to con - trol! Kids! With their aw - ful clothes and their
Kids to - day? Kids! Who could guess that they would turn

want to do!
rock and roll!
out that way!

Why can't they be like { we } were?
{ you }

Per - fect in ev - 'ry way. What's the mat - ter with Kids to - day?

478. Long, Long Ago

Words & Music by Thomas H. Bayly

With movement

mf Tell me the tales that to me were so dear, Long, long a - go, long, long a - go.
(Verses 2 & 3 see block lyrics)

Sing me the songs I de - light - ed to hear, Long, long a - go, long a - go.

Now you are come, all my grief is re - moved, Let me for - get that so long you have roved.

Let me be - lieve that you love as you loved, Long, long a - go, long a - go.

2. Do you remember the path where we met
Long, long ago, long, long ago?
Ah, yes, you told me you ne'er would forget
Long, long ago, long ago
Then to all others my smile you preferred
Love, when you spoke, gave a charm to each word
Still my heart treasures the praises I heard
Long, long ago, long ago.

3. Tho' by your kindness my fond hopes were raised
Long, long ago, long, long ago
You by more eloquent lips have been praised
Long, long ago, long ago
But, by long absence your truth has been tried
Still to your accents I listen with pride
Blessed as I was when I sat by your side
Long, long ago, long ago.

479. Lead Kindly Light

Words & Music by C. H. Purday

1. Lead kind-ly light, a-mid the'en-circl-ing gloom, Lead Thou me on;
(Verses 2 & 3 see block lyrics)

The night is dark, and I am far from home; Lead Thou me on. Keep Thou my

feet; I do not ask to see the dis-tant scene one step e-nough for me.

2. I was not ever thus, nor prayed that Thou
 Shouldst lead me on
I loved to choose and see my path, but now
 Lead Thou me on
I loved the garish day, and, spite of fears
Pride ruled my will; remember not past years.

3. So long Thy power hath blessed me, sure it still
 Will lead me on
O'er moor and fen, o'er crag and torrent, till
 The night is gone
And with the morn those angel faces smile
Which I have loved long since, and lost awhile.

480. Kissing Bug

Music by Billy Strayhorn & Rex Stewart. Words by Joya Sherrill

You say that I'm the one you love _ You swear by ev-'ry star a-bove, _

And then you kiss some oth-er miss, _ You're noth-ing but _ a kiss-ing bug. _

You pro-mised that you'd take my hand _ And lead me to the preach-er man, _

But now I find it's just a line, _ You're noth-ing but _ a kiss-ing bug. _ You would-n't,

You could-n't be true if you tried. __ I've told you, won't scold you, I

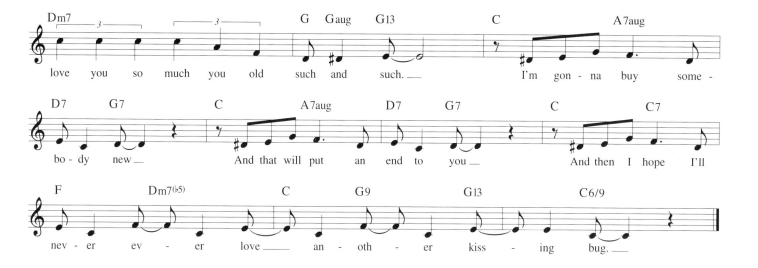

481. King Creole

Words & Music by Jerry Leiber & Mike Stoller

482. Ladybyrd

Music by Tadd Dameron. Words by Moira Heath

483. Laura

Words by Johnny Mercer. Music by David Raksin

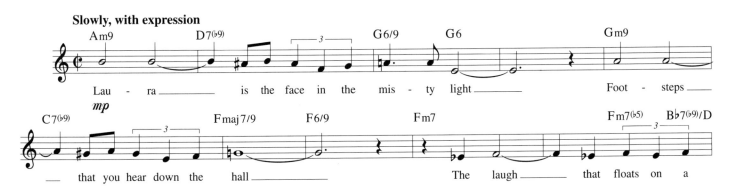

sum - mer night_____ That you can nev - er quite_____ re - call_____ And you see

Lau - ra_____ on the train that is pass - ing thru_____ Those eyes_____

— how fa - mil - iar they seem_____ She gave_____ your ve - ry first

kiss to you_____ That was Lau - ra_____ but she's on - ly a

dream.

dream._____

484. La Donna E Mobile (from 'Rigoletto')

Composed by Giuseppe Verdi

485. Lay All Your Love On Me

Words & Music by Benny Andersson & Bjorn Ulvaeus

I was-n't jeal - ous be -
It was like shoot - ing a
I've had a few lit - tle

- fore we met, now ev - 'ry wo - man I see is a po - ten - tial threat,
sit - ting duck, a lit - tle small - talk, a smile and, ba - by, I was stuck.
love af - fairs, they did - n't last ve - ry long and they've been pret - ty scarce.

and I'm pos - ses - sive, it is - n't nice, you've heard me say - ing that
I still don't know what you've done with me, a grown - up wo - man should
I used to think that was sen - si - ble, it makes the truth ev - en

smok - ing was my on - ly vice. But now it is - n't true,
nev - er fall so ea - si - ly. I feel a kind of fear
more in - com - pre - hen - si - ble. 'Cause ev - 'ry - thing is new,

now ev - 'ry - thing is new and all I've learned has
when I don't have you near, un - sat - is - fied I
and ev - 'ry - thing is you, and all I've learned has

ov - er - turned, I beg of you: Don't go wast - ing your e -
skip my pride, I beg you dear:
ov - er - turned, what can I do?

1.

- mo - tion, lay all your love on me.

2.

Don't go shar - ing your de - vo - tion, lay all your love on

me.

sharing your devotion, lay all your love on me.
wasting your emotion,

Don't go
Don't go

Repeat to fade

486. The Lady's In Love With You

Music by Frank Loesser. Words by Burton Lane

Moderately

If there's a gleam in her eye ___ each time she straightens your tie, ___ you'll know the

lady's in love ___ with you. If she can dress for a date ___ without that

waiting you hate ___ it means the lady's in love ___ with you.

And when your friends ask you over to join their table ___ but

she picks that faraway booth for two, well, sir, here's

just how it stands, ___ you've got romance on your hands ___ because the

lady's in love ___ with you. If there's a

you.

487. Les Poissons

Words by Howard Ashman. Music by Alan Menken

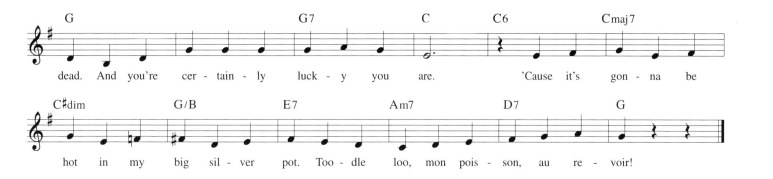

488. Lilli Marlene

Music by Norbert Schultze. Words by Hans Leip. English Words by Tommie Connor & Jimmy Phillips

489. Let It Rain

Words & Music by Mortimer, Kean, Harding & Curnow

don't want to see it, just wan-na feel it.

Love knows no boun-da-ry ____ got-ta be-lieve it and you'll re-ceive it.

Coda

Love, let ____ it rain, love, let ____ it rain, love, let ____ it rain, let ____ it rain.

2. Tribes 1 4 4 on the mount
Like an exodus to the final count
Music is blasting, silence everlasting
The call of the cosmos got the planets dancing
To send a new vibe, new ray, new day
A spiritual experience is gonna come your way
A vision, a vibe with a touch too tender
Your love to the lord, now it's time to surrender.

490. Like Dreamers Do

Words & Music by John Lennon & Paul McCartney

1. Dreams, I saw a girl in my dreams, ____ And so it seems
2. You, You came just one dream a-go, ____ And now I know

that I will love her. Oh ____ you, you are the girl in my
that I will love you. Oh ____ I know when you first said "hel-

dreams, ____ And so it seems that I will love you. } And ____
-lo," ____ That's how I know that I will love you.

I yi yi yi yi ____ wait-ed for your kiss, ____ Wait-ed for the bliss,

like dream-ers do. And I ____ yi yi yi yi yi: ____ Oh, I'll be

there yeh, wait-ing for you, you, you, you, you, you.

Coda

491. Let Me Try Again

Music by Caravelli. French Words by Michel Jourdan.
English Words by Paul Anka & Sammy Cahn

Moderately slow

I know I said that I was leav-ing, but I just could-n't say good-
I was such a fool to doubt you, to try to go it all a-

bye. It was on-ly self de-ceiv-ing to walk a-way from some-one who means
lone. There's no sense to life with-out you. Now all I do is just ex-ist and

ev-'ry-thing in life to you. You learn from ev-'ry lone-ly day. I've learned and I've come back to
think a-bout the chance I've missed. To beg is not an eas-y task. But pride is such a fool-ish

stay. Let me try a-gain! Let me try a-gain! Think of all we had be-fore,
mask.

let me try once more. We can have it all, you and I a-gain.

Just for-give me or I'll die, please let me try a-gain! gain!

492. Laughing On The Outside
(Crying On The Inside)

Words by Ben Raleigh. Music by Bernie Wayne

Moderately

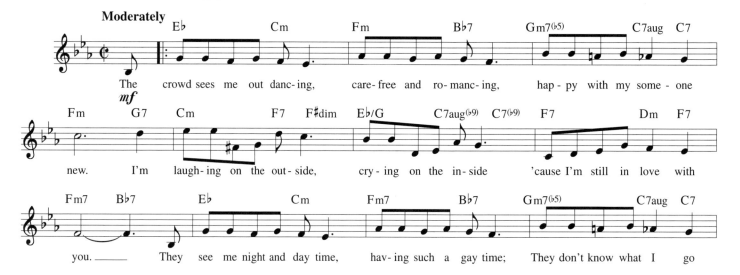

The crowd sees me out danc-ing, care-free and ro-manc-ing, hap-py with my some-one

new. I'm laugh-ing on the out-side, cry-ing on the in-side 'cause I'm still in love with

you. They see me night and day time, hav-ing such a gay time; They don't know what I go

476

493. Lords Of The Air

Words & Music by Michael North & Davy Burnaby

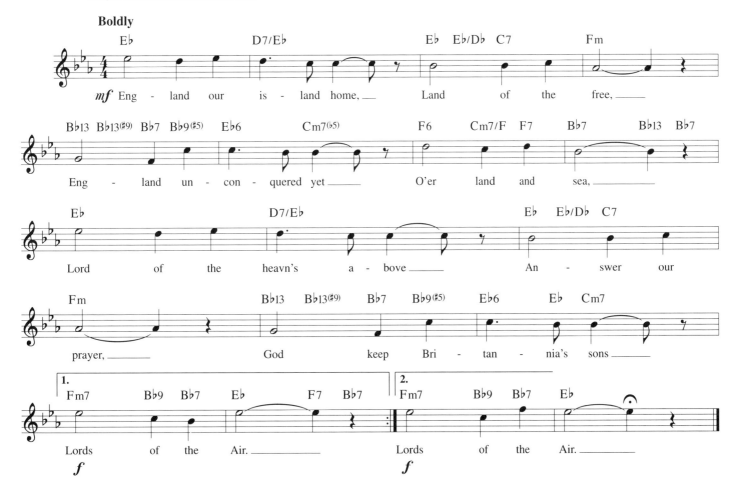

494. Let The Good Times Roll

Words & Music by Leonard Lee

2. Come on baby, gonna have a ball
Put your troubles up against the wall
Come on baby, let the good times roll
Roll on and on
Come on baby, let us paint the town
Don't let nothin' ever bring us down
Come on baby, let the good times roll
Roll on and on.

495. Lonely Ballerina

Words by Michael Carr. Music by Michael Carr & P. Lambrecht

496. Let The Music Play

Words & Music by Ed Chisolm & Chris Barbosa

3. He tried pretending a dance is just a dance, but I see
   He's dancing his way back to me
   Guess he's discovered
   We are truly lovers
   Magic from the very start. 'Cause
   Love just kept me groovin', and
   He felt me movin'
   Even though we danced apart
   So we started dancing and love put us back in the groove
   As soon as we started to move
   As soon as we started to move. *(To Chorus)*

497. The Lincolnshire Poacher

Traditional

2. As me and my companions were setting of a snare
   'Twas when we spied the gamekeeper, for him we did not care
   For we can wrestle and fight, my boys, and jump out anywhere.
   Chorus

3. As me and my companions were setting four or five
   And taking on 'em up again, we caught a hare alive
   We took a hare alive, my boys, and through the woods did steer.
   Chorus

4. I threw him on my shoulder and then we trudged home
   We took him to a neighbour's house and sold him for a crown
   We sold him for a crown, my boys, but did not tell you where.
   Chorus

5. Success to ev'ry gentleman that lives in Licolnshire
   Success to ev'ry poacher that wants to sell a hare
   Bad luck to ev'ry gamekeeper that will not sell his deer.
   Chorus

498. Let Your Soul Be Your Pilot

Words & Music by Sting

dow pane to the lights — up - on the hill. The dis-tance seems so

strange to you now and the dark room — seems so still. 3. Let your

D.℅.al Coda

⊕Coda

Let your soul guide — you, let your soul guide — you up - on — your —

way. Let your soul guide you a - long the way, let your soul guide you a - long the way.

Repeat to fade

Let your soul guide you a - long the way, let your soul guide you a - long the way.

2. When the doctors failed to heal you
When no medicine chest can make you well
When no counsel leads to comfort
When there are no more lies they can tell.
No more useless information
And the compass spins
The compass spins between heaven and hell
Let your soul be your pilot
Let your soul guide you
He'll guide you well.

3. Let your pain be my sorrow
Let your tears be my tears too
Let your courage be my model
That the north you find will be true.
When there's no more information
And the compass turns to nowhere that you know well
Let your soul be your pilot
Let your soul guide you…

499. The Lord's My Shepherd

Music by Jessie Irvine. Words by Francis Rous

© Copyright 1999 Dorsey Brothers Music Limited, 8/9 Frith Street, London W1.
All Rights Reserved. International Copyright Secured.

Moderately

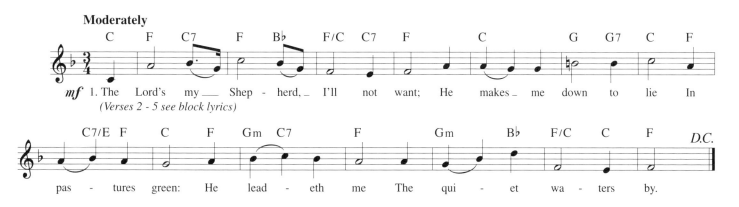

mf 1. The Lord's my — Shep - herd, — I'll not want; He makes — me down to lie In
(Verses 2 - 5 see block lyrics)

pas - tures green: He lead - eth me The qui - et wa - ters by. D.C.

2. My sould He doth restore again
And me to walk doth make
Within the paths of righteousness
E'en for His own name's sake.

3. Yea, though I walk in death's dark vale
Yet will I fear no ill
Fir Thou art with me, and Thy rod
And staff me comfort still.

4. My table Thou hast furnished
In presence of my foes
My head Thou dost with oil annoint
And my cup overflows.

5. Goodness and mercy all my life
Shall surely follow me
And in God's house for evermore
My dwelling place shall be.

500. Let's Hear It For The Boy

Words & Music by Ian Pitchford & Tom Snow

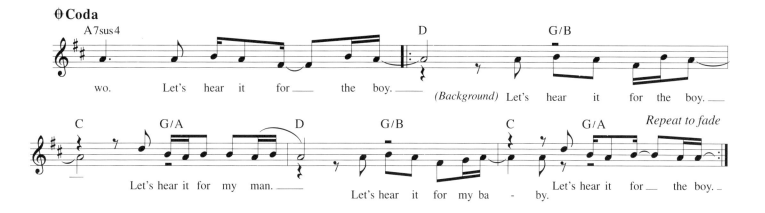

501. Learn To Croon

Music by Arthur Johnston. Words by Sam Coslow.

502. Life Is So Peculiar

Words by Johnny Burke. Music by Jimmy Van Heusen

503. Look Around (And You'll Find Me There)

Music by Francis Lai. Words by Lowell Mark & Norman Simon

487

504. Like A Child

Words & Music by Fitzgerald Scott

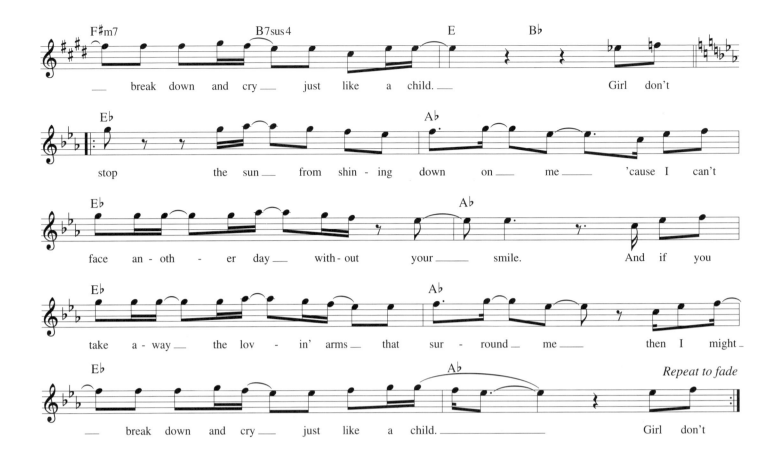

break down and cry __ just like a child. __ Girl don't

stop the sun __ from shin - ing down on __ me __ 'cause I can't

face an - oth - er day __ with - out your __ smile. And if you

take a - way __ the lov - in' arms __ that sur - round __ me __ then I might

break down and cry __ just like a child. __ Girl don't

505. The Little Boy That Santa Claus Forgot

Words & Music by Tommie Connor, Michael Carr & Jimmy Leach

Moderately slow

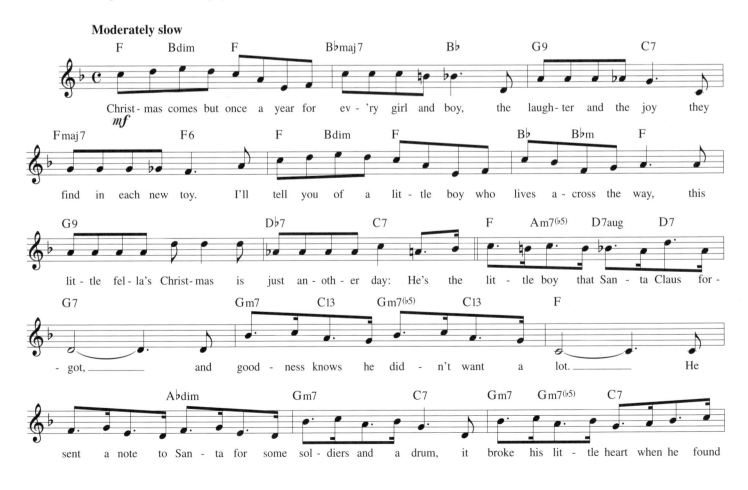

Christ - mas comes but once a year for ev - 'ry girl and boy, the laugh - ter and the joy they

find in each new toy. I'll tell you of a lit - tle boy who lives a - cross the way, this

lit - tle fel - la's Christ - mas is just an - oth - er day: He's the lit - tle boy that San - ta Claus for -

- got, __ and good - ness knows he did - n't want a lot. __ He

sent a note to San - ta for some sol - diers and a drum, it broke his lit - tle heart when he found

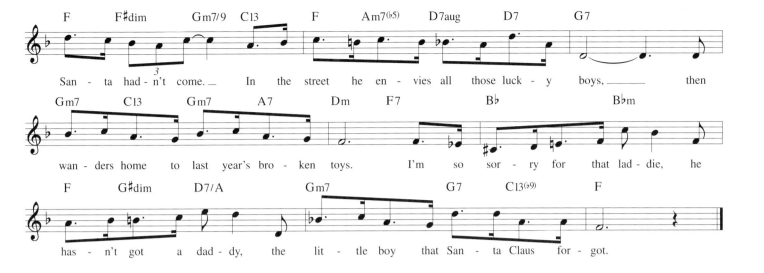

San - ta had - n't come. ___ In the street he en - vies all those luck - y boys, ___ then wan - ders home to last year's bro - ken toys. I'm so sor - ry for that lad - die, he has - n't got a dad - dy, the lit - tle boy that San - ta Claus for - got.

506. Light My Fire

Words & Music by The Doors

With a beat

1. You know that it would be un - true; ___ You know that I would be a liar; ___
time to hes - i - tate is through, ___ No time to wal - low in the mire, ___

If I was to say ___ to you; ___ Girl, we could - n't get much higher; ___
Try now we can on - ly lose, ___ And our love be - come a fune - ral pyre. ___

1.2. Come on, ba - by, light my fire, ___ Come on, ba - by, light my fire, ___

1. Try to set the night on fire. 2. The

2. 3. The time to hes - i - tate is through,

No time to wal - low in the mire, ___ Try now we can on - ly lose, ___ And our

love be - come a fune - ral pyre. ___ Come on, ba - by, light my fire, ___ Come on, ba - by, light my fire, ___

Repeat 3 times

Try to set the night on fire, ___ Try to set the night on fire.

491

507. Like A Rolling Stone

Words & Music by Bob Dylan

Like a roll - ing   stone?

Repeat 4 times   fade

2. You've gone to the finest school all right Miss Lonely
   But you know you only used to get
   Juiced in it.
   And nobody's ever taught you how to live on the street
   And now you're gonna have to get
   Used to it.
   You said you'd never compromise
   With the mystery tramp. but now you realize
   He's not selling any alibis
   As you stare into the vacuum of his eyes
   And ask him do you want to
   Make a deal?

3. You never turned around to see the frowns on the jugglers and the clowns
   When they all come down
   And did tricks for you.
   You never understood that it ain't no good
   You shouldn't let other people
   Get your kicks for you.
   You used to ride on the chrome horse with your diplomat
   Who carried on his shoulder a Siamese cat
   Ain't it hard when you discovered that
   He really wasn't where it's at
   After he took from you everything
   He could steal.

4. Princess on the steeple
   And all the pretty people're drinkin', thinkin'
   That they got it made.
   Exchanging all kinds of precious gifts and things
   But you'd better lift your diamond ring
   You'd better pawn it babe.
   You used to be so amused
   At Napoleon in rags and the language that he used
   Go to him now, he calls you, you can't refuse
   When you got nothing, you got nothing to lose
   You're invisible now, you got no secrets
   To conceal.

508. London Bridge Is Falling Down

Traditional

Brightly

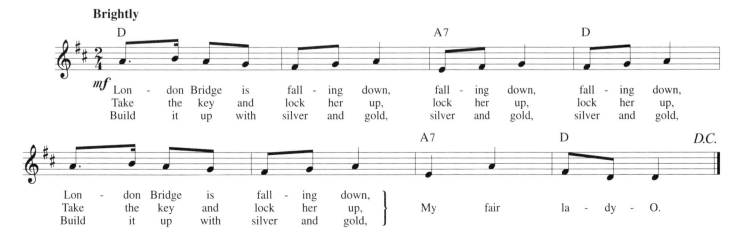

Lon - don Bridge is fall - ing down, fall - ing down, fall - ing down,
Take the key and lock her up, lock her up, lock her up,
Build it up with silver and gold, silver and gold, silver and gold,

Lon - don Bridge is fall - ing down,
Take the key and lock her up,   My fair la - dy - O.
Build it up with silver and gold,

509. Linger

Music by Dolores O'Riordan & Noel Hogan. Words by Dolores O'Riordan

510. Little April Shower

Words by Larry Morey. Music by Frank Churchill

Drip, drip, drop, lit-tle A - pril show - er, beat-ing a tune as you fall all a - round.
Drip, drip, drop, lit-tle A - pril show - er, beat-ing a tune ev - 'ry - where that you fall.

Drip, drip, drop, lit-tle A - pril show - er, what can com-pare with your beau - ti - ful sound.
Drip, drip, drop, lit-tle A - pril show - er, I'm get-ting wet and I don't care at all.

Drip, drip, drop, when the sky is cloud - y your pret - ty mu - sic can bright - en the day.

Drip, drip, drop, when the sun says, "How - dy" you say "Good - bye" right a - way.

Drip! Drop! Drip! Drop! I'll nev - er be a - fraid of a

good lit - tle gay lit - tle A - pril ser - e - nade.

511. Like A Baby

Words & Music by Jesse Stone

1. You gave me love ___ to en - joy like a
   fool's ___ heart you took and I
   found ___ how you lied then I

bright shin - ing toy, ___ Like a ba - by. ___ No mat - ter what ___ you would do I de -
fell 'cause you look, ___ Like a ba - by. ___ To wo - men's ways ___ I was blind 'cause I
broke down and cried, ___ Like a ba - by. ___ That was the time ___ I could see you were

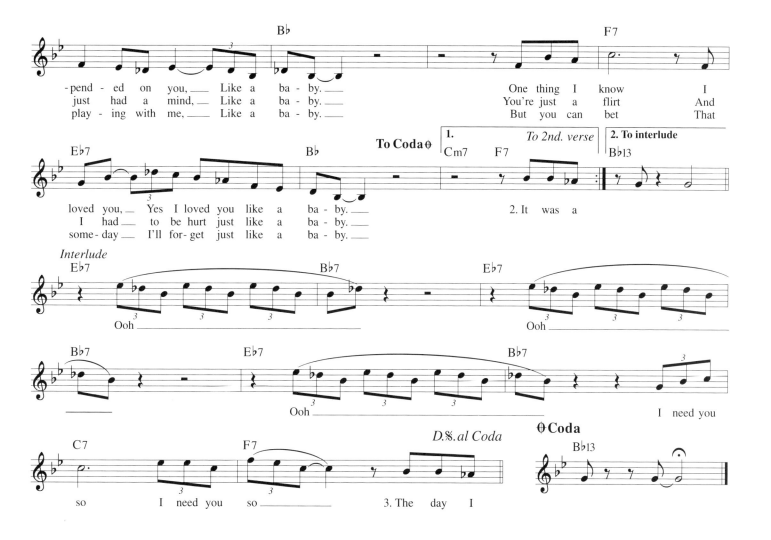

-pend- ed on you,___ Like a ba - by. One thing I know I
just had a mind,___ Like a ba - by. You're just a flirt And
play - ing with me,___ Like a ba - by. But you can bet That

Eb7   Bb   To Coda ⊕   1.   To 2nd. verse   2. To interlude
                                                                 Cm7   F7   Bb13

loved you,___ Yes I loved you like a ba - by.   2. It was a
I had___ to be hurt just like a ba - by.
some - day___ I'll for - get just like a ba - by.

Interlude
Eb7   Bb7   Eb7

Ooh ___   Ooh ___

Bb7   Eb7   Bb7

___   Ooh ___   I need you

                                                D.𝄋.al Coda   ⊕ Coda
C7   F7   Bb13

so   I need you so ___   3. The day I

512. Love Letters

Music by Victor Young. Words by Edward Heyman

© Copyright 1945 Famous Music Corporation, USA.
All Rights Reserved. International Copyright Secured.

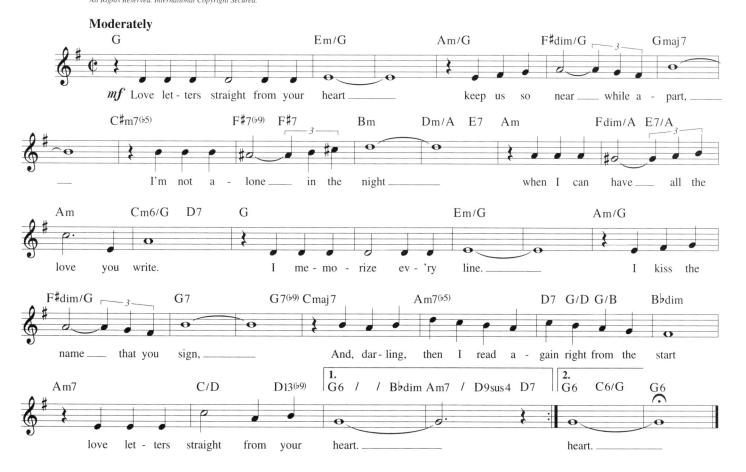

Moderately
G   Em/G   Am/G   F#dim/G   Gmaj7

mf Love let - ters straight from your heart ___ keep us so near ___ while a - part, ___

C#m7(b5)   F#7(b9) F#7   Bm   Dm/A E7 Am   Fdim/A E7/A

___ I'm not a - lone ___ in the night ___ when I can have ___ all the

Am   Cm6/G   D7   G   Em/G   Am/G

love you write.   I me - mo - rize ev - 'ry line. ___   I kiss the

F#dim/G   G7   G7(b9) Cmaj7   Am7(b5)   D7 G/D G/B   Bbdim

name ___ that you sign,   And, dar - ling, then I read a - gain right from the start

Am7   C/D   D13(b9)   1.   2.
                                      G6 / / Bbdim Am7 / D9sus4 D7   G6   C6/G   G6

love let - ters straight from your heart. ___   heart. ___

513. Little Bird

Words & Music by Annie Lennox

2. I walk along the city streets so dark with rage and fear
   And I, I wish that I could be that bird and fly away from here
   I wish I had the wings to fly away from here, yeah.

3. (D.C.) For I am just a troubled soul who's weighted
   Weighted to the ground
   Give me the strength to carry on
   Till I can lay this burden down
   Give me the strength to lay this burden
   Down, down, down, yeah.

514. Little Buttercup
(from 'H.M.S. Pinafore')

Words by W. S. Gilbert. Music by Arthur Sullivan

Moderately

I'm called Lit - tle But - ter - cup, dear Lit - tle But - ter - cup, though I could nev - er tell why;
buy of your But - ter - cup, dear Lit - tle But - ter - cup, sail - ors should nev - er be shy;

but still I'm called But - ter - cup, poor Lit - tle But - ter - cup, sweet Lit - tle But - ter - cup, I.
so buy of your But - ter - cup,

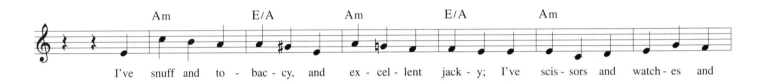

I've snuff and to - bac - cy, and ex - cel - lent jack - y; I've scis - sors and watch - es and

knives; I've rib - bons and lac - es to set off the fac - es of pret - ty young

sweet - hearts and wives. I've trea - cle and tof - fee, I've tea and I've cof - fee, soft

tom - my and suc - cu - lent chops; I've chick - ens and co - nies, and

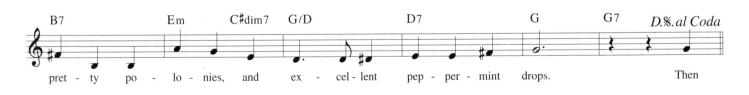

pret - ty po - lo - nies, and ex - cel - lent pep - per - mint drops.   Then

⊕ Coda

poor Lit - tle But - ter - cup; come, of your But - ter - cup buy. _____

500

515. Lovin' You

Words & Music by Minnie Riperton & Richard Rudolph

516. Lilliburlero

Music Traditional. Words by Patrick Michael

Here we all are as gay as can be, Join in and sing this grand me-lo-dy.
Noth-ing's so bad what-e'er may be wrong, But you feel bet-ter sing-ing a song.

Nev-er a care shall fur-row the brow, Lift up your voi-ces hear-ti-ly now.
So here's a dit-ty cat-chy and gay, Helps you to chase your wor-ries a-way.

Le-ro, Le-ro, Lil-li-bur-le-ro, Ev-'ry-one sing till the raf-ters all ring, The

great day is near-ing, When clouds will be clear-ing, So Lil-li-bur-le-ro let us all sing.

517. The Little Man

Words & Music by Johnny Cash

Moderately

It seems ___ like some good peo-ple ___ do get messed up ___ on their chanc - es.
like peo - ple would get ___ tired of look-in' ___ down on peo - ple. ___ It

Ain't no doubt, ___ it's all been planned ___ out be - fore ___ they were born. ___
seems like peo - ple got to have ___ some - one ___ to kick a - round.

Al - ways ___ go - in' up ___ that long down - hill road. ___
Al - ways feel - in' like ___ they need to ___ be looked up ___ to and

Al - ways ___ at the lit - tle end ___ of the horn. ___ } Oh, the lit - tle man don't
al - ways some - one there when they look down. ___

count, they look right ov - er his head, and they turn him and they burn him

an - y way they can. ___ Just some - bod - y's ___ lean - in' post, ___ ev - 'ry -

- bod - y's ___ un - der dog. Oh! heav - en help, ___ 'Cause no one else ___ will

help the lit - tle man! ___ It seems ___

518. Lonely Man

Words & Music by Bennie Benjamin & Sol Marcus

Moderately slow

It's a lone - ly man who wan - ders all a - round. ___ It's a lone - ly man

who roams from town to town. ___ Search - in' ___ al - ways search - in' ___ for

some - thing ___ he can't find. Hop - in', ___ al - ways hop - in' ___ that some - day fate will be

kind. It's a lone - ly man who trav - els all a - lone. ___ When he

has no one that he can call his own. ___ Al - ways ___ so un -

- hap - py, ___ tak - in' shel - ter ___ where he can. Here I am; come meet a

lone - ly, lone - ly man. It's a man. ___

519. Livin' On A Prayer

Words & Music by Jon Bon Jovi, Richie Sambora & Desmond Child

Liv - in' on ___ a prayer. ___ *(instrumental)*

Oh, ___ we've got to hold ___ on ___

read - y or ___ not, you live for the fight when it's all that you've got.

Wo, ___ we're half - way there. ___ Wo, ___ liv - in' on a prayer. ___

Repeat to fade

Take my hand ___ and we'll make it, I swear. ___ Wo, ___ liv - in' on a prayer. ___

520. Theme From Lassie

By Basil Poledouris

521. Long Black Limousine

Words & Music by Bobby George & Vern Stovall

522. A Lot Of Livin' To Do

Music by Charles Strouse. Words by Lee Adams

523. Lover

Music by Richard Rodgers. Words by Lorenz Hart

524. Love Is All Around

Words & Music by Reg Presley

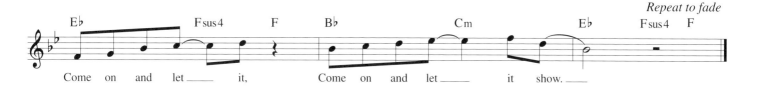

Come on and let ___ it, Come on and let ___ it show. ___

2. I see your face before me as I lay on my bed
   I cannot get to thinking of all the things you said
   You gave your promise to me, and I gave mine to you
   I need someone beside me in everything I do.

525. Theme From London's Burning

By Simon Brint & Roddy Matthews

526. Love Is Wonderful Ev'rywhere

Words & Music by Matt Dennis & L. Ted Steele

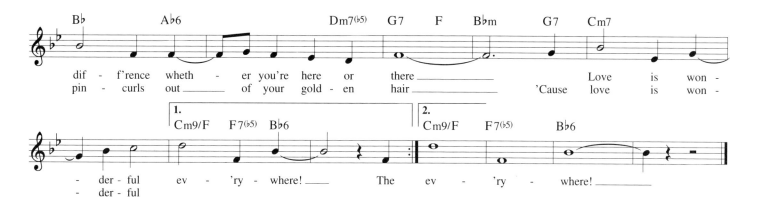

diff'rence wheth- er you're here or there _____ Love is won- der-ful ev-'ry- where! _____ The ev-'ry- where! _____

pin- curls out _____ of your gold- en hair _____ 'Cause love is won- der-ful

527. Lonesome Cowboy

Words & Music by Sid Tepper & Roy C. Bennett

Moderately slow

Just be- yond the moun- tain lies a ci- ty And I hear it call- ing me; _____

"Sad- dle up and ride, you lone- some cow- boy; Here is where you'll find your des- ti- ny." _____

In my dreams the lights shine bright and pret- ty, Near to me and yet so far. _____

Will I al- ways be a lone- some cow- boy; Am I on- ly reach- ing for a star? _____

_____ Ride, _____ ride a- long, cow- boy. _____ Sing, _____

_____ sing your song, cow- boy. _____ Will I ev- er leave this lone- some val- ley,

Real- ly see the lights that shine? _____ Got- ta find what lies be- yond the moun- tains;

Got- ta rope and tie that dream of mine. _____ mine. _____

528. A Love Like This

Music by Victor Young. Words by Ned Washington

529. Look Homeward, Angel

Words & Music by Wally Gold

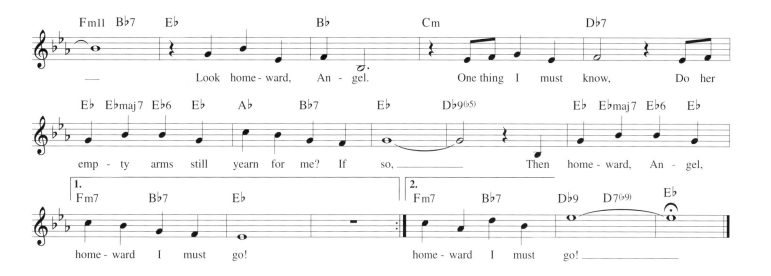

530. Lonesome Town

Words & Music by Baker Knight

2. You can buy a dream or two
   To last you all through the years
   And the only price you pay
   Is a heart full of tears.

3. In the town of broken dreams
   The streets are filled with regret
   Lay me down in Lonesome Town
   I can learn to forget.

531. Love Me Tender

Words & Music by Elvis Presley & Vera Matson

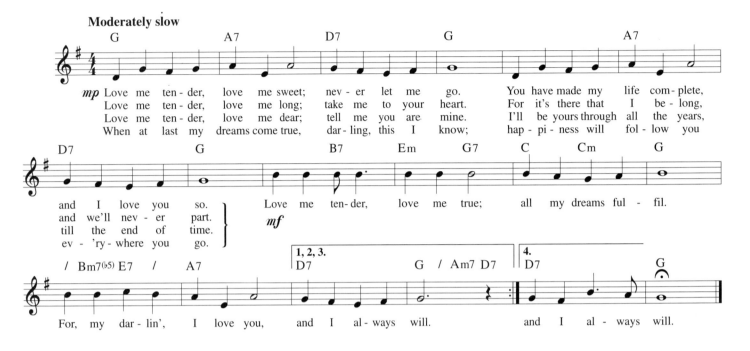

532. Look Out The Window (The Winter Song)

Words & Music by Lew Porter & Teepee Mitchell

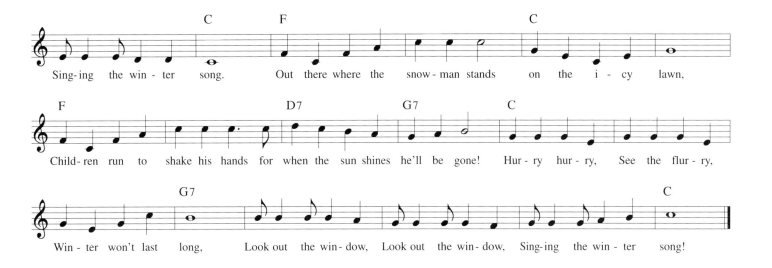

Singing the win - ter song. Out there where the snow - man stands on the i - cy lawn,

Child - ren run to shake his hands for when the sun shines he'll be gone! Hur - ry hur - ry, See the flur - ry,

Win - ter won't last long, Look out the win - dow, Look out the win - dow, Sing - ing the win - ter song!

533. Love Is

Words & Music by Leslie Bricusse

Medium bounce

1. Love is ___ a Bom - bay cur - ry, Love is ___ but not to wor - ry Love is ___ too
2. Love is ___ a bash - ful rein - deer Love is ___ a mid - night train dear Love is ___ a

hot to hur - ry Love is ___ Love is ___ a red - hot can - dle
month in Spain, dear Love is ___ Love is ___ the cap - tain's ta - ble

Love is ___ a white - hot scan - dal Love is ___ too hot to han - dle Love is ___
Love is ___ the Tower of Ba - bel Love is ___ a coat of sa - ble Love is ___

Love is ___ hap - py as a sand - boy ___ Fit to beat the
Love is ___ sleep - y as a pil - low ___ Weep - y as a

band, boy ___ But as shy as Hold my hand boy Love is ___ an
wil - low ___ Creep - y as a Late U - tril - lo Love is ___ with -

A - pril show - er Love is ___ a sun - kissed flow - er Love is ___ a
- out py - ja - mas Love is ___ the hot Ba - ha - mas Love is ___ a

1.
fate - ful hour ___ Love is. ___

2.
ring like ma - ma's
Love is. ___

517

534. Loving You

Words & Music by Jerry Leiber & Mike Stoller

Moderately slow

I will spend my whole life through lov-ing you, _ lov-ing you. _ Win-ter, sum-mer, spring-time, too, lov-ing you, _ lov-ing you. _ Makes no dif-f'rence where I go or what I do, you know that I'll al-ways be lov-ing you. if I'm seen with some-one new, don't be blue, _ don't be blue. _ I'll be faith-ful, I'll be true, al-ways true, _ true to you. _ There is on-ly one for me, and you know who. You know that I'll al-ways be lov-ing you.

535. Love Is Just Around The Corner

Music by Lewis Gensler. Words by Leo Robin

Moderately

Love is just a-round the cor-ner, An-y co-sy lit-tle cor-ner, Love is just a-round the cor-ner when I'm a-round you. I'm a sen-ti-men-tal mour-ner, And I could-n't be for-lorn-er When you keep me on a cor-ner just wait-ing for you. _ Ve-nus de Mi-lo was not-ed for her charms, But strict-ly be-tween us, You're

536. Love Thy Neighbour

Music by Harry Revel. Words by Mack Gordon

537. Love In Bloom

Words & Music by Leo Robin & Ralph Rainger

538. Love Me Forever

Music by Gary Lynes. Words by Beverly Guthrie

539. Magic Moments

Words & Music by Burt Bacharach & Hal David

540. Theme From Madson

By Denis King

541. The Man With The Golden Arm

Music by Jimmy Van Heusen. Words by Sammy Cahn

542. Make It Easy On Yourself

Music by Burt Bacharach. Words by Hal David

break- ing up ___ is so ve - ry hard to do.

2. And if the way I hold you can compare to his grace,
No words of consolation will make me miss you less.
My darling, if this is goodbye I just know I'm gonna cry,
So run to him before you start crying too.
And make it easy *(etc.)*

543. **March** (from 'Scipione')

Composed by George Frideric Handel

544. Make Yourself Comfortable

Words & Music by Bob Merrill

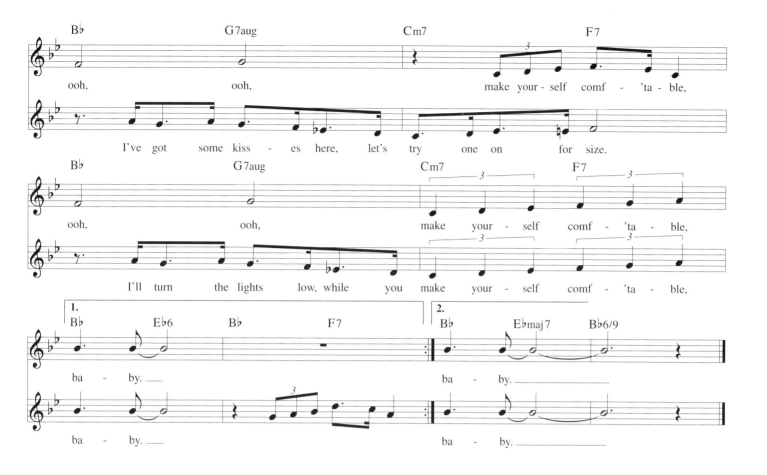

ooh,   ooh,   make your-self comf-'ta-ble,

I've got some kiss-es here, let's try one on for size.

ooh,   ooh,   make your-self comf-'ta-ble,

I'll turn the lights low, while you make your-self comf-'ta-ble,

ba-by.   ba-by.

ba-by.   ba-by.

545. **March Of The Grenadiers**

Words by Clifford Grey. Additional Words by Reg Connelly.
Music by Victor Schertzinger

1. Gren-a-diers   stead-y and strong, march-ing a-long, Sing-ing a song of
2. Gren-a-diers   stead-y in war, read-y in love, Liv-ing to serve no

moth-er-land.   land.   Ev-'ry un-i-form
oth-er

tak-ing the hearts   by storm. Who could be true as the Gren-a-

diers?   Stead-y and strong, march-ing a-long, He-roes who scorn all

fears.   Loy-al men the Roy-al Gren-a-diers.

546. Mama

Words & Music by Matthew Rowbottom, Richard Stannard, Melanie Brown,
Victoria Aadams, Geri Halliwell, Emma Bunton & Melanie Chisholm

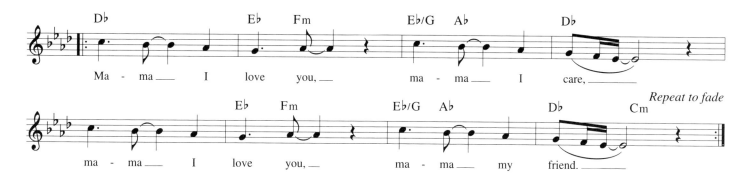

2. I didn't want to hear it then but I'm not ashamed to say it now
Every little thing you said and did was right for me
I had a lot of time to think about, about the way I used to be
Never had a sense of my responsibility.

Back then I didn't know why, why you were misunderstood
So now I see through your eyes, all that you did was love
Mama I love you, Mama I care
Mama I love you, Mama my friend
My friend.

547. Mean Woman Blues

Words & Music by Claude DeMetrius

548. Mambo In The Moonlight

Words & Music by Buddy Kaye & Jules Loman

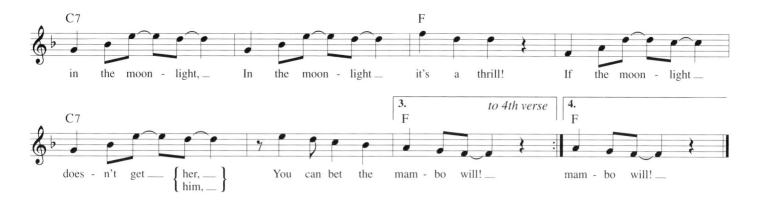

in the moon - light, __ In the moon - light __ it's a thrill! If the moon - light __

does - n't get __ {her, __} {him, __} You can bet the mam - bo will! __ mam - bo will! __

3.
F
to 4th verse
4.
F

549. Mad Passionate Love

Words & Music by Dick Sherman & Dave Coleman

Medium bounce

They were mak - in' mad pas - sion - ate love, __ mad pas - sion - ate love. __

There in the park, they were hap - py as a lark, bill - in' and coo - in'. They were mak - in'

mad pas - sion - ate love, __ mad pas - sion - ate love. __ There all a - lone in a

world of their own, do - in' their woo - in' he whis - per'd, "I love you, my

heart's all a twit - ter o - ver you; __ I'll feath - er a love nest if you'll love me

too." __ They were mak - in' mad pas - sion - ate love, __ mad pas - sion - ate love. __ 'Til the

light - nin' flash'd and the thund - er crash'd, so the two lit - tle bir - dies flew a -

1.
C
2.
C

way, __ so the two lit - tle bir - dies flew a - way. They were mak - in' way.

531

550. Mambo Italiano

Words & Music by Bob Merrill

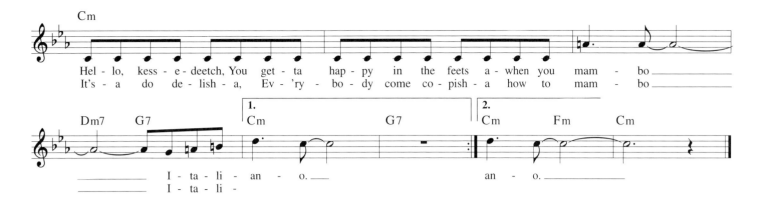

Hel - lo, kess - e - deetch, You get - a hap - py in the feets a - when you mam - bo ___
It's - a do de - lish - a, Ev - 'ry - bo - dy come co - pish - a how to mam - bo ___

Dm7 G7

1.
Cm   G7
___ I - ta - li - an - o. ___
___ I - ta - li -

2.
Cm   Fm   Cm
an - o. ___

551. The Marvellous Toy

Words & Music by Tom Paxton

Moderately

1. When I was just a wee lit - tle lad, Full of health and joy, My Fa - ther home - ward

mf (Verses 2 - 4 see block lyric)

came one night, And gave to me a toy. A won - der to be - hold it was, With

man - y col - ours bright, And the mo - ment I laid eyes on it, It be - came my heart's de -

Chorus
light, It went "Zip" when it moved, And "Bop" when it stopped, And "Whirr" when it stood

still. I nev - er knew just what it was, And I guess I nev - er will.

2. The first time that I picked it up I had a big surprise
For right on its bottom were two big buttons that looked like big green eyes
I first pushed one and then the other, and then I twisted its lid
And when I set it down again, this is what it did.

3. It first marched left then marched right and then marched under a chair
And when I looked where it had gone, it wasn't even there!
I started to sob and my daddy laughed, for he knew what I would find
When I turned around, my marvellous toy, chugging from behind.

4. Well, the years have gone by too quickly, it seems, I have my own little boy
And yesterday I gave to him my marvellous little toy
His eyes nearly popped right out of his head and he gave a squeal of glee
Neither one of us knows just what it is, but he loves it, just like me.

Last Chorus:
It still goes "Zip" when it moves and "Bop" when it stops
And "Whirr" when it stands still
I never knew just what it was
And I guess I never will.

552. The Man Who Shot Liberty Valance

Music by Burt Bacharach. Words by Hal David

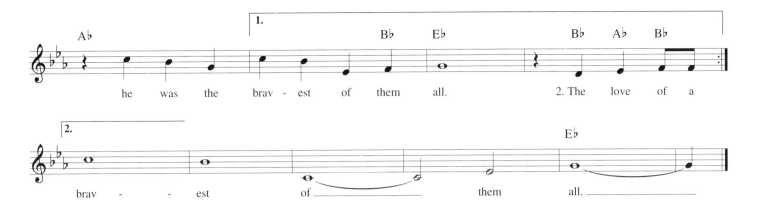

553. May I Never Love Again

Words & Music by Sano Marco & Jack Erickson

554. Many Rivers To Cross

Words & Music by Jimmy Cliff

D.%.and repeat 3rd time to fade

and I mere - ly sur - vive   be - cause of my   pride.

2. Many rivers to cross,
    But just where to begin
    I'm playing for time
    There've been times when I find myself
    Thinking of committing some dreadful crime.

    I've got many rivers to cross
    But I can't seem to find
    My way over
    Wandering, I am lost
    As I travel along
    The white cliffs of Dover

3. I've got many rivers to cross
    But I can't seem to find
    My way over
    Wandering, I am lost
    As I travel along
    The white cliffs of Dover.

    I've got many, many
    Rivers to cross
    Oh...
    Wandering, I am lost
    Oh...
    Oh...

555. Mellow Yellow

Words & Music by Donovan Leitch

2. I'm just mad about Fourteen
    Fourteen's mad about me
    I'm just mad about Fourteen
    She's just mad about me.

    To Chorus:

3. Born high, forever to fly
    Wind velocity: nil
    Born high, forever to fly
    If you want your cup I will fill.

    To Chorus:

4. *Instrumental:*

5. Electrical banana
    Is going to be a sudden craze
    Electrical banana
    Is bound to be the very next phase.

    To Chorus:

6. I'm just mas about Saffron
    I'm just mad about her
    I'm just mad about Saffron
    She's just mad about me.

    To Chorus:

556. Mary Ann

Traditional

Moderately

mf 1. Mar - y Ann, oh Mar - y Ann, oh you're the girl for me, e - ven though your
(Verse 2 see block lyric)

dear old ma - ma will not say "Si si." Mar - y Ann, oh Mar - y Ann oh

won't you please a - gree? You and I should mar - ry, raise a fam - i - ly,

Chorus

All day, all night, Mar - y Ann, _____ down by the sea - side

sift - in' sand, _____ all the lit - tle chil - dren love Mar - y Ann, _____

down by the sea - side sift - in' sand. _____

2. When I met sweet Mary Ann, her mother said to me
"Would you care to tell me where you stand financially?"
She does not approve of me 'cause I'm no millionaire
But I love her daughter, more than I can bear.

557. Me And You And A Dog Named Boo

Words & Music by Kent LaVoie

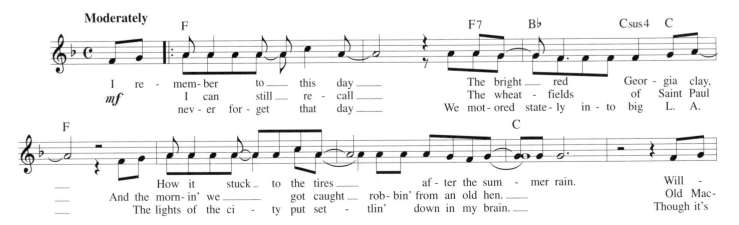

Moderately

mf I re - mem - ber to _____ this day _____ The bright _____ red Geor - gia clay,
I can still _____ re - call _____ The wheat - fields of Saint Paul
nev - er for - get that day _____ We mot - ored state - ly in - to big L. A.

How it stuck _____ to the tires _____ af - ter the sum - mer rain. Will -
And the morn - in' we _____ got caught _____ rob - bin' from an old hen. _____ Old Mac -
The lights of the ci - ty put set - tlin' down in my brain. Though it's

power made that old car go, _____ A wom-an's mind told me that it's so, _____
-Don-ald, he made us work, _____ But then he paid us for what it was worth. _____ An-
on-ly been a month or so, _____ That old car's bug-gin' us to go. _____ You

Oh, how I wish _____ we were back _____ on the road _____ a-gain.
-oth-er tank of gas _____ and back _____ on the road _____ a-gain.
got-ta get a-way and get back _____ on the road _____ a-gain.

Me and you _____ and a dog _____ named Boo _____ Trav-el-lin' and liv-in' off the

land. Me and you _____ and a dog _____ named Boo _____ How I love _____

be-in' a free man. _____

2. _____
3. I'll

558. Minuetto (Theme from 'Haffner Symphony')

By Wolfgang Amadeus Mozart

Moderately

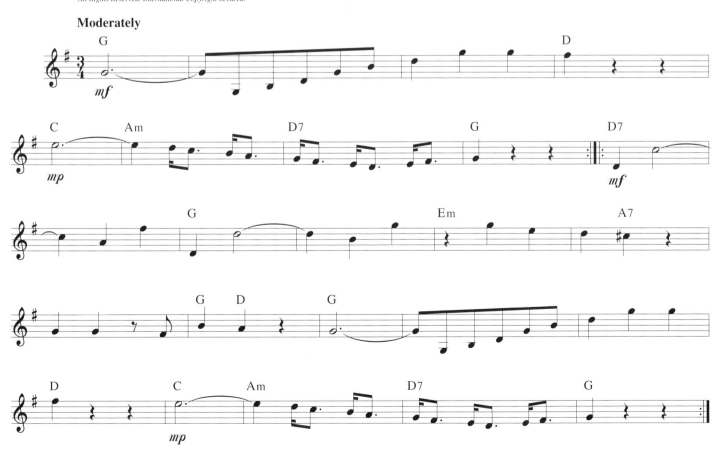

559. Masters Of War

Words & Music by Bob Dylan

2. You that never do nothin'
But build to destroy
You play with my world
Like it's your little toy
You put a gun in my hand
And you hide from my eyes
And you turn and run farther
When the fast bullets fly

3. Like Judas of old
You lie and deceive
A world war can be won
You want me to believe
But I see through your eyes
And I see through your brain
Like I see through the water
That runs down my drain

4. You fasten the triggers
For the others to fire
Then you sit back and watch
When the death count gets higher
You hide in your mansion
As young people's blood
Flows out of their bodies
And is buried in the mud.

5. You've thrown the worst fear
That can ever be hurled
Fear to bring children
Into the world
For threatenin' my baby
Unborn and unnamed
You ain't worth the blood
That runs in your veins

6. How much do I know
To talk out of turn
You might say that I'm young
You might say (I'm unlearned)
But there's one thing I know
Though I'm younger than you
Even Jesus would never
Forgive what you do

Let me ask you one question
7. Is your money that good?
Will it buy you forgiveness?
Do you think that it could?
I think you will find
When your death takes its toll
All the money you made
Will never buy back your soul

8. And I hope that you die
And your death'll come soon
I will follow your casket
On a pale afternoon
And I'll watch while you're lowered
Down to your death bed
And I'll stand o'er your grave
'Till I'm sure that you're dead.

560. Merry Christmas Everybody

Words & Music by Neville Holder & James Lea

561. Melting Pot

Words & Music by Roger Cook & Roger Greenaway

562. "Murder" He Says

Music by Jimmy McHugh. Words by Frank Loesser

563. Memphis Blues

Words & Music by W. C. Handy

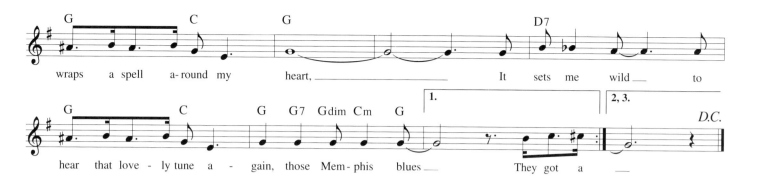

564. Mine Eyes

Words & Music by Earl K. Brent & Matt Dennis

565. Merry Merry Christmas Baby

Words & Music by Margo Sylvia & Gilbert Lopez

566. The Minute Waltz

Composed by Frédéric Chopin

567. A Mess Of Blues

Words & Music by Doc Pomus & Mort Shuman

568. Moon River

Music by Henry Mancini. Words by Johnny Mercer

548

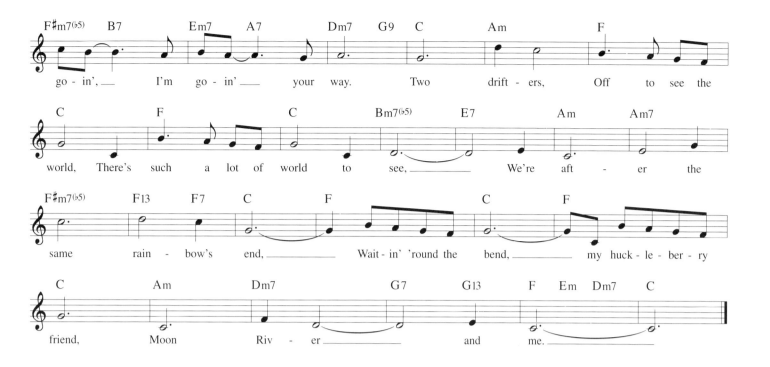

go - in', ___ I'm go - in' ___ your way. Two drift - ers, Off to see the world, There's such a lot of world to see, ___ We're aft - er the same rain - bow's end, ___ Wait - in' 'round the bend, ___ my huck - le - ber - ry friend, Moon Riv - er ___ and me. ___

569. My Love She's But A Lassie Yet

Scottish Traditional

My love, she's but a lass - ie yet, my ___ love, she's but a lass - ie yet, we'll ___ let her stand a year or twa, she'll no ___ be ___ half sae sau - cy yet. 1. I ___ rue the day I

(Verses 2 & 3 see block lyrics)

sought her, Oh! I ___ rue the day I sought her, Oh! Wha ___ gets her need - na say he's woo'd, but

he ___ may ___ say he's bought her. Oh! My ___ think - in' o't. My ___ love, she's but a lass - ie yet, my ___

love, she's but a lass - ie yet, we'll ___ let her stand a year or twa, she'll no ___ be ___ half sae sau - cy yet.

2. Came draw a drap o' the best o't yet
Came draw a drap o' the best o't yet!
Gae seek for pleasure where ye will
But here I never missed it yet
Chorus

Chorus
My love, she's but a lassie yet
My love, she's but a lassie yet!
We'll let her stand a year or twa
She'll no be half sae saucy yet!

3. We're a' dry wi' drinkin' o't
We're a' dry wi' drinkin' o't!
The minister kiss't the fiddler's wife
He couldna preach for thinkin' o't!
Chorus

570. Mexican Hat Dance (Chiapanecas)

Traditional

571. M-I-S-S-I-S-S-I-P-P-I

Words & Music by Curly Williams & Billy Simmons

By the M, i, crook-ed let-ter, crook-ed let-ter, i, crook-ed let-ter, crook-ed let-ter,
i, hump-back, hump-back, i,___ Mis-sis-sip-pi, Flow-in' down to New Or-leans___
And it flows right by___ my___ Ten-nes-see home___ Where his-to-ry was made by Steam-boat
Bill, M-e-m-p-h-i-s,___ Mem-phis is the town I mean,___

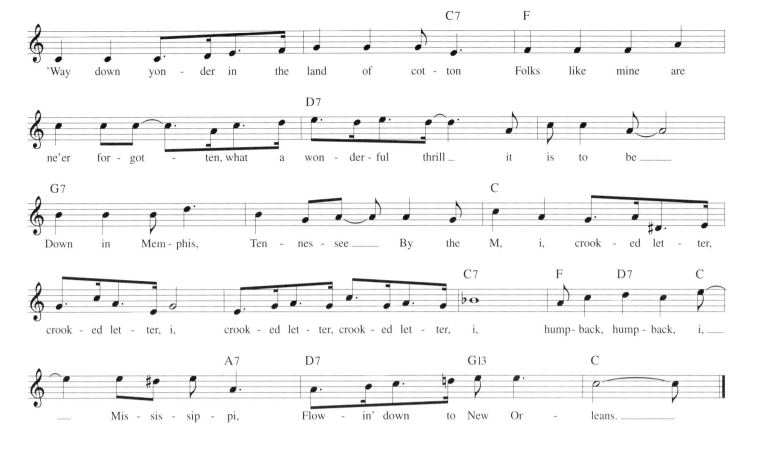

572. Mother Machree

Words & Music by Rida Johnson Young, Chauncy Olcott & Ernest R. Ball

573. Mickey Mouse March

Words & Music by Jimmie Dodd

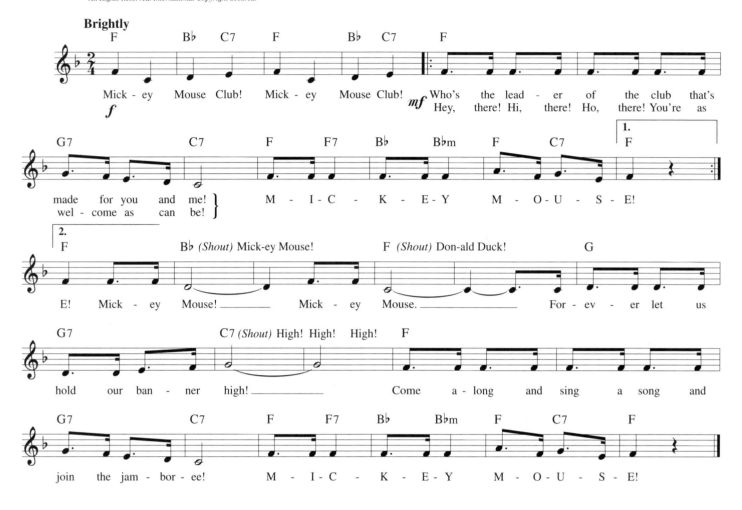

574. March Of The Priests (from 'The Magic Flute')

Composed by Wolfgang Amadeus Mozart

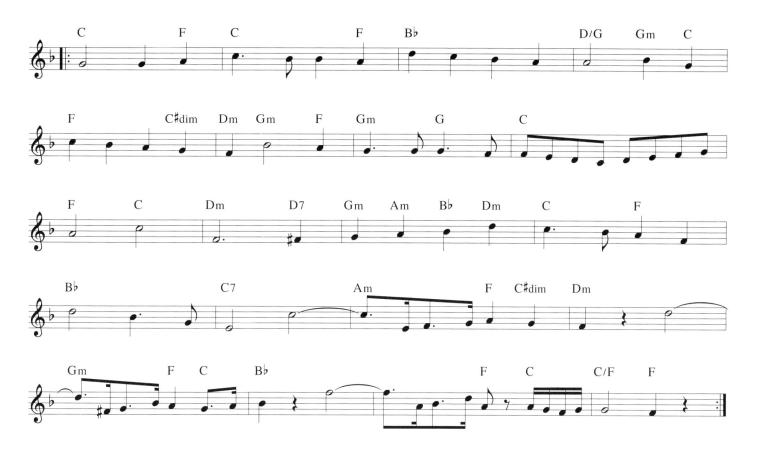

575. The Minstrel Boy

Traditional

1. The min-strel boy __ to the war is gone, In the ranks of death __ you'll
2. The min-strel fell __ but the foe-man''s chain could not bring that proud __ soul

find __ him, His fa-ther's sword __ he hath gird-ed on, And his
un-der, The harp he lov'd __ ne'er __ spoke a-gain, For he

wild harp slung __ be-hind __ him. *f* "Land of song!" said the
tore its chords __ a-sun-der, And said "No chains shall __

war-rior bard, "Tho' all the world be-trays __ thee, One sword, at least, thy
sul-ly thee, Thou soul of love and brav-'ry! Thy songs were made __ for the

rights shall guard, One __ faith-ful harp __ shall __ praise __ thee!"
pure and free, They shall nev-er sound __ in __ sla-ve-ry!"

D.C.

576. Midnight Train To Georgia

Words & Music by Jim Weatherly

577. The Mountains Of Mourne

Traditional

2. I believe that when writin', a wish you expressed
   As to how the fine ladies in London were dressed
   Well if you'll believe me, when asked to a ball
   Faith, they don't wear a top to their dresses at all
   Oh, I've seen them meself, and you could not, in thrath
   Say if they were bound for a ball or a bath
   Don't be startin' them fashions now, Mary Macree
   Where the mountains o' Mourne sweep down to the sea.

3. I've seen England's King from the top of a bus
   I never knew him, tho' he means to know us
   And tho' by the Saxon we once were oppressed
   Still I cheered (God forgive me) I cheered with the rest
   And now that he's visited Erin's green shore
   We'll be much better friends than we've been heretofore
   When we've got all we want we're as quite as can be
   Where the mountains o' Mourne sweep down to the sea.

4. You remember young Peter O'Loughlin, of course?
   Well now he is here at the head o' the force
   I met him today, I was crossin' The Strand
   And he stopped the whole street wid wan wave of his hand
   And there we stood talking of days that are gone
   While the whole population of London looked on
   But for all these great powers he's wishful, like me
   To be back where dark Mourne sweeps down to the sea.

5. There's beautiful girls here, oh! niver mind!
   Wid beautiful shapes nature niver designed
   And lovely complextions all roses and crame
   But O'Loughlin remarked wid regard to the same
   "That if those roses you venture to sip,
   The colours might all come away on your lip."
   So I'll wait for the wild rose that's waitin' for me
   Where the mountains of Mourne sweep down to the sea.

578. Mis-shapes

Music by Pulp. Lyrics by Jarvis Cocker

556

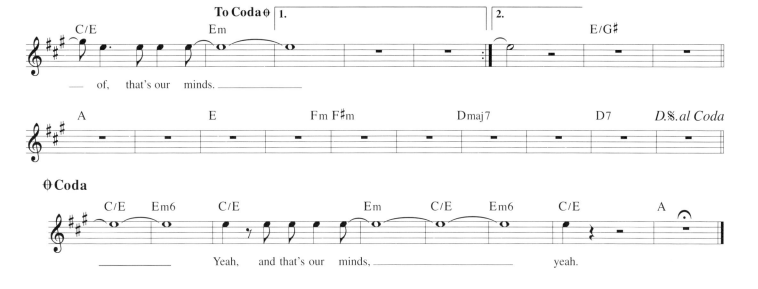

2. Check your lucky numbers
   That much money could drag you under, oh
   What's the point of being rich
   If you can't think what to do with it
   'Cause you're so bleeding thick
   Oh, we weren't supposed to be
   We learnt too much at school
   Now we can't help but see
   The future that you've got mapped out
   Is nothing much to shout about.

579. Moonlight Becomes You

Music by Jimmy Van Heusen. Words by Johnny Burke

580. Miss You Nights

Words & Music by Dave Townsend

(Play down) ___ play down all dreams and themes once re-mem-bered   It's just the same ___

This miss you game

Yet these miss you nights   are the long-est. ___

581. Meditation (from 'Thais')

By Jules Massenet

582. Missing

Music by Ben Watt. Words by Tracey Thorn

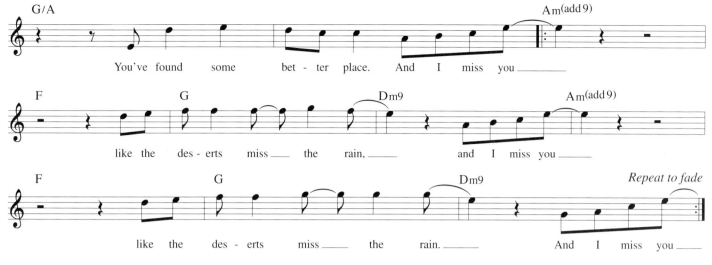

You've found some better place. And I miss you like the deserts miss the rain, and I miss you like the deserts miss the rain. And I miss you

2. Could you be dead?
   You always were two steps ahead of everyone
   We'd walk behind while you would run
   I look up at your house
   And I can almost hear you shout down to me
   Where I always used to be
   And I miss you.

3. Back on the train
   I ask why did I come again?
   Can I confess I've been hanging 'round your old address
   And the years have proved
   To offer nothing since you moved
   You're long gone but I can't move on
   And I miss you.

583. Mona Lisa

Words & Music by Jay Livingston & Ray Evans

Mona Lisa, Mona Lisa men have named you, You're so like the lady with the mystic smile, Is it only 'cause you're lonely they have blamed you for that Mona Lisa strangeness in your smile? Do you smile to tempt a lover, Mona Lisa? Or is this your way to hide a broken heart? Many dreams have been brought to your doorstep, They just lie there, and they die there, Are you warm, are you real, Mona Lisa, or just a cold and lonely, lovely work of art?

584. Theme From Mission: Impossible

By Lalo Schifrin

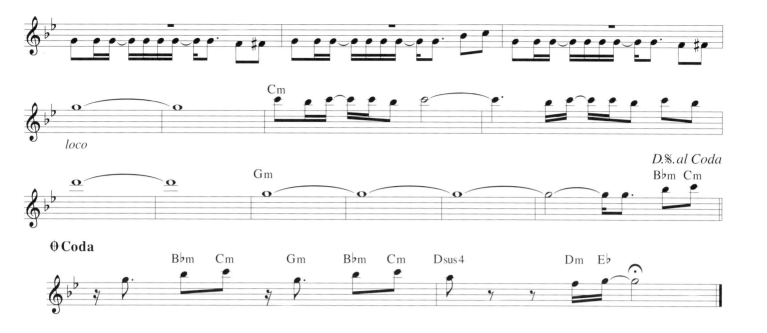

585. Mister Brown Of London Town

Words & Music by R. Arkell & Noel Gay

Mis - ter Brown of Lon - don Town Had a job __ to do. Meant to see __ it

through, And he did __ it, too. Mis - ter Brown __ of Lon - don Town __

Sent the wife __ a - way, Sent the kids __ to play Miles and miles __ a -

way. Things blew up __ and things blew down, __ Seemed a blink - in' shame,

Bloom - in' fire __ and flame, Bli - mey, what __ a game! But

who stood up __ and saved the town, __ When Lon - don Bridge __ was fall - ing down? __

Mis - ter Brown of Lon - don Town __ "Oi," Mis - ter Brown! __

586. Mister Taptoe

Words & Music by Terry Gilkyson, Richard Dehr & Frank Miller

587. Mmmm Mmmm Mmmm Mmmm

Words & Music by Brad Roberts

2. Once there was a girl who
   Wouldn't go and change with the girls in the change room
   But when they finally made her
   They saw birthmarks all over her body
   She couldn't quite explain it
   They'd always just been there.

3. 'Cause then there was this boy whose
   Parents made him come directly home right after school
   And when they went to their church
   They shook and lurched all over the church floor
   He couldn't quite explain it
   They'd always just gone there.

588. Mony Mony

Words & Music by Bobby Bloom, Ritchie Cordell, Bo Gentry & Tommy James

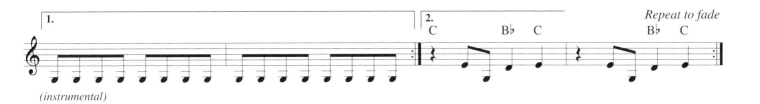

(instrumental)

589. Mis'ry And The Blues

Words & Music by Charles La Vere

Moderately slow

Blues ___ in the morn - in', mis' - ry in the eve - nin', Meet the sad - dest man you
Blues ___ in the morn - in', mis' - ry in the eve - nin', Keep me won - d'rin what I

ev - er knew. Got my share of sor - row, same ol' thing to - mor - row,
ought to do. Al - most out of mon - ey, guess you think that's fun - ny,

Since you've gone the dawn is al - ways o - ver - due. ___ love with you.
Ev - en though you know I'm still in

Ba - by, ___ when you told me good - bye ___ with a smile in your eye, Ba - by, ___

had to laugh so that I _____ would - n't cry. Now there's noth - in' but

blues ___ in the morn - in', mis' - ry in the eve - nin', Wake up cry - in' like a

child of two. Wish I'd nev - er met you, let the dev - il get you,

Then you'll know the heart - aches of a fool ___ full of mis - er - y and blues.

567

590. The Moon's A Window To Heaven

Music by Jerry Goldsmith. Words by John Bettis

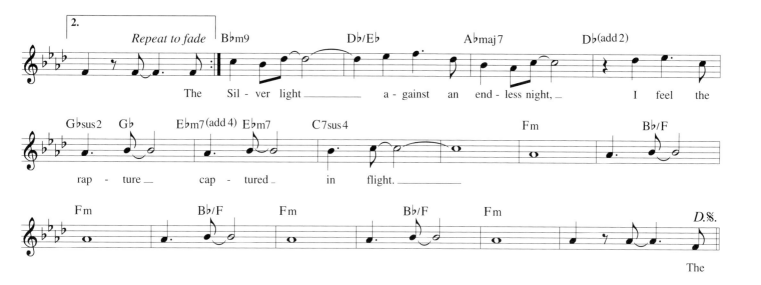

The Sil - ver light _____ a - gainst an end - less night, _____ I feel the

rap - ture _____ cap - tured _____ in flight. _____

The

591. Minuet (from 'Berenice')

Music by George Frideric Handel

Moderately

592. Mother Goose Jumps

Words & Music by Woody Herman, Ralph Burns & Willie Stein

593. Moonlighting

Music by Lee Holdridge. Words by Al Jarreau.

594. Mrs Robinson

Words & Music by Paul Simon

Moderately

And here's to you, __ Mrs. __ Rob - in - son, __ Je - sus loves you more __ than you __ will

know, _____ Wo wo wo. ____ God bless you, please, Mrs. __ Rob - in - son, __

Heav - en holds __ a place __ for those __ who pray, _____ Hey hey hey, _____ Hey hey hey.

1. We'd like to know a lit - tle bit __ a - bout __ you for our files,

We'd like to help __ you learn to help your - self. _____

Look a - round you, all ____ you see __ are sym - pa - the - tic eyes. ____

Stroll a - round __ the grounds __ un - til you feel at home. __ And here's to you

2. Hide it in a hid - ing place __ where no one ev - er goes, ____

Put it in your pan - try with __ your cup - cakes. ____ It's a lit - tle se -

- cret, just __ the Rob - in - son's __ af - fair, _____ Most of all

__ you've got to hide __ it from the kids. __ Coo coo ca - choo, __ Mrs. __ Rob -

God bless you, please, Mrs. Robinson, Heaven holds a place for those who pray,

Hey hey hey, Hey hey hey.

2. Sitting on a sofa on a Sunday afternoon
Going to the candidate's debate
Laugh about it, shout about it
When you've got to choose
Every way you look at it, you lose
Where have you gone, Joe Dimaggio?
A nation turns its lonely eyes on you
Woo woo woo
What's that you say, Mrs. Robinson?
"Joltin' Joe" has left and gone away
Hey hey hey
Hey hey hey.

595. O Come, O Come, Emmanuel

Traditional Christmas Song

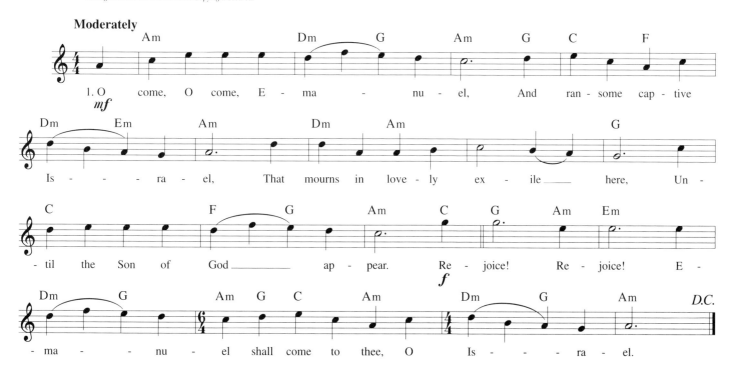

1. O come, O come, E-ma-nu-el, And ran-some cap-tive Is-ra-el, That mourns in love-ly ex-ile here, Un-til the Son of God ap-pear. Re-joice! Re-joice! E-ma-nu-el shall come to thee, O Is-ra-el.

2. O come, Thou Dayspring, Come and cheer
Our spirits by thine advent here
Disperse the gloomy clouds of night
And death's dark shadows put to flight
Rejoice! Rejoice! *(etc.)*

3. O come, thou Wisdom from on high
And order all things far and nigh
To us the path of knowledge show
And cause us in her ways to go
Rejoice! Rejoice! *(etc.)*

4. O come, Desire of nations bind
All peoples in one heart and mind
Bid envy, strife, and quarrels cease
Fill the whole world with heaven's peace
Rejoice! Rejoice! *(etc.)*

596. Mulder And Scully

Words & Music by Cerys Matthews & Mark Roberts

- lone here. Things are get-ting strange, I'm start-ing to wor-ry, this could be a case for Mul-der and Scul-ly. things are get-ting strange now I can't see a - lone. So what have you got to say a-bout that, and what does some-one do with-out love, and what does some-one do with love, and what have you got to say a-bout that?

Play 3 times

Repeat to fade

2. I'd rather be jumping ship
I find myself jumping straight in
Stop doing what you
Keep doing it to.

Forever be dozy and dim
I wake myself thinking of him
Stop doing what you
Keep doing it to.

3. And as for some happy ending
I'd rather stay single and thin
Stop doing what you
Keep doing it to me.

597. My Object All Sublime

Words by W. S. Gilbert. Music by Sir Arthur Sullivan

Moderately fast

mf

My ob-ject all sub-lime I shall a-chieve in time To let the pun-ish-ment fit the crime, The pun-ish-ment fit the crime: And make each pris-'ner pent Un-will-ing-ly re-pre-sent A source of in-no-cent mer-ri-ment, Of in-no-cent mer-ri- ment!

598. Music Box

Words & Music by Mariah Carey & Walter Afanasieff

now and for-ev-er, my love.

All I have I want to give to thee.

599. My Old Kentucky Home

Words & Music by Stephen Foster

The sun shines bright in the old Ken-tuck-y home, 'Tis sum-mer, the old folks are
young folks roll on the lit-tle cab-in floor, All mer-ry, all hap-py and
(Verses 2 & 3 see block lyrics)

gay.   The corn-top's ripe and the mead-ow's in the bloom, While the
bright.   By'n by hard times come a-knock-in' at the door, Then my

birds make mu-sic all the day.   The old Ken-tuck-y home, good-night.

Chorus
Weep no more, my la-dy, Oh, weep no more to-day.   We will

sing one song for the old Ken-tuck-y home, For the old Ken-tuck-y home, far a-way.

2. They hunt no more for the possum and the coon
    On the meadow, the hill, and the shore
    They sing no more by the glimmer of the moon
    On the bench by the old cabin door
    The day goes by like a shadow o'er the heart
    With sorrow where all was delight
    The time has come when the old folks have to part
    Then my old Kentucky home, good-night.
    Chorus

3. The head must bow and the back will have to bend
    Wherever the wanderer may go
    A few more days, and the trouble all will end
    In the field where the sugar canes grow
    A few more days for to tote the weary load
    No matter, 'twill never be light
    A few more days will we totter on the road
    Then my old Kentucky home, good-night.
    Chorus

600. The Music Of Goodbye

Music by John Barry. Words by Alan & Marilyn Bergman

601. My Precious World (The Man)

Words & Music by Desmond Dacres & Leslie Kong

602. My Baby Loves Lovin'

Words & Music by Roger Cook & Roger Greenaway

2. My baby loves love, your baby loves lovin'
    She's got what it takes and she knows how to use it
    My baby loves love, my baby loves lovin'
    She's got what it takes and she knows how to use it
    She's the only one makes me feel so good
    Can't believe my luck so I knock on wood
    All my silent fears seem to fly away
    She looks at me as if to say.

3. Your baby loves love, my baby loves lovin'
    She's got what it takes and she knows how to use it
    My baby loves love, my baby loves lovin'
    She's got what it takes and she knows how to use it
    I was lonely once in this great big world
    Just a nowhere man without a girl
    Till that lucky day when she came my way
    And she smiled at me as if to say.

603. Moonlight Cocktail

Words & Music by Lucy Roberts & Kim Gannon

604. My Bonnie Lies Over The Ocean

Traditional

605. The Moon And I

Music by Sir Arthur Sullivan. Words by W. S. Gilbert

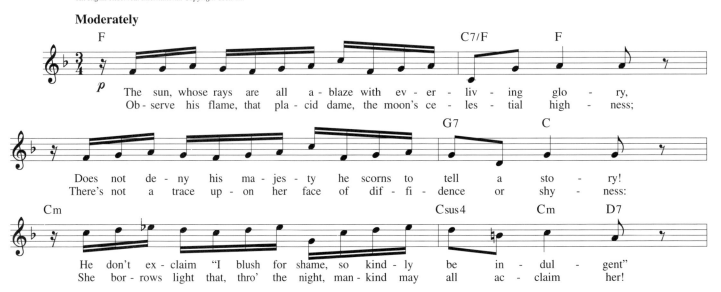

582

But, fierce and bold, in fier-y gold, he glor-ies all ef-ful-gent!
And, truth to tell, she lights up well, so I, for one, don't blame her.

I mean to rule the earth, as he the sky we
Ah, pray make no mis-take, we are not shy: We're

real-ly know our worth, the sun and I!
ve-ry wide a-wake, the moon and I!

I mean to rule the earth, as he the sky we
Ah, pray make no mis-take, we are not shy; we're

real-ly know our worth, the sun and I!
ve-ry wide a-wake, the moon and I!

606. My Heart & I

Music by Frederick Hollander. Words by Leo Robin

Moderately

My heart and I were dis-cuss-ing your charms, We de-cid-ed that

you should be in my arms. My arms and I felt a thrill at the

start, We de-cid-ed that you should be in my heart. We're so in

love with you, both my heart and I. Love me too,

Then as years go by, Both my heart and I will for-ev-er be true, For

all that I want is your heart and you. My you.

607. My Kind Of Town (Chicago Is)

Words by Sammy Cahn. Music by Jimmy Van Heusen

* Any city name of three syllables can replace Chicago, i.e., Manhattan, Las Vegas, etc.

584

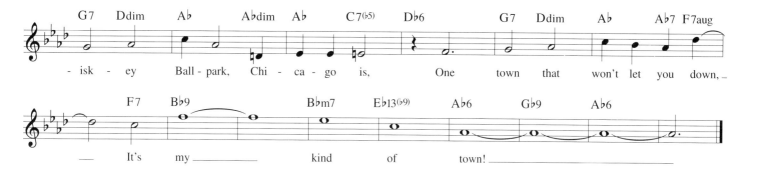

-isk- ey Ball - park, Chi - ca - go is, One town that won't let you down, _

It's my _____ kind of town! _____

608. The Moon Is Blue

Music by Herschel Burke Gilbert. Words by Sylvia Fine

Moderately

Mon - ey grows on trees, ___ the de - sert starts to freeze, cats con - verse in per - fect Pe - kin -
So per - haps could be _____ that or - di - na - ry me stands a chance with ex - tra spe - cial

- ese. And some - times _____ a dream like you comes true, Now and then when the
you. They tell me _____ that mi - ra - cles come thru',

moon is blue. ___ just ter - rif' _____ if the moon is blue. I'm in your

spell _____ and folks are talk - ing, _____ they might as well, _____ can't be de -

- nied, _____ How can I hide the fact that I go walk - ing _____ with both my

feet ten feet a - bove the side - walk? Now I think I see _____ a

ta - xi up a tree, _____ a lamp post and a span - iel drink - ing tea. So tell me _____ that

you can see it too, ___ A month of Sun - days com - ing up in June be - cause the moon is blue.

585

609. My Resistance Is Low

Words by Harold Adamson. Music by Hoagy Carmichael

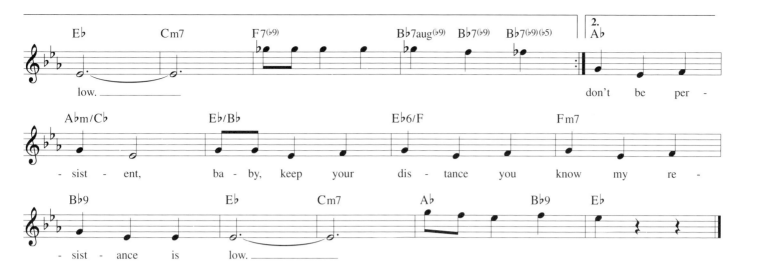

low. don't be per-

-sist- ent, ba- by, keep your dis- tance you know my re-

-sist- ance is low.

610. Musetta's Waltz (from 'La Bohème')

Composed by Giacomo Puccini

611. My Dear Little Sweetheart

Words & Music by George David Weiss & Johnny Smith

612. My, My Ain't That Somethin'

Words & Music by Harry Tobias & Pinky Tomlin

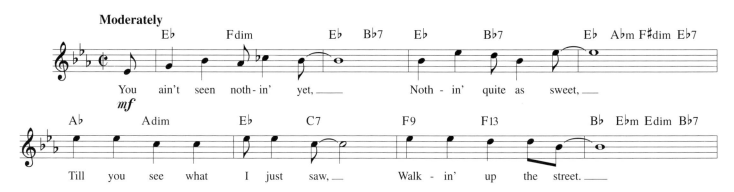

My, my ___ ain't that some-thin' (Whistle) Where's my hat? ___
My, my ___ ain't that some-thin' (Whistle) Shut my mouth ___

Oh! boy, ___ My heart's thum-pin' Ain't ___ seen noth-in' that looks like that, ___
Oh! joy ___ My heart's jump-in' jum - pin' north and a jump-in' south, ___

It real - ly walks, It real-ly talks, It real-ly moves a-bout, ___

It must be real, A sol-id deal, And I'm gon-na fig-ure it out, ___

My, my ___ Ain't that some-thin' (Whistle) Hear me shout, ___

Oh! boy, ___ ain't that some-thin', Ain't ___ that some-thin' to talk a-bout. ___

613. Michael Row The Boat Ashore

Traditional

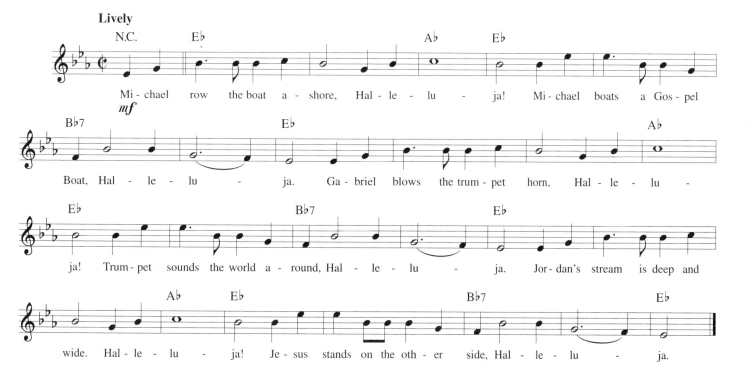

Mi - chael row the boat a - shore, Hal - le - lu - ja! Mi - chael boats a Gos - pel

Boat, Hal - le - lu - ja. Ga - briel blows the trum - pet horn, Hal - le - lu -

ja! Trum - pet sounds the world a - round, Hal - le - lu - ja. Jor - dan's stream is deep and

wide. Hal - le - lu - ja! Je - sus stands on the oth - er side, Hal - le - lu - ja.

614. My Old Flame

Words & Music by Arthur Johnston & Sam Coslow

615. Morning (from 'Peer Gynt Suite No.1')

Composed by Edvard Grieg

616. Mazel Tov

Jewish Traditional Song

617. Native New Yorker

Words & Music by Sandy Linzer & Denny Randell

618. Nobody Does It Better

Words by Carole Bayer Sager. Music by Marvin Hamlisch

619. Need You Tonight

Words & Music by Andrew Farriss & Michael Hutchence

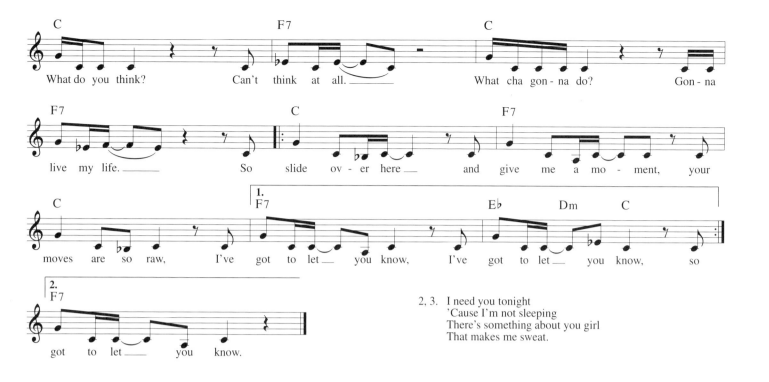

What do you think? Can't think at all. ___ What cha gon - na do? Gon - na

live my life. ___ So slide ov - er here ___ and give me a mo - ment, your

1.
moves are so raw, I've got to let ___ you know, I've got to let ___ you know, so

2.
got to let ___ you know.

2, 3. I need you tonight
'Cause I'm not sleeping
There's something about you girl
That makes me sweat.

620. The Night Has A Thousand Eyes

Words & Music by Buddy Bernier & Jerome Brainin

Don't whis - per things to me you don't mean, ___ For words deep down in -
ro - mance may have called in the past ___ My love for you will

- side can be seen by the night. ___ The night ___ has a thou - sand eyes ___ and it
be ev - er - last - ing and bright ___ As bright ___ as the star - lit skies ___ And this

1.   **2.**
knows a truth - ful heart from one that lies. ___ Tho' ___ I've lived my life ___
won - d'rous night that has a thou - sand eyes. ___

walk - ing thru a dream. ___ For I knew that I would find this mo - ment su -

- preme. ___ A night of bliss ___ and ten - der sighs ___ And the smil - ing down

___ of a thou - sand eyes. The night ___ has a thou - sand eyes.

621. Never Mind

Words & Music by Harlan Howard

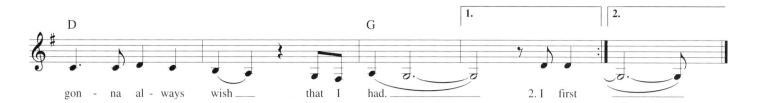

gon - na al - ways wish ___ that I had. _____ 2. I first

2. I first saw you picking oranges in Orlando
And all day you kept your ladder close to mine
We froze in Georgia, burned up in Chicago
And I alway thought that we
But never mind
And did you know today my baby called you daddy?
Sometimes I've wished that she was yours and mine
I could call my brother, Milt, in Cincinnati
And ask him for a loan
But never mind
Never mind, never mind *(etc.)*

622. The Nearness Of You

Music by Hoagy Carmichael. Words by Ned Washington

623. Never Say Die

Words & Music by Jon Bon Jovi

624. No More "I Love You's"

Words & Music by D. Freeman & J. Hughes

2. I used to have demons in my room at night
   Desire, despair, desire, so many monsters
   Oh, but now
   I don't find myself bouncing home
   Whistling buttonhole tunes to make me cry.

625. No Woman, No Cry

Words & Music by Bob Marley & Vincent Ford

626. Not A Second Time

Words & Music by John Lennon & Paul McCartney

627. The Odd Couple

By Neal Hefti

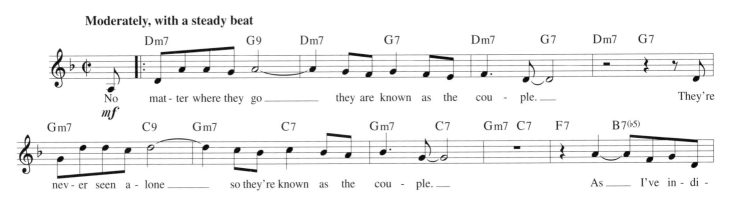

604

-ca - ted __ they __ are nev - er quite se - pa - ra - ted, they __ are peas in a

pod. Don't you think that it's odd? Their hab - its, I con - fess, __ none can guess with the

cou - ple. __ If one says no it's yes __ more or less, with the cou - ple. __

But __ they're laugh pro - vok - ing; __ yet __ they real - ly don't

know they're jok - ing. Don't you find __ when love is blind __ it's kind of odd!

No odd! Don't you think it's odd? __

Don't you think it's odd? __ Don't you think it's odd? __

628. Now The Day Is Over

Music by Joseph Barnby. Words by Sabine Baring-Gould

Moderately

Now the day is o - ver, Night is draw - ing __ nigh,
(Verses 2 & 3 see block lyrics)

Shad - ows of the even - ing Steal a - cross the sky.

2. Through the long night watches, may thine angels spread
Their white wings above me, watching round my bed.

3. When the morning wakens, then may I arise
Pure and fresh and sinless, in thy holy eyes.

629. Nothing Ever Happens

Words & Music by Justin Currie

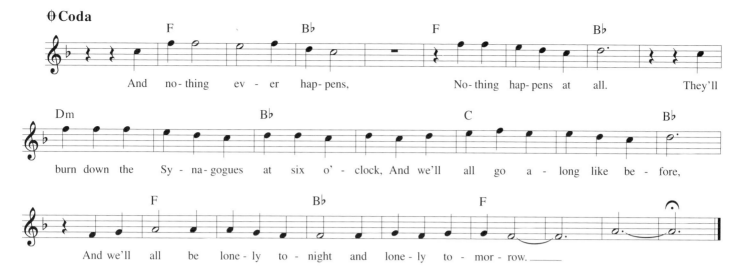

And no-thing ev- er hap- pens, No-thing hap-pens at all. They'll

burn down the Sy - na- gogues at six o' - clock, And we'll all go a - long like be - fore,

And we'll all be lone - ly to - night and lone - ly to - mor - row. _____

2. Gentlemen time please, you know we can't serve anymore
   Now the traffic lights change to stop when there's nothing to go
   And by five o'clock everything's dead
   And every third car is a cab
   And ignorant people sleep in their beds
   Like the doped white mice in the college lab.

3. Telephone exchanges click while there's nobody there
   The Martians could land in the car park and no one would care
   Closed-circuit cameras in department stores
   Shoot the same movie every day
   And the stars of these films neither die not get killed
   Just survive constant action replay.

4. And bill hoardings advertise products that nobody needs
   While angry of Manchester writes to complaint about
   All the repeats on T.V.
   And computer terminals report some gains
   On the values of copper and tin
   While American businessmen snap up Van Goghs
   For the price of a hospital wing.

630. O God Our Help In Ages Past

Music by Dr. William Croft. Words by Isaac Watts

Moderately

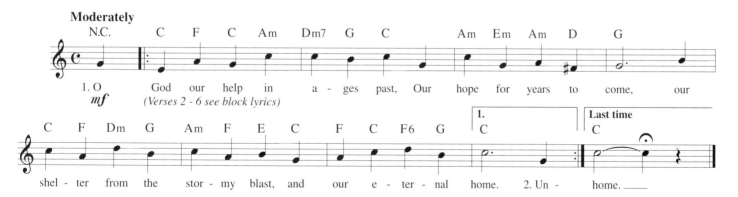

1. O God our help in a - ges past, Our hope for years to come, our
(Verses 2 - 6 see block lyrics)

shel - ter from the stor - my blast, and our e - ter - nal home. 2. Un - home. _____

2. Under the shadow of Thy throne
   Thy saints have dwelt secure
   Sufficient is Thine arm alone
   And our defence is sure.

3. Before the hills in order stood
   Or earth received her frame
   From everlasting Thou art God
   To endless years the same.

4. A thousand ages in Thy sight
   Are like an evening gone
   Short as the watch that ends the night
   Before the rising sun.

5. Time, like an ever-rolling stream
   Bears all its sons away
   They fly forgotten, as a dream
   Dies at the opening day.

6. O God our help in ages past
   Our hope for years to come
   Be thou our guard while troubles last
   And our eternal home.

631. Ocean Drive

Words & Music by Paul Tucker

2. He left you black and blue
   Without a word of explanation
   And he took your love for granted
   And he left you high and dry
   And you know someday
   Well you'll wonder what you see in him anyway
   When that day arrives
   We'll live on Ocean Drive.

632. On Days Like These

Music by Quincy Jones. Words by Don Black

633. Ode To My Family

Words & Music by Dolores O'Riordan & Noel Hogan

as fun — and take — it if — we can. — My moth - er, my moth - er, she hold —

— me, she hold — me when I was out there. — My fa - ther,

my fa - ther, he liked — me, oh, he liked — me. Does an - y - one care?

1.
me. Does an - y - one care? — Does an - y - one care? —

Does an - y - one care? — Does an - y - one care? — Does an - y - one care? —

2.
— Doo, doo, doo, doo, — doo, doo, doo, doo, — doo,

doo, doo, doo, — doo, doo, doo, doo, — Doo.

Vocal Tacet 4th time

2. Understand what I've become
It wasn't my design
And people ev'rywhere think
Something better than I am
But I miss you, I miss, 'cause I liked it
'Cause I liked it when I was out there
Do you know this
Do you know you did not find me
You did not find me,
Does anyone care?

611

634. On The Road Again

Words & Music by Willie Nelson

635. Once Upon A Time

Music by Charles Strouse. Music by Lee Adams

636. One

Words & Music by U2

637. Oh Baby Doll

Words & Music by Chuck Berry

638. One Meat Ball

Words & Music by Hy Zaret & Louis Singer

639. Old Love

Words & Music by Eric Clapton & Robert Cray

640. OK Fred

Words & Music by John Holt, Monty Babson & Terry Cramer

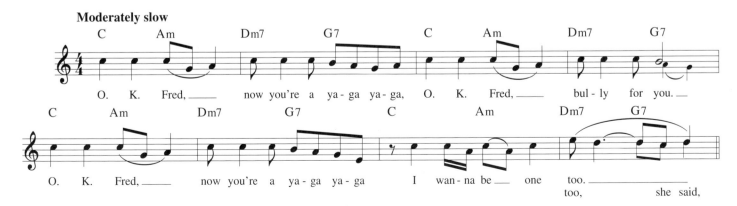

O. K. Fred, ____ now I'm a ya-ga ya-ga, O. K. Fred, ____ what do I do? ____

O. K. Fred, ____ now I'm a ya-ga ya-ga, I am ____ just like you, ____ she said,

"I like the way that you do it ____ when you do it on the quick." ____ She said,

D.C. al Coda

"I like the way that you move, ____ I like the way ____ that you groove," ____ she said,

Coda

O. K. Fred, ____ now you're a ya-ga ya-ga, O. K. Fred, ____ bul-ly for you.

"I like the way that you do it ____ when you do it on the quick." ____ She said,

Repeat to fade

"I like the way that you groove dar-ling I like the way ____ that you move, ____ she said.

641. Prelude Op.28 No.20

Composed by Frédérik Chopin

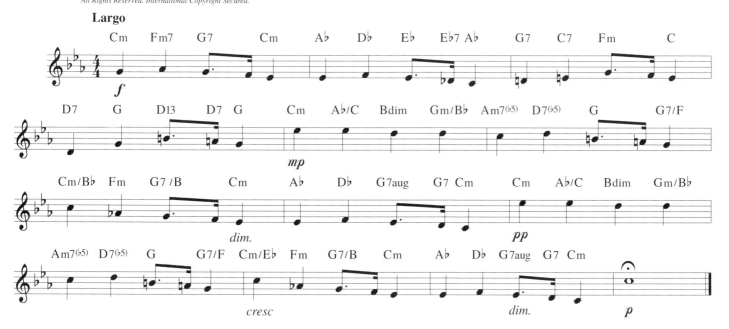

642. Old Toy Trains

Words & Music by Roger Miller

643. Oops Upside Your Head

Words & Music by Rudy Taylor, Lonnie Simmons,
Charlie Wilson, Robert Wilson & Ronnie Wilson

644. On The Sunny Side Of The Street

Words by Dorothy Fields. Music by Jimmy McHugh

645. Once Is Not Enough

Music by Harry Tobias. Words by Larry Kusik

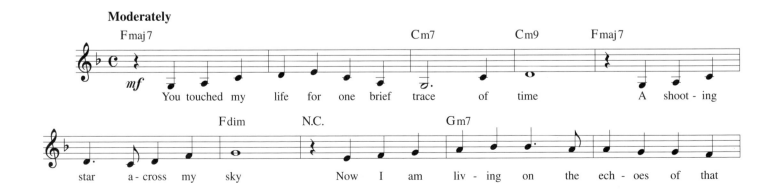

yes - ter - day ___ Re - liv - ing dreams my heart can't put a - way ___ Love wrote our
stor - y once ___ but once is not e - nough ___ Now that I've learned how kiss - es
warm the night. In arms that shut the world out - side ___ I tast - ed
love just once ___ but once is not e - nough ___ for all the lov - ing needs I
feel deep in - side. side. ___

646. Onward Christian Soldiers

Music by Sir Arthur Sullivan. Words by Sabine Baring-Gould

Moderately

mf 1. On - ward, Chris - tian sol - diers, March - ing as to war, With the cross of Je - sus
(Verses 2 - 4 see block lyrics)
Go - ing on be - fore! Christ, the roy - al mas - ter, Leads a - gainst the foe;
For - ward in - to bat - tle, ___ See! His ban - ners go! *Refrain* On - ward, Chris - tian sol - diers, ___
March - ing as to ___ war, With the cross of Je - sus Go - ing on be - fore!

2. At the sign of triumph
Satan's host doth flee
On then, Christian soldiers
On to victory!
Hell's foundations quiver
At the shout of praise
Brothers lift your voices
Loud your anthems raise.
Refrain

3. Crowns and thrones may perish
Kingdoms rise and wane
But the Church of Jesus
Constant will remain
Gates of hell can never
'Gainst that Church prevail
We have Christ's own promise
And that cannot fail.
Refrain

4. Onward, then, ye people!
Join our happy throng
Blend with ours your voices
In the triumph-song
Glory, laud, and honour
Unto Christ the King!
This through countless ages
Men and angels sing:
Refrain

647. The Only Thing That Looks Good On Me Is You

Words & Music by Bryan Adams & Robert John "Mutt" Lange

good on me ___ is you.

2. I'm not satisfied with Versace's style
Put those patent leather pants in the circular file
Sometimes I think I might be looking good
But there's only one thing that fits like it should.

648. Only A Northern Song

Words & Music by George Harrison

649. Only You (And You Alone)

Words & Music by Buck Ram & Ande Rand

650. Only Fools And Horses

By John R. Sullivan

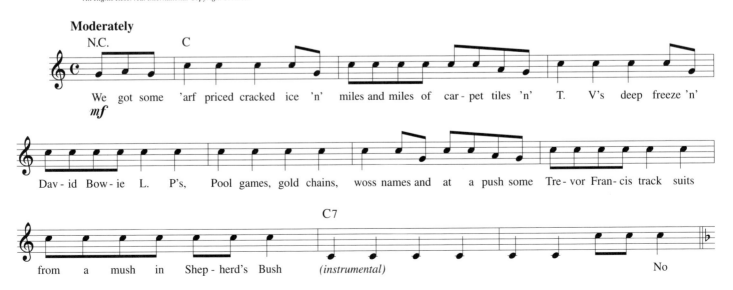

in - come tax, no V. A. T., ___ No mon - ey back, ___ no gua - ran - tee, ___

Black and white, ___ rich or broke, ___ We'll cut pri - ces at a stroke. ___

___ God bless Hook - ey Street, ___ Vi - va

Hook - ey Street, ___ Long live Hook - ey Street, ___ C'est mag - ni - fique,

Hook - ey Street, ___ Mag - ni - fique, Hook - ey Street. ___

651. Psycho (Prelude)

By Bernard Herrmann

Agitato

652. Open Your Heart

Words & Music by Mike Pickering & Paul Heard

(Ba - by ba - by ba - by)

1. If I on -
(Verse 2 see block lyric)

- - ly knew ___ how you ___ feel, ___ I would give ___ my heart ___

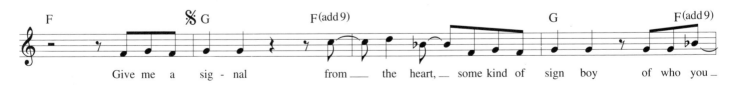

___ to you. ___ And if you ___ let ___ me in ___ on

your ___ deal, ___ may - be I ___ won't feel ___ so blue.

Give me a sig - nal from ___ the heart, ___ some kind of sign boy of who you ___

___ real - ly are ___ don't waste my time 'cause we've come ___ too far, ___ you must de -

2. Why don't you wear your heart on my sleeve
   Then you can take your place by me
   And I've got more to give than you need
   Come on and end this misery
   Give me a signal from the heart
   Some kind of sign, boy, of who you really are
   Don't waste my time now, we've come too far
   It makes no sense now when we're apart.

653. Out Of Sight, Out Of Mind

Words & Music by Ivory Joe Hunter & Clyde Otis

654. Outstanding

Words & Music by Raymond Calhoun

655. Out Of Nowhere

Music by John Green. Lyrics by Edward Heyman

656. Out Of The East

Words & Music by Harry Noble

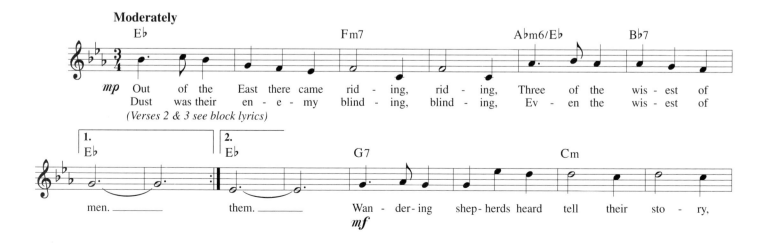

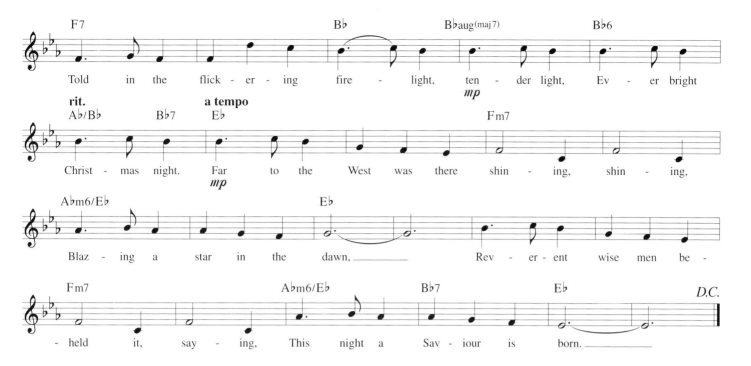

Told in the flick-er-ing fire - light, ten - der light, Ev - er bright
Christ - mas night. Far to the West was there shin - ing, shin - ing,
Blaz - ing a star in the dawn, _____ Rev - er - ent wise men be -
- held it, say - ing, This night a Sav - iour is born. _____

2. Into the West they went riding, riding
   Following after the star
   Over a quiet town shining, shining
   Lighting their way from afar
   Under its glory sat Mother Mary
   Tenderly singing a lullaby, hush-a-bye
   Don't you cry, lullaby
   Into the stable came riding, riding
   Three of the wisest of men
   Gifts did they bring for that babe in a manger
   Gifts for the Saviour of men.

3. Low in a manger they found Him, found Him
   Bathed in the light of yon star
   Gold did they bring Him and frankincense
   And myrhh from a land that was far
   Shepherds crept in singing praises, praises
   Guardian angels were near to Him, dear to Him
   One with Him, praising Him
   Into the East then went riding, riding
   Three of the wisest of men
   Found was the babe in a lowly manger
   Crowned was the Saviour of men.

657. A Place In The Sun

Music by Franz Waxman. Words by Jay Livingston

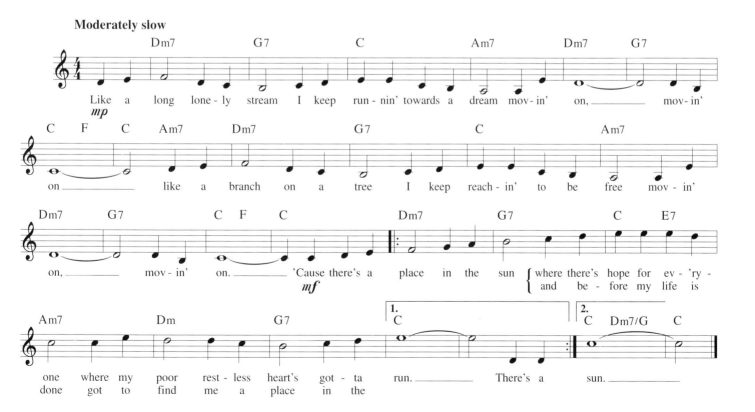

Like a long lone - ly stream I keep run - nin' towards a dream mov - in' on, _____ mov - in'
on _____ like a branch on a tree I keep reach - in' to be free mov - in'
on, _____ mov - in' on. _____ 'Cause there's a place in the sun { where there's hope for ev - 'ry - and be - fore my life is
one where my poor rest - less heart's got - ta run. There's a sun. _____
done got to find me a place in the

658. Paramount On Parade

Words & Music by Elsie Janis & Jack King

659. Piggies

Words & Music by George Harrison

Slow 4

1. Have you seen the lit - tle pig - gies crawl - ing in the dirt? And for all the lit - tle pig - gies life is get - ting worse. Al - ways hav - ing dirt to play a - round in.

2. Have you seen the big - ger pig - gies in their starched white shirts? You will find the big - ger pig - gies stir - ring up the dirt. Al - ways have clean shirts to play a - round in.

In their styles with all their back - ing, They don't care what goes on a - round; In their eyes there's some - thing lack - ing, What they need's a damn good whack - ing!

3. Ev - 'ry - where there's lots of pig - gies liv - ing pig - gy lives, You can see them out for din - ner with their pig - gy wives; Clutch - ing forks and knives to eat their ba - con.

660. (Let's Have A) Party

Words & Music by Jessie Mae Robinson

Medium bright rock

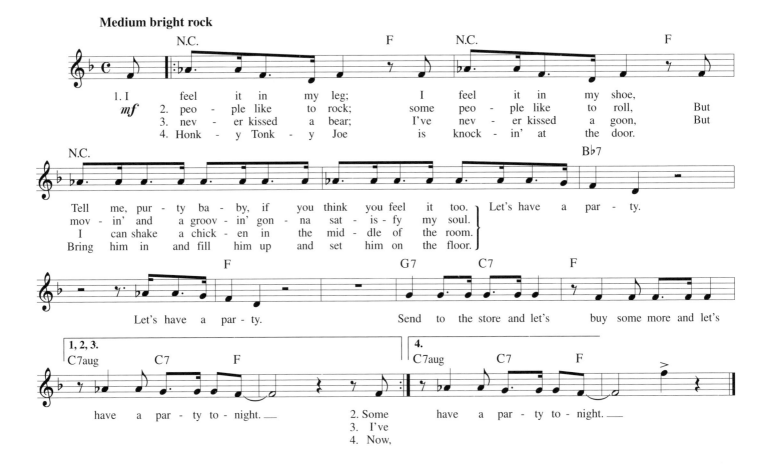

1. I feel it in my leg; I feel it in my shoe,
2. peo - ple like to rock; some peo - ple like to roll, But
3. nev - er kissed a bear; I've nev - er kissed a goon, But
4. Honk - y Tonk - y Joe is knock - in' at the door.

Tell me, pur - ty ba - by, if you think you feel it too. ⎫
mov - in' and a groov - in' gon - na sat - is - fy my soul. ⎬ Let's have a par - ty.
I can shake a chick - en in the mid - dle of the room. ⎭
Bring him in and fill him up and set him on the floor. ⎭

Let's have a par - ty. Send to the store and let's buy some more and let's

1, 2, 3. have a par - ty to - night. **4.** have a par - ty to - night.

2. Some
3. I've
4. Now,

661. Paralyzed

Words & Music by Otis Blackwell & Elvis Presley

Bright shuffle

When you looked in - to my eyes, I stood there like I was hyp - no -
When we kissed, ooh, what a thrill. You took my hand and ooh, ba - by, what a

- tized. You sent a feel - ing to my spine, a feel - ing warm and smooth and fine, But
chill. I felt like grab - bin' you real tight, squeeze and squeeze with all my might, But

all I could do was stand there pa - ra - lyzed. - lyzed. Oh, yah, luck - y me, I'm
all I could do was stand there pa - ra

sing - in' ev - 'ry day, Ev - er since that day you came my way. You

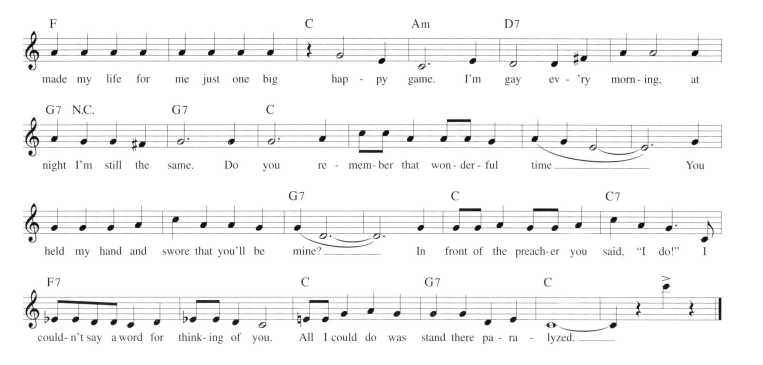

made my life for me just one big hap - py game. I'm gay ev - 'ry morn - ing, at
night I'm still the same. Do you re - mem - ber that won - der - ful time ___ You
held my hand and swore that you'll be mine? ___ In front of the preach - er you said, "I do!" I
could-n't say a word for think - ing of you. All I could do was stand there pa - ra - lyzed. ___

662. Portrait Of My Love

Words by David West. Music by Cyril Ornadel

Moderately slow

There could nev - er be A por - trait of my love For no - bo - dy could paint a
dream ___ You will nev - er see A por - trait of my love For mi - ra - cles are
nev - er seen ___ An - - - y one who sees her ___
soon ___ for - gets the Mo - na Li - za It would take, I know a
Mi - chel - an - ge - lo And he would need the glow of dawn that paints the sky a - bove, To
try and paint a por - trait of my love.   love. ___

663. Pass The Dutchie

Words & Music by Jackie Mittoo, Lloyd Ferguson & Fitzroy Simpson

664. Patience Of Angels

Words & Music by Boo Hewerdine

1. D(add 9) | **2.** D(add 9) | Bm7 | A/C♯ | D | E7sus4

There's a | She's the pa-tience of an - gels, the pa-tience
Tacet 2nd time

Bm7 | A/C♯ | **1.** D | E7sus4 | **2.** D | E7sus4 | A | E/G♯

of, _____ of an - gels. _ It would try the pa-tience of

Bm7 | **1, 2, 3.** D | E | **4.** D | E | Bm7 | A/C♯ | D | E13 | Bm7

an - gels. _ It would An - gels.

2. And you know something's wrong
When the morning hurts your eyes
And the baby won't stop crying,
You'll be waiting till you die.
Would I be any good
And if I was would I find
That it would try
The patience of angels *(etc.)*

665. Please Don't Drag That String Around

Words & Music by Otis Blackwell & Winfield Scott

Moderately

E♭ | F7 | A♭

1. You like to keep me a - dan - gling on a string, _ 'Cause you know with-out _
mf

B♭7 | E♭ | A♭

— you my life don't mean a thing. _ So I beg you, Please don't drag that string a-round,

E♭ | B♭7 | E♭

— oh, no, Well, what if it should break, _ (oh tell me) What would _ I do then?

E♭7 | A♭ | E♭

— (ba - by) Keep that string up off the ground, _ oh, yeah, Re - mem - ber, my

B♭7 | **1, 2.** E♭ | B♭7 | **3.** E♭ | A♭ | E♭

heart is tied _ to the oth - er end. _ (Mm) _

2. Yes, I'm your puppet, my heart is in your hand
One twist of the wrist and I jump to your command
So I beg you,

3. I feel inside me, as sure as anything
One day I'll mean more to you than a puppet on a string
So I beg you,

666. Peacock Suit

Words & Music by Paul Weller

642

Did you think I should? _____

F7

Play 3 times

Fade

2. I'm Narcissus in a puddle
   In shop windows I gloat
   Like a ball of fleece lining
   In my camel skin coat.
   I don't need a ship
   To sail in stormy weather
   Don't need you to ruffle the feathers
   Of my peacock suit
   Did you think I should?

3. Nemesis in a muddle
   In a mirror I look
   Like a streak of sheet light'nin'
   In my rattlesnake shoes.
   I don't need a ship
   To sail in stormy weather
   Don't need you to ruffle the feathers
   Of my peacock suit
   Did you think I should?

667. Praise My Soul

Music by J. Goss. Words by H. F. Lyte

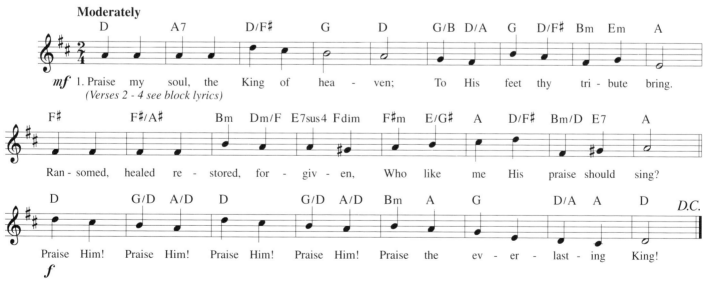

Moderately

D   A7   D/F#   G   D   G/B D/A G   D/F# Bm Em   A

mf 1. Praise my soul, the King of hea - ven; To His feet thy tri - bute bring.
(Verses 2 - 4 see block lyrics)

F#   F#/A#   Bm Dm/F E7sus4 Fdim F#m E/G# A   D/F# Bm/D E7   A

Ran - somed, healed re - stored, for - giv - en, Who like me His praise should sing?

D   G/D A/D D   G/D A/D Bm   A   G   D/A   A   D   *D.C.*

Praise Him! Praise Him! Praise Him! Praise Him! Praise the ev - er - last - ing King!

f

2. Praise Him for His grace and favour
   To our fathers in distress
   Praise Him, still the same as ever
   Slow to chide, and swift to bless
   Praise Him! Praise Him!
   Praise Him! Praise Him!
   Glorious in His faithfulness.

3. Father-like He tends and spares us
   Well our feeble frame He knows
   In His hands He gently bears us
   Rescues us from all our foes
   Praise Him! Praise Him!
   Praise Him! Praise Him!
   Widely as His mercy flows.

4. Angels in the height, adore Him
   Ye behold Him face to face
   Sun and moon, bow down before Him
   Dwellers all in time and space
   Praise Him! Praise Him!
   Praise Him! Praise Him!
   Praise with us the God of grace!

668. Pilgrims' Chorus (from 'Tannhäuser')

Composed by Richard Wagner

669. Please Help Me Get Him Off My Mind

Words & Music by Bessie Smith

2. I've come to see you gypsy, beggin' on my bended knees
   I've come to see you gypsy, beggin' on my bended knees
   That man's put something on me, oh take it off me, please.

3. It starts at my forehead and goes clean down to my toes
   It starts at my forehead and goes clean down to my toes
   Oh, how I'm sufferin' gypsy, nobody but the good Lawd knows.

4. Gypsy, don't hurt him, fix him for me one more time
   Oh, don't hurt him gypsy, fix him for me one more time
   Just make him love me, but, please mam, take him off my mind.

670. Pipes Of Peace

Words & Music by McCartney

671. A Place In Paris

Music by Michel Legrand. Words by Hal Shaper

672. Please

Words & Music by Leo Robin & Ralph Rainger

Please lend your lit- tle ear to my pleas, Lend a ray of cheer to my pleas, Tell me that you love me too.

Please let me hold you tight in my arms, I could find de- light in your

charms, Ev- 'ry night my whole life through. Your eyes re- veal that you have the

soul of { an an- gel, white as snow; / the ni- cest man I've met; } But how long must I play the role of { a / a

gloom- y Ro- me- o? / tear- ful Ju- li- et? } Oh! Please say you're not in- ten- ding to tease,

Spend the hap- py end- ing and please Tell me that you love me too.

673. Parklife

Words & Music by Damon Albarn, Graham Coxon, Alex James & David Rowntree

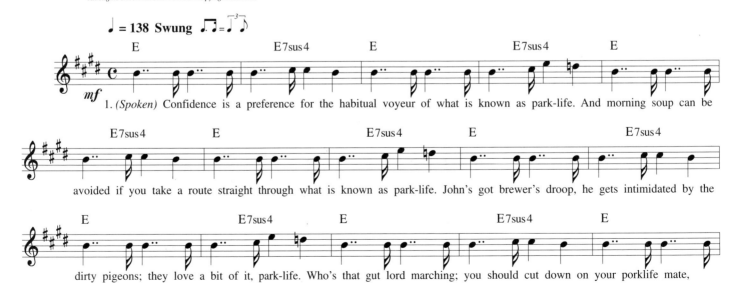

1. *(Spoken)* Confidence is a preference for the habitual voyeur of what is known as park-life. And morning soup can be

avoided if you take a route straight through what is known as park-life. John's got brewer's droop, he gets intimidated by the

dirty pigeons; they love a bit of it, park-life. Who's that gut lord marching; you should cut down on your porklife mate,

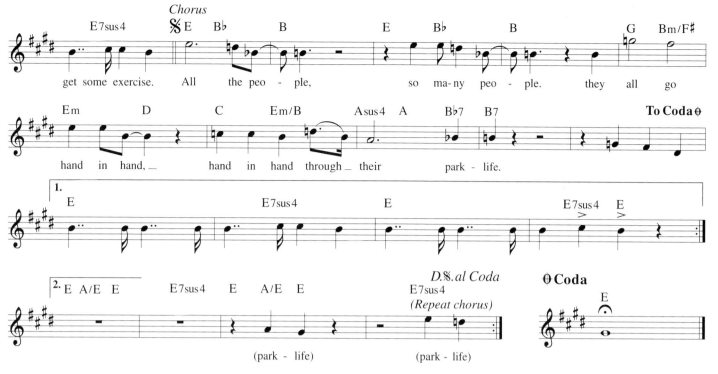

get some exercise. All the peo - ple, so ma-ny peo - ple. they all go hand in hand, — hand in hand through their park - life.

(park - life) (park - life)

(Spoken 3 & 4) It's got nothing to do with your vorsprung durch technic, you know, and it's not about you joggers who go round and round and round.

2. I get up when I want except on Wednesday when I get rudely awakened by dustmen - (parklife)
I put my trousers on, have a cup of tea and I think about leaving the house - (parklife)
I feed the pigeons, I sometimes feed the sparrows too. It gives me a sense of enormous well-being - (parklife)
And then I'm happy for the rest of the day safe in the knowledge there will always be a bit of my heart devoted to it.

674. Picnic

Music by George Dunning. Words by Steve Allen

On a pic - nic morn - ing, with - out a warn - ing, I looked at you and some - how I knew. _____ On a day for sing - ing, my heart went wing - ing, a pic - nic grove was our ren - dez - vous. _____ You and I in the sun - shine, we strolled the field and farms, _____ at the last light of eve - ning, I held you in my arms. Now when days grow storm - y, and lone - ly for me, I just re - call pic - nic time with you. _____

675. Please Don't Make Me Cry

Words & Music by Winston Tucker

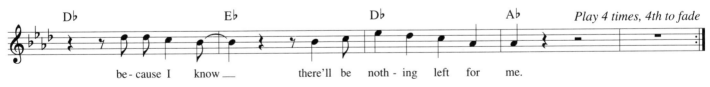

2. All them good good times we stayed together
   You say you're with me and no other
   At night you wanna make me pain inside
   Darling I know you're gonna make me cry.

3. *Instrumental 8 bars*
   All this pain I can't stand
   You're gonna leave, you're gonna leave this poor man on his own.

4. All this pain I can't stand
   You're gonna leave, you're gonna leave this poor man on his own
   Please don't make me cry, baby I'm feeling
   Oh, oh, oh, oh.

676. Pretty Flamingo

Words & Music by Mark Barkan

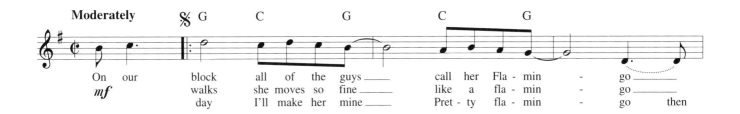

On our block all of the guys ___ call her Flamin - go
walks she moves so fine ___ like a flamin - go ___
day I'll make her mine ___ Pret - ty fla - min - go then

'cause her hair glows like the sun ___ and her eyes can light the skies.
crim - son dress that clings so tight ___ she's out of reach and out of sight.
ev - 'ry one will en - vy me, ___ 'cause par - a - dise is where I'll be

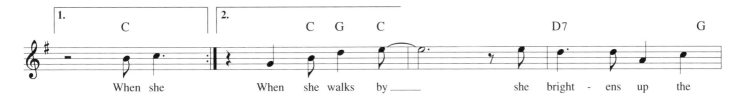

1. When she
2. When she walks by ___ she bright - ens up the

neigh - bour - hood ___ oh, ev - 'ry guy ___ would

make her his if he just could if she just would. Some sweet

Coda

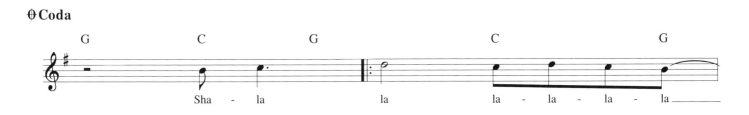

Sha - la la la - la la - la ___

Repeat to fade

Pret - ty fla - min - go Sha - la

677. Power Of A Woman

Words & Music by Evan Rogers & Carl Sturken

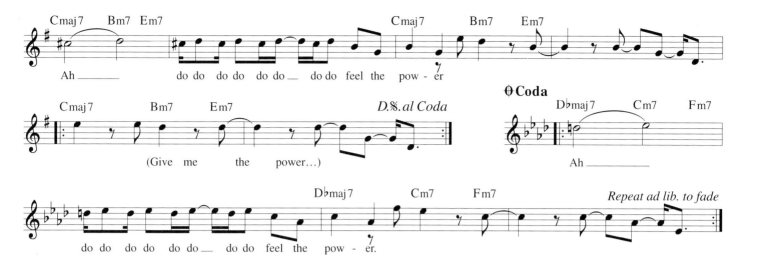

Ah _____ do do do do do do _ do do feel the pow-er

Cmaj7   Bm7   Em7

Cmaj7   Bm7   Em7   D.%.al Coda   Coda   Dbmaj7   Cm7   Fm7

(Give   me   the   power...)   Ah _____

Dbmaj7   Cm7   Fm7   Repeat ad lib. to fade

do do   do do   do do _   do do feel the pow-er.

2. Please don't misunderstand
   I need a strong man
   Who'll be my soldier
   Never give up the fight
   I gotta know now
   Baby let it show now
   Can you keep the fire burning
   Morning till night?

   You're always caught up
   In a one-way love affair
   Livin' with your heart on the run
   I've got the real thing
   Come and get it if you dare
   Let me tell you baby
   Don't you know I'm the one.

678. Rock Of Ages

Words by A. M. Toplady. Music by R. Redhead.

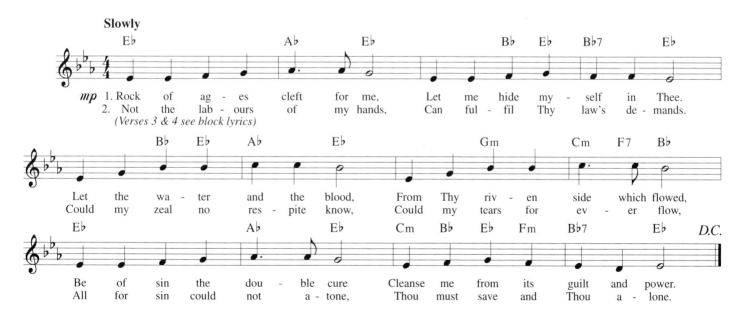

Slowly

Eb   Ab   Eb   Bb   Eb   Bb7   Eb

mp 1. Rock of ag - es cleft for me, Let me hide my - self in Thee.
     2. Not the lab - ours of my hands, Can ful - fil Thy law's de - mands.
     (Verses 3 & 4 see block lyrics)

Bb   Eb   Ab   Eb   Gm   Cm   F7   Bb

Let the wa - ter and the blood, From Thy riv - en side which flowed,
Could my zeal no res - pite know, Could my tears for ev - er flow,

Eb   Ab   Eb   Cm   Bb   Eb   Fm   Bb7   Eb   *D.C.*

Be of sin the dou - ble cure Cleanse me from its guilt and power.
All for sin could not a - tone, Thou must save and Thou a - lone.

3. Nothing in my hand I bring
   Simply to Thy Cross I cling
   Naked, come to Thee for dress
   Helpless, look to Thee for grace
   Foul, I to the fountain fly
   Wash me, Saviour, or I die.

4. While I draw this fleeting breath
   When mine eyes shall close in death
   When I soar through tracts unknown
   See Thee on Thy judgement throne
   Rock of ages, cleft for me
   Let me hide myself in Thee.

679. Power To The People

Words & Music by John Lennon

680. Put On A Happy Face

Music by Charles Strouse. Words by Lee Adams

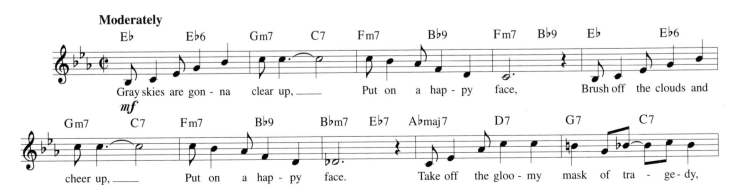

it's not your style; You'll look so good that you'll be glad___ ya' de-
-cid-ed to smile.___ Pick out a pleas-ant out-look,___ Stick out that no-ble
chin; Wipe off that "full of doubt" look,___ Slap on a hap-py
grin! And spread sun-shine all ov-er the
place. Just put on a hap-py face!___

681. The Road To Morocco

Music by Johnny Burke. Words by Jimmy van Heusen

Let's meet on the road___ tp Mo-roc-co,___ In-
meet on the road___ to Mo-roc-co,___ Though
-stead of the tun-nel of love;___ The de-sert night, the Ar-ab tents, the
our Brook-lyn moon shines a-bove;___ I'll whis-per how I love you to the
har-em at-mos-phere, It's the best at-trac-tion Con-ey Is-land has this
strains of na-tive flutes, And your arms will thrill me more than all the chute-the-
year. Let's chutes. Tell the gang so they won't___ hang a-round___
Like Web-ster's Dic-tion-ar-y, we're Mo-roc-co bound.

682. Praise The Lord And Pass The Ammunition

Words & Music by Frank Loesser

683. Promise Her Anything

Music by Burt Bacharach. Words by Hal David

684. Quit Playing Games (With My Heart)

Words & Music by Max Martin & Herbert Crichlow

2. I live my life the way
   To keep you comin' back to me
   Everything I do is for you
   So what is it that you can't see?
   Sometimes I wish I could turn back time
   Impossible as it may seem
   But I wish I could so bad, baby
   You better quit playing games with my heart.

685. Raincloud

Music by Paul Tucker, Emmanuel Baiyewu & Martin Brammer. Words by Paul Tucker

2. There ain't no point holding back desire
   Still gonna get ya
   Strangers on a train driving through the night
   Soon overtakes ya
   If someone feels the same as you
   Might as well just do what you want to do
   There ain't no point holding back desire
   Don't waste your time.

686. Rip It Up

Words & Music by Robert Blackwell & John Marascalco

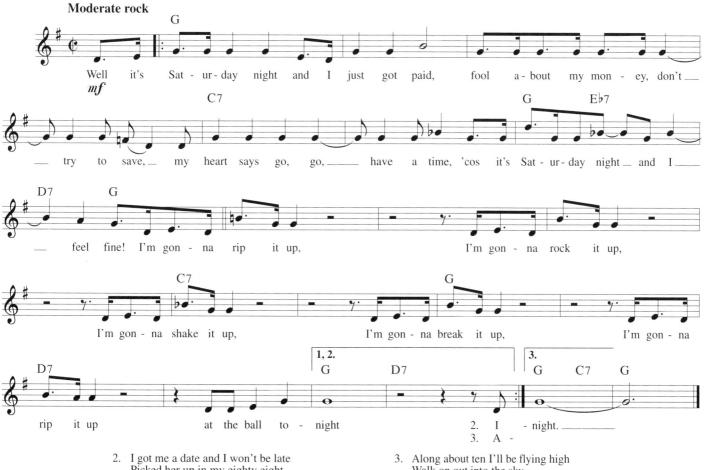

2. I got me a date and I won't be late
   Picked her up in my eighty eight
   Shag on down by the social hall
   When the joint starts jumpin' I'll have a ball.
   I'm gonna rip it up *(etc.)*

3. Along about ten I'll be flying high
   Walk on out into the sky
   But I don't care if I spend my dough
   'Cos tonight I'm gonna be one happy soul.
   I'm gonna rip it up *(etc.)*

687. Ready Teddy

Words & Music by John Marascalco & Robert Blackwell

688. Re-Enlistment Blues

Words & Music by James Jones, Frederick Karger & Robert Wells

Moderately slow

ADDITIONAL CHORUSES

4. I woke up on Thursday
   The walls was movin', I swear, movin' I swear
   I reach'd down in my trousers
   All my pockets was bare, nothin' was there
   I really blew my fuse
   Re-enlistment blues, oh them blues.

5. Hit the bar again on Friday
   Ask'd for a free glass of beer, free glass of beer
   Bar man he don't know me
   He just say no credit here, no credit here
   What I done then ain't news
   Re-enlistment blues, oh them blues.

6. The jail was cold Sa'day
   Just like the people outside, people outside
   I ain't no guardhouse lawyer
   But even I got my pride, I got my pride
   Ain't much left to choose
   Re-enlistment blues, oh them blues.

7. Slep' in the park Sunday
   Seen all those folks go to church, folks go to church
   Your belly feels so empty
   When you've been left in the lurch, left in a lurch
   Dog soljers don't own pews
   Re-enlistment blues, oh them blues.

8. Short timbers, I'll tell you
   Don't you get throw'd in the can, throw'd in the can
   You might as well be dead
   Or be a thirty year man, thirty year man
   Guy always seem to lose
   Re-enlistment blues, oh them blues.

689. Ready To Take A Chance Again

Words & Music by Charles Fox & Norman Gimbel

664

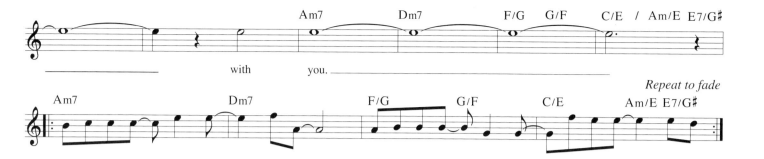

with you.

Repeat to fade

690. **Rêverie**

Composed by Claude Debussy

691. Real Real Gone

Words & Music by Van Morrison

2. I'm real real — I'm real _____ gone, _____ oh _____

Lord I got hit by a bow and ar - row, got me down

— to the ve - ry mar - row, you're a friend ___ of mine, _____

and I'm real ___ real gone. ___

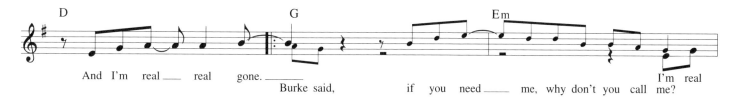

And I'm real ___ real gone. _____
Burke said, if you need ___ me, why don't you call me?
I'm real

gone.
James Brown said, when you're tired of what you got, try me
Wil - son Pick - ett said, in the Mid - night Hour _
Gene Chand - ler said, _

Repeat to fade

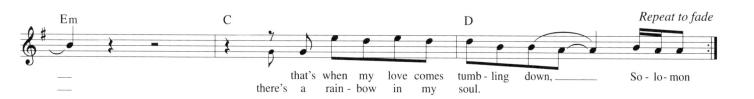

—
— that's when my love comes tumb - ling down, _____ So - lo - mon
there's a rain - bow in my soul.

2. I'm real real gone
   I can't stand up by myself
   Don't you know I need your help
   You're a friend of mine
   And I'm real real gone.

   And Sam Cooke is on the radio
   And the night is filled with space
   And your fingertips touch my face
   You're a friend of mine
   I'm real real gone.

692. Return To Me

Words & Music by Carmen Lombardo & Daniel Di Minno

Moderately

Re-turn to me, Oh, my dear, I'm so lone-ly; Hur-ry back, hur-ry back, Oh, my
Ri-tor-na a me, Non la-scia-re mi so-lo; Vien-i tu, vien-i tu, Vien-i

love, hur-ry back, I am yours. Re-turn to me, For my heart wants you
tu, vien-i tu, mi a-mor. Ri-tor-na a me, Ca-ra mi-a ti

on-ly. Hur-ry home, hur-ry home, Won't you please hur-ry home, to my
a-mo; So-lo tu, so-lo tu, So-lo tu, so-lo tu, mi-o

heart. My dar-ling, if I hurt you I'm sor-ry; For-
cuor Bam-bi-na, dar il cuor-a nes-su-no; Man-

give me, and please say you are mine: Re-turn to me,
tie-ni, so-la-men-te per me. Ri-tor-na a me,

___ Please come back, bel-la mi-a; Hur-ry back hur-ry home to my
___ E la san-ta ve-nu-ta; Vien-i tu, vien-i tu so-lo

1.
arms, to my lips, and my heart. Re-turn to heart.
tu, so-lo tu mi a-mor!

2.
Re-turn to heart.
Ri-tor-na a mor!

693. A Root'n Toot'n Santa Claus

Words & Music by Oakley Haldeman & Peter Tinturin

Bright tempo

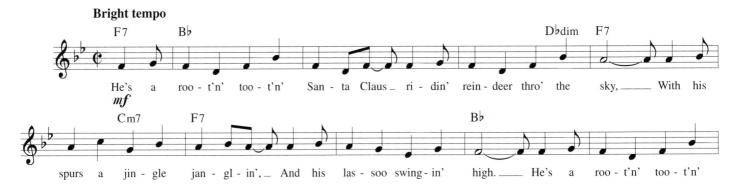

He's a roo-t'n' too-t'n' San-ta Claus ri-din' rein-deer thro' the sky, With his

spurs a jin-gle jan-gl-in', And his las-soo swing-in' high. He's a roo-t'n' too-t'n'

San - ta Claus, Sad - dle bags all packed with toys, — Down the chim - ney he will bring them all — to the

dream - ing girls and boys. — Git a - long lit - tle rein - deer git a - long, — Co - ver all the range to - night,

— It's a long long trail, — An all night trail, — But you can bet your boots that

San - ta won't fail! He's a roo - t'n' too - t'n' San - ta Claus, — And he's on his mer - ry

way, — He will round up all your Christ - mas dreams with a yip - py - yo - ki - yay! —

694. Romance (from 'The Pearl Fishers')

By Georges Bizet

Andante

cresc   dim.

695. Rêve de Printemps

Composed by Johann Strauss

696. The Raider's March

By John Williams

697. Rhythm Of My Heart

Words & Music by Marc Jordan & John Capek

672

673

698. Right By Your Side

Words & Music by A. Lennox & D. A. Stewart

699. Rain

Words & Music by John Lennon & Paul McCartney

700. The Right Place

Words & Music by Mark E. Nevin

3. Now I don't mind if the sun goes down, — the night — can't hurt me now. — The sum-mer's young and the road is clear, — I thank what-ev-er brought me here. — I've — been in the wrong place, I've — been in the wrong place, I've — been in the wrong place, — long e-nough to know. — I'm in the right place — now. — I'm in the right place

Repeat ad lib. to fade

2. Five or ten lifetimes ago
   There lived a girl that you don't know
   She walked about
   And answered to my name
   But let's not talk of strangers now
   Of where and when or why and how
   I've turned around
   And I'm looking at a new day.

701. Right Said Fred

Music by Ted Dicks. Words by Myles Rudge

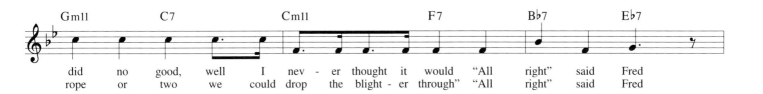

did   no   good,   well   I   nev - er   thought   it   would   "All   right"   said   Fred
rope   or   two   we   could   drop   the   blight - er   through"   "All   right"   said   Fred

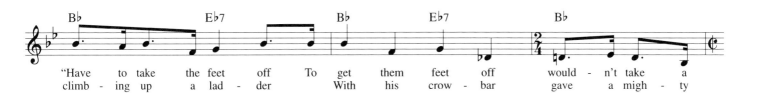

"Have   to   take   the   feet   off   To   get   them   feet   off   would - n't   take   a
climb - ing   up   a   lad - der   With   his   crow - bar   gave   a   migh - ty

mo."   Took   it's   feet   off   ev - en   took   the   seat   off
blow.   Was   he   in   trou - ble   half   a   ton   of   rub - ble

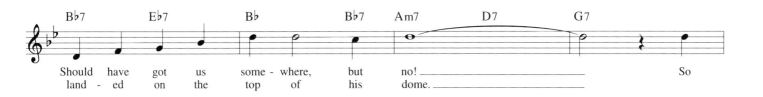

Should   have   got   us   some - where,   but   no! _____   So
land - ed   on   the   top   of   his   dome. _____

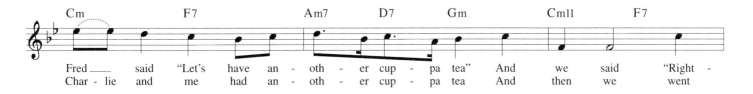

Fred _____   said   "Let's   have   an - oth - er   cup - pa   tea"   And   we   said   "Right -
Char - lie   and   me   had   an - oth - er   cup - pa   tea   And   then   we   went

1.

- o." _____

2.

home. _____

702. Rinky Dink

Words & Music by David Clowney & Paul Winley

Moderate cha-cha

703. Romantica

Music & Original Lyrics by Dino Verde & Renato Rascel. English Lyric by Al Stillman

Moderately beguine

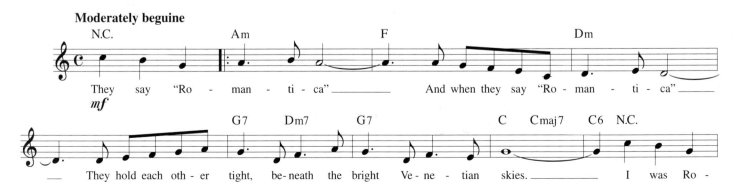

They say "Ro - man - ti - ca" _____ And when they say "Ro - man - ti - ca" _____

_____ They hold each oth - er tight, be - neath the bright Ve - ne - tian skies. _____ I was Ro -

-man-ti-ca, _____ And you were so Ro-man-ti-ca, _____ I felt it in your
kiss, I saw it glis-ten in your eyes, _____ I gave my love to you, _____
— I gave my heart to you, And if you ask me to, _____ I'd do it
ov-er a-gain, Now tho' you're far from me, You nev-er leave my me-mo-ry, _____
— If I but close my eyes, I see your smi-ling face, And then _____ I am Ro-
-man-ti-ca _____ a-gain. _____ They say "Ro- -gain. _____

704. Release Me

Words & Music by Eddie Miller, Dub Williams & Robert Yount

Moderately

Please re-lease me, let me go
I have found a new love, dear, _____
Please re-lease me, can't you see _____

For I don't
And I will
You'd be a

love you an-y-more.
al-ways want her near.
fool to cling to me.

To waste our lives would be a sin. _____
Her lips are warm while yours are cold. _____
To live a lie would bring us pain, _____

Re-lease me and let me love a-gain.
Re-lease me, my dar-ling, let me go.
So re-lease me and let me love a- -gain. _____

705. The Riverboat Song

Words & Music by Simon Fowler, Steve Cradock, Oscar Harrison & Damon Minchella

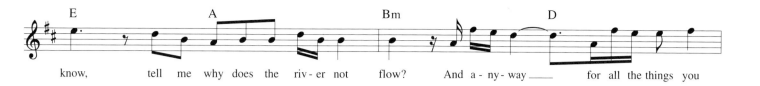

know, tell me why does the riv-er not flow? And a-ny-way _____ for all the things you

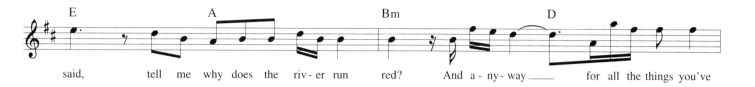

said, tell me why does the riv-er run red? And a-ny-way _____ for all the things you've

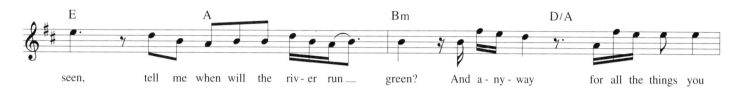

seen, tell me when will the riv-er run _ green? And a-ny-way for all the things you

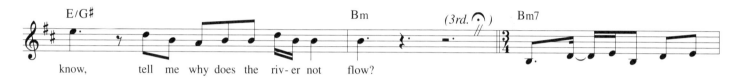

know, tell me why does the riv-er not flow?

D.%.al Coda

⊕ Coda

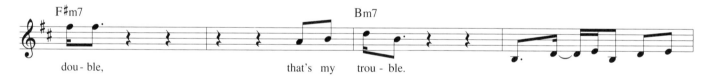

dou-ble, that's my trou-ble.

Repeat to fade

2. I see trouble up the road
   Like the things you found in love are by the way
   And like to cheat on your soul
   Like the best and worst of thoughts that lose control
   Before you lie on your bed
   It's more or less the same as the things that you said.

3. *Instrumental 4 bars*
   It's more or less the things you fail to say in your way
   That's the trouble
   Like a king who stalks the wings
   And shoots the moon and the stars and his double
   It's more or less the same as the things that you said.

4. **(D.S.)**
   I see double up ahead
   Where the riverboat swayed beneath the sun
   Is where the river runs red
   I see double, that's my trouble.

683

706. Rivers Of Babylon

Words & Music by Farian, Reyam, Dowe & McNaughton

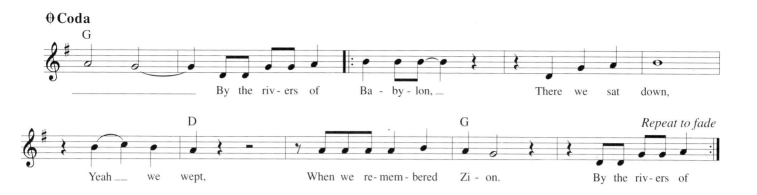

707. Rondo Alla Turca

Composed by Wolfgang Amadeus Mozart

708. (They Call Me) The Rock Of Gibraltar

Words & Music by Terry Gilkyson

709. Return To Sender

Words & Music by Otis Blackwell & Winfield Scott

710. Rockin' Roll Baby

Words & Music by Tom Bell & Linda Creed

Moderate rock

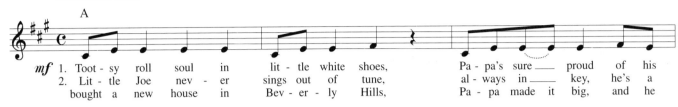

mf
1. Toot - sy roll soul in lit - tle white shoes, Pa - pa's sure ___ proud of his
2. Lit - tle Joe nev - er sings out of tune, al - ways in ___ key, he's a
bought a new house in Bev - er - ly Hills, Pa - pa made it big, and he

lit - tle bit - ty rock - in' roll ba - by, sing - ing at the age ___ of two. ___
soul - ful lit - tle rock - in' roll ba - by, Pa - pa loves the way ___ he grooves.
did it for the rock - in' roll ba - by, A lit - tle bit of rhy - thm and blues. ___

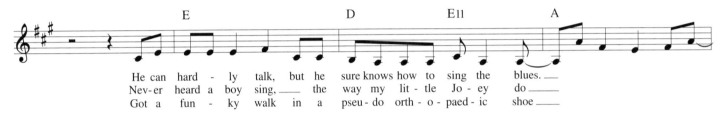

He can hard - ly talk, but he sure knows how to sing the blues. ___
Nev - er heard a boy sing, ___ the way my lit - tle Jo - ey do ___
Got a fun - ky walk in a pseu - do orth - o - paed - ic shoe ___

1.
2, 3.
He was born ___

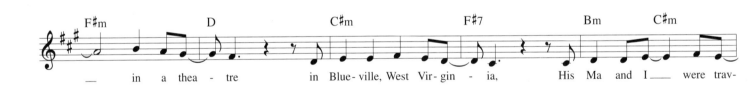

___ in a thea - tre in Blue - ville, West Vir - gin - ia, His Ma and I ___ were trav -

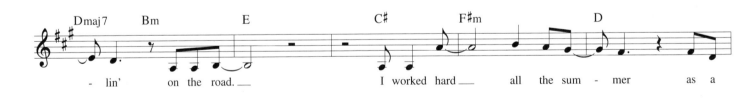

- lin' on the road. ___ I worked hard ___ all the sum - mer as a

fill in for the drum - mer, one - night stands ___ weren't eas - y for lit - tle Joe. ___

To Coda ✛ *D.C. al Coda* **✛ Coda**

3. We ___

711. Romance

Composed by Anton Rubinstein

712. Roll Over Beethoven

Words & Music by Chuck Berry

Moderate rock

Well I'm a- write a lit-tle let-ter, gon-na mail it to my lo-cal D. J. ___

Yes it's a jump-in' lit-tle re-cord I want ___ my jock-ey to play, Roll ov-

-er Beet-ho-ven, I got-ta hear it a-gain to day. ___ You know my

tem-p'ra-ture's ris-in' and the juke box blow-in' a fuse, My heart's beat-in' rhy-thm and my

soul keeps a-sing-in' the blues. ___ Roll ov-er Beet-ho-ven and

tell Tchai-kow-sky the news. ___ I got the rock-in' pneu-mo-nia, I

need a shot of rhy-thm and blues, ___ I caught the roll-in' ar-thri-tis, sit-tin'

down at a rhy-thm re-view, ___ Roll ov-er Beet-ho-ven they're rock-in' in two by two.

Well if you feel you like it, go get your lov-er, Then reel and rock it,

roll it ov - er, Then move on up just a tri - fle fur - ther, Then reel and rock with

one an - oth - er, Roll ov - er Beet - ho - ven, Dig these rhy - thm and blues. _____

Well ear - ly in the morn - in' and I'm giv - in' you my warn - in', Don't you step on my blue suede

shoes, Hey did - dle did - dle I'm a play - in' my fid - dle, Ain't got noth - in' to lose, _ Roll ov -

- er Beet - ho - ven and tell Tchai - kow - sky the news. _ You know she wig - gles like a glow - worm,

Dance like a spin - in' top, _____ She got a cra - zy part - ner, You

ought - a see 'em reel an' rock, Long as she's got a dime _ the mu - sic won't ev - er stop.

_ Roll ov - er Beet - ho - ven, Roll ov - er Beet - ho - ven,

Roll ov - er Beet - ho - ven, Roll ov - er Beet - ho - ven,

Roll ov - er Beet - ho - ven and dig these rhy - thm and blues. _____

713. Rotterdam

Words & Music by Paul Heaton & David Rotheray

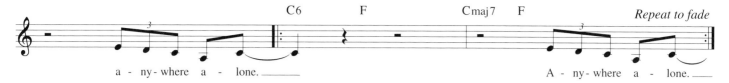

a - ny- where a - lone. _____ A - ny- where a - lone. _____

2. And everyone is blonde
   And everyone is beautiful
   And when blonde and beautiful are multiple
   They become so dull and dutiful
   And when faced with dull and dutiful
   They fire a warning flare
   Pedal khaki personality
   With red underwear.

714. Rockin' Rollin' Rover

Words & Music by J. Leslie McFarland

Moderate rock

Rock- in' Roll- in' Ro - ver, Cut- est dog I ev- er did see, Rock- in' Roll- in' Ro - ver,

Cut- est lit- tle dog I ev- er did see.
1. One day I heard some mu- sic while walk- ing down the
2. Now Ro- ver's just a pup- py who's on- ly eight weeks

street, I saw a crowd of peo- ple rock 'n' roll- in' with a beat, I stretch'd my neck a -
old, Yet he has taught a les- son and it's worth much more than gold, A hap- py heart is

- bove the crowd and what a great sur- prise, A cute lit- tle dog- gy was danc- ing and I
hap- py on- ly if you share your wealth, So he just had to show the world ex-

could- n't be- lieve my eyes. He was wag- gin' his tail to the rock 'n' roll, _____ He was wig- glin' his
act- ly how he felt.

ears to the rock 'n' roll, _____ From all a- round the town _____ the peo- ple came; _____

_____ He was roll- in' his eyes to the rock 'n' roll, _____ He was tap- pin' his paws to the rock 'n' roll, _

1.
_____ And that's how lit- tle Ro- ver got his name. _____

2.
name. _____

715. Roustabout

Words & Music by Bill Giant, Bernie Baum & Florence Kaye

Till I find my place, there's no   doubt, _____   I'll be a rov - in' roust - a - bout. _____

716. Rock And Roll Music

Words & Music by Chuck Berry

Moderate rock

Just let me hear some of that Rock And Roll _____ Mu - sic,   An - y old way you

choose it,   It's got a back beat you can't lose _____ it,   An - y old time you use _____

_____ it,   It's got - ta be Rock Roll   Mu - sic,   If you wan - na dance with me, _____

_____   If you wan - na dance with me. _____   I got no kick a - gainst mod - ern jazz, _____

(Verses 2 - 4 see block lyrics)

Un - less they try to play it   too darn   fast, _____   And change the beau - ty of the

me - lo - dy, _____   Un - til they sound just like a   sym - pho - ny, _____   That's why I go for that

⊕ Coda

If you wan - na dance with me, _____   If you wan - na dance with me.

2. I took my loved one over 'cross the tracks
    So she can hear my man a-wail a sax
    I must admit they have a rockin' band
    Man they were goin' like a hurrican'
    That's why I go for that Rock And Roll Music *(etc.)*

3. Way down South they gave a jubilee
    The jokey folks that had a jamboree
    They're drinkin' home brew from a water cup
    The folks dancin' got all shook up
    And started playin' that Rock And Roll Music *(etc.)*

4. Don't care to hear 'em play a tango
    I'm in the mood to hear a mambo
    It's way too early for a congo
    So keep a-rockin' that piano
    So I can hear some of that Rock And Roll Music *(etc.)*

717. Roxanne

Words & Music by Sting

Moderately

1. Rox - anne you don't have to put on the red light,
(Verse 2 see block lyric)

those days are ov - er; you don't have to sell your bo - dy to the night. Rox -

- anne, you don't have to wear that dress to - night

Walk the streets for mon - ey, you don't care if it's wrong or if it's right. Rox -

- anne, you don't have to put on the red light, Rox -

To Coda

- anne, you don't have to put on the red light Rox - anne

(Put on the red light) Rox - anne (Put on the red light) Rox - anne

(Put on the red light) Rox - anne (Put on the red light) Rox - anne

(Put on the red light) oh.

D.%.al Coda

Coda

(Put on the red light) Rox - anne

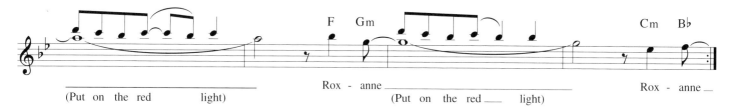

(Put on the red   light)   Rox - anne _____ (Put on the red ___ light)   Rox - anne _____

> 2. I loved ya since I knew ya,
> I wouldn't talk down to ya
> I have to tell you just how I feel
> I won't share you with another boy
> I know my mind is made up
> So put away your make up
> Told you once I won't tell you again
> It's a crime the way...
>
> Roxanne... *(etc.)*

718. Rubber Biscuit

Words & Music by Nathaniel Epps, Charles Johnson,
Paul Fulton, Shedrick Lincoln & Samuel Strain.

Moderately

Ba, ba her wa da her da wa da her wa - oo. Her wa da her da wa ja ja er wa da

oo. Ah wa da ah da wa ma jig er wa da oo. Ah wa da her ba wa da jig er ma a

oo. Her wa da her da wa da her da wa da oo. Her wa da her da wa ja ja er wa da

oo. Ah wa da her da wa ma jig er wa da oo. Ah wa da

her da wa da jig er ma a oo. Her wa da her da wa da her da wa da

Spoken verses:

1. Do that again! *(To Chorus)*

2. Hm, have you ever heard of a wish sandwich?
   A wish sandwich is the kind of a sandwich where
   You have two slices of bread and you– Hm…
   Wish you had some meatball. *(To Chorus)*

3. The other day I had a ricochet biscuit.
   A ricochet biscuit is the kind of a biscuit that's
   Supposed to bounce back off the wall into your mouth.
   If it don't bounce back. Hm…
   You go hungry. *(To Chorus)*

4. The other day I had a "cool water" sandwich
   And a Sunday "go to meetin'" bun. *(To Chorus)*

5. Hm. . . . what do you want for nothin',
   Rubber Biscuit? *(To Ending)*

Ball ball oo oo oo, oo. _____

719. The Rose Of Allendale

Traditional

2. Where'er I wandered, to the East or West, and fate began to lower
   Consoling still she was to me in sorrow's lonely hour
   Oh tempests wrecked my lonely boat and wrecked the quivering sail
   One maiden form withstood the storm
   'Twas the rose of Allendale
   Sweet rose of Allendale, sweet rose of Allendale
   By far the sweetest flower there
   Was the rose of Allendale.

3. And when my fever'd lips were parched on Africa's burning sands
   She whispered hopes of happiness and tales of foreign lands
   My life had been a wilderness, unblest by fortune's gain
   Had fate not linked my knot to hers
   Sweet rose of Allendale
   Sweet rose of Allendale, sweet rose of Allendale
   By far the sweetest flower there
   Was the rose of Allendale.

720. Saddle Up

Words & Music by Philo Robinson & James Bolden

721. Save Your Love

Words & Music by John & Sue Edward

love for sum-mer nights with moon and stars a-bove. A se-ren-ade I long to sing you the red-dest rose I al-ways bring you save your love for Ro-ma and for me.

722. Red Cheeks And White Whiskers

Words & Music by Al Hoffman & Bob Merrill

How are you at rid-dles? Ve-ry ve-ry good no doubt! Well I've got one, It's lots of fun, Let me try you out: He's got red cheeks and white whis-kers, Rein-deer and a red cheeks and white whis-kers, Don't you know his sleigh, And a bag of toys for the girls and boys to play. He's got same. name? If you have-n't guessed, well he's al-ways dressed the He's such a mer-ry fel-low, And when he starts to laugh, Ha! Ha! Ha! Ho! Ho! Ho! Near-ly bends in half! Mis-ter red cheeks and white whis-kers soon will come your way. Ev-'ry-bo-dy loves him so, And if his name you still don't know, Be good and you'll find out on Christ-mas day!

723. Sand In My Shoes

Music by Victor Schertzinger. Words by Frank Loesser

724. Santa Claus Is Back In Town

Words & Music by Jerry Leiber & Mike Stoller

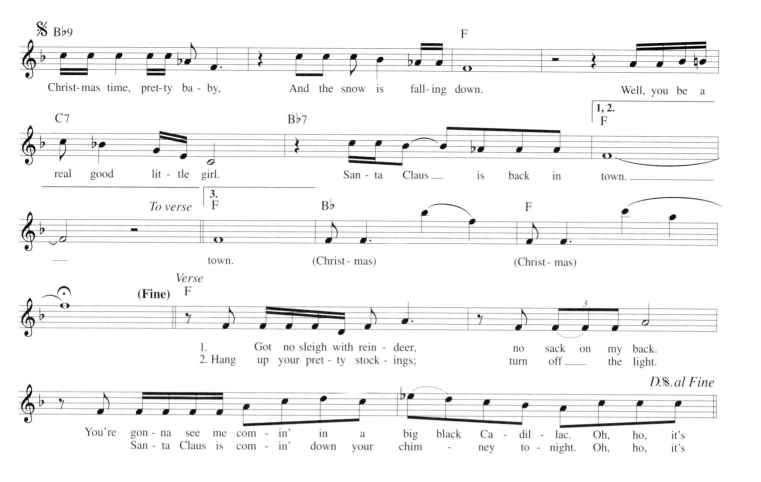

Christ-mas time, pret-ty ba - by, And the snow is fall-ing down. Well, you be a

real good lit - tle girl. San - ta Claus ___ is back in town. ___

To verse 3. town. (Christ - mas) (Christ - mas)

Verse (Fine)
1. Got no sleigh with rein - deer, no sack on my back.
2. Hang up your pret - ty stock - ings; turn off ___ the light.

D.%.al Fine

You're gon-na see me com-in' in a big black Ca - dil - lac. Oh, ho, it's
San - ta Claus is com - in' down your chim - ney to - night. Oh, ho, it's

725. So This Is Love (The Cinderella Waltz)

Words & Music by Mack David, Al Hoffman & Jerry Livingston

So this is love! Mm ___ So this is love! ___ So this is what

makes life di - vine! ___ I'm all a - glow, Mm ___ and now I know ___

the key to all heav - en is mine. ___ My heart has wings, Mm ___ and I can

fly, ___ I'll touch ev - 'ry star in the sky. ___ So this is the mir - a - cle that

I've been dream - ing of! Mm ___ mm, so this is love! ___

726. Santa, Bring My Baby Back To Me

Words & Music by Aaron Schroeder & Claude DeMetrius

727. She's Not You

Words & Music by Jerry Leiber, Mike Stoller & Doc Pomus

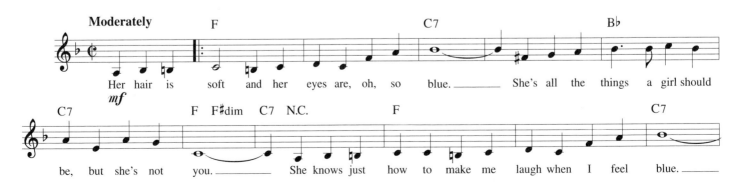

728. Some Day

Words & Music by Brian Hooker & Rudolf Friml

729. Santa Claus March

Words & Music by Redd Evans & Joe Cowen

730. Sea Of Heartbreak

Words & Music by Hal David & Paul Hampton

731. Save The Best For Last

Words & Music by Jon Lind, Wendy Waldman & Philip Galdston

our chance had passed __ You go and save __ the best __ for last __

Some-times the ve - ry thing __ you're __ look-

- ing for __ Is the one thing __ you can't __ see Some-times the snow __

comes down __ in June __ Some-times the sun __ goes round __ the moon __

Just when I thought __ our chance had passed __ You go and save __ the best __ for last __

You went and saved __ the best __ for last. __

732. The Sailor's Hornpipe

Traditional

Fast

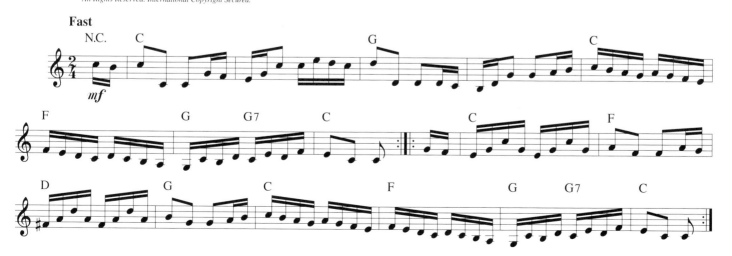

733. Say Has Anybody Seen My Sweet Gypsy Rose?

Words & Music by Irwin Levine & L. Russell Brown

734. Semi-Detached Suburban Mr James

Words & Music by John Carter & Geoff Stephens

735. Say You'll Be There

Words & Music by Eliot Kennedy, Melanie Brown,
Victoria Aadams, Emma Bunton, Geri Halliwell & Melanie Chisholm

say you will be there,   won't you sing it with me.

Coda

give you eve-ry-thing on this I swear just pro-mise you'll al-ways be there.

I'm giv-ing you eve - ry-thing all that joy can bring this I swear.

And   all that I want from you is a pro - mise you will be there.

2. If you put two and two together you will see what our friendship is for
If you can't work this equation then I guess I'll have to show you the door
There is no need to say you love me it would be better left unsaid.

I'm giving you everything all that joy can bring this I swear
And all that I want from you is a promise you will be there
Yeah I want you.

3. *(Instrumental)*
Any fool can see they're falling, gotta make you understand.

736. **Serpico** (Rock Theme)

By Mikis Theodorakis

Moderately

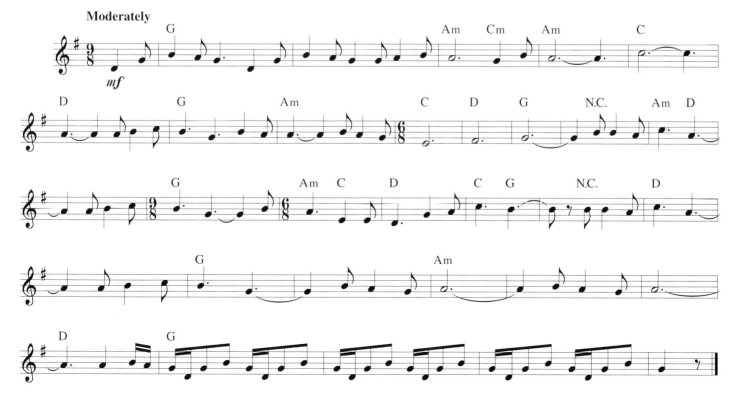

737. The Second Star To The Right

Words by Sammy Cahn. Music by Sammy Fain

738. September In The Rain

Music by Harry Warren. Words by Al Dubin

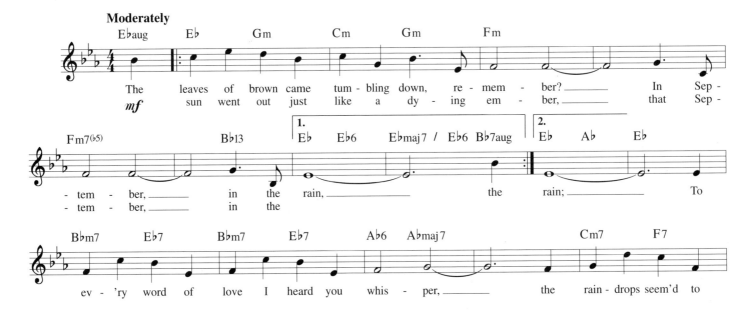

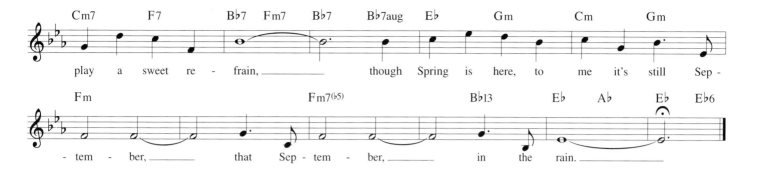

739. Serenata

Composed by Enrico Toselli

740. Semper Fidelis

Music by John Philip Sousa

741. She Said She Said

Words & Music by John Lennon & Paul McCartney

742. 7000 Dollars And You

Words & Music by Hugo Peretti, Luigi Creatore & George David Weiss

743. Sexy Sadie

Words & Music by John Lennon & Paul McCartney

744. Shadow Of The Sun

Words & Music by Paul Weller

In the sha-dow of __ the sun, _____ in the sha-dow of __ the

sun. __

745. The Siamese Cat Song

Words & Music by Peggy Lee & Sonny Burke

Moderately slow

We are Si-am-ee-iz if you plee-iz,   We are Si-am-ee-iz if you don't please.

We are for-mer res-i-dents of Si-am.   There { is / are } no fin-er cat than { I / we } am.

We are Si-am-ese with ver-y dain-ty claws.

Please ob-serv-ing paws con-tain-ing dain-ty claws.   Now we look-in' o-ver our new dom-i-cile.

If we like we stay for may-be quite a while.

746. **Shakedown**

Words & Music by Keith Forsey, Harold Faltermeyer & Bob Seger

Shake - down, break - down, take - down; ev - 'ry - bo - dy wants in - to the

crowd - ed light. _____ Break - down, take - down; you're bust - ed. _____

{ Shake - down, break - down; } hon - ey, just a - bout the time you think that it's al - right. _____
{ Let down your guard, }

Repeat to fade

Break - down, take - down; you're bust - ed. _____

747. Sealed With A Kiss

Words by Peter Udell. Music by Gary Geld

© Copyright 1960 Post Music Incorporated, USA.
Worldwide print rights controlled by Warner Bros. Publishing Incorporated/IMP Limited.
All Rights Reserved. International Copyright Secured.

Moderately

Tho' we got - ta say good - bye for the sum - mer, dar - ling I prom - ise you
cold lone - ly sum - mer, I'll fill the emp - ti -

this, I'll send you all my love ev - 'ry day in a let - ter, sealed with a
- ness, I'll send you all my dreams ev - 'ry day in a let - ter, sealed with a

kiss. Guess it's gon - na be a kiss. I'll see you in the sun - light, I'll

hear your voice ev - 'ry - where, I'll run to ten - der - ley hold you, but dar - ling you won't be

there, I don't wan - na say good - bye for the sum - mer, know - ing the love we'll

miss, oh let us make a pledge to meet in Sep - tem - ber, and seal it with a kiss. _____

748. Shalom Chaveyrim

Jewish Traditional

Sha - lom cha - vey - rim, sha - lom cha - vey - rim, sha - lom, sha -
Sha - lom, my friend, sha - lom, my friend, sha - lom, sha -

lom. L' - hit - ra - ot, l' - hit - ra - ot, sha - lom, sha - lom.
lom. We'll meet a - gain, we'll meet a - gain, sha - lom, sha - lom.

749. A Stranger's Just A Friend

Words & Music by Gilbert Gibson & Jim Reeves

If ev - er your life is lone - ly, if ev - er
warm smile can bring me true love, a warm heart

you're feel - ing low, there's one thing you must re - mem - ber, a
can make it grow, there's no need for be - ing lone - ly,

stran - ger's just a friend you do not know. I'll pass a - long this

way just one time on - ly, a fleet - ing mo - ment in e - ter - ni - ty.

Why should I spend my life a - lone and lone - ly, if just a word of

friend - ship is the key?

Coda

No - mat - ter where you go of

724

this you can be sure, a stran-ger's just a friend you do not know.

750. Symphony No.104 in D (London)
Theme from 2nd Movement

Composed by Franz Joseph Haydn

751. She Caught The Katy

Words & Music by Taj Mahal & James Rachel

* Katy is the nickname for the Missouri-Kansas-Texas Railroad (MKT)

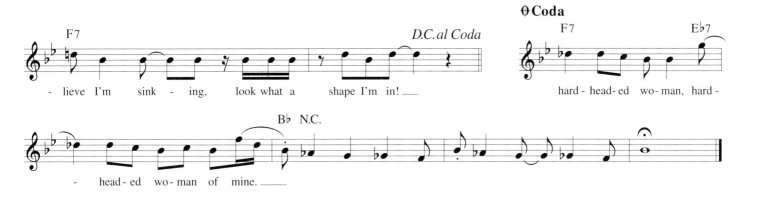

752. Shadow Of Love

By Mercer Ellington

753. She Makes My Day

Words & Music by Robert Palmer

she just has to touch my hand to make me stay. — She's all good lov-in' at once. — She's

all good lov-in' at once. She's all good lov-in' at once. — She's all good lov-in' at once. — She's

2. Our love was unintentional
She says we're not responsible
She thinks with her chin up
She always makes uncommon sense
Always knows just what to say
She always takes me unawares
In less time than it takes to fall
I'm here and there are you
We never fought it any way
I'll never be lonely now I know her, *etc.*

754. Some Day My Prince Will Come

Words by Larry Morey. Music by Frank Churchill.

Some day my Prince will come, Some day I'll find my

love, And how thrill-ing that mo-ment will be, ___ When the Prince of my

dreams comes to me. ___ He'll whis-per, "I love you,"

And steal a kiss or two, Though he's far a-way, I'll find my love some

day, Some day when my dreams come true. ___ true. ___

755. She-She Little Sheila

Words & Music by Jerry Merritt & Whitey Pullen

756. Shrimp Boats

Words & Music by Paul Mason Howard & Paul Weston

731

757. Shoo-Shoo Baby

Words & Music by Philip Moore

758. Slowly But Surely

Words & Music by Sid Wayne & Ben Weisman

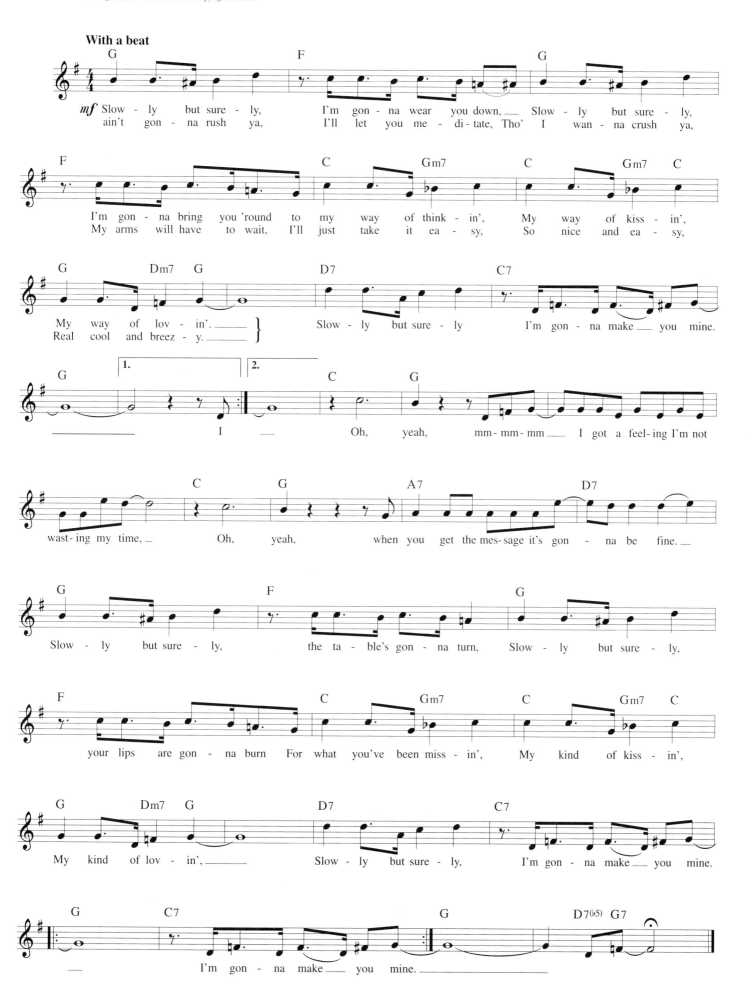

759. Simply Irresistible

Words & Music by Robert Palmer

1. How can it be per-mis-si-ble to

(Verses 2 & 3 see block lyrics)

com-pro-mise my prin-ci-ples? Yeah, __ yeah. __ That

kind of love is my-thi-cal; she's an-y-thing but ty-pi-cal. __

She's a craze, you ought-ta know it; she's a

pow-er-ful force __ you're o-bliged to con-form __ with, there's no oth-er choice. __ She

To Coda

used to look good to me, __ but now I find her. __ Sim-ply ir-re-

-sis-ti-ble, Sim-ply ir-re-sis-ti-ble.

1.

2.

2. Her Sim-ply ir-re-

(-sis-ti-ble.) there's no tell-ing where the mo-ney went. Sim-ply ir-re-
She's so fine,

(-sis-ti-ble.) there's no oth-er way to go. __
She's all mine, __

She's un-a-void-ab-le, I'm backed a-gainst the wall. She gives me feel-ings that I

nev-er felt be-fore. __ I'm break-ing pro-mi-ses, she's break-ing eve-ry law.

She used to look __ good to me, now I find __ her sim-ply ir-re-(sis-ti-ble.) She's so fine,

there's no tell-ing where the mo-ney went. Sim-ply ir-re-(sis-ti-ble.) She's all mine, ____

there's no oth-er way to go. __ Woh. ____

D.%.al Coda

3. Her

⊕ Coda

Sim-ply ir-re-(sis-ti-ble.) She's so fine, there's no tell-ing where the

Sim-ply ir-re-(sis-ti-ble.) She's all mine, ____ there's no oth-er way to

1.
Sim-ply ir-re-

2.
Sim-ply ir-re-sis-ti-ble.

go. __

2. Her loving is so powerful
It's simply unavoidable. Woh, woh
The trend is irreversible
She's a natural law
And she leaves me in awe
She deserves the applause
I surrender the cause
She used to look good to me
But now I find her
Simply irresistible.

3. Her methods are inscrutable
The proof is irrefutable
She's so completely kissable
Her eyes are indivisible
She's a craze, you ought to know it, *etc.*

760. Sing

Words & Music by Joe Raposo

761. Sing, You Sinners

Music by Franke W. Harling. Words by Sam Coslow.

762. Sisters Are Doing It For Themselves

Words & Music by A. Lennox & D. A. Stewart

has got a new ex - te - ri - or.___ We got doc - tors, law - yers, pol -

- i - ti - cians, too.___ Ev - 'ry - bod - y ___

take ___ a look a - round. ___ Can you see, can you

C   E♭   D.%.al Coda

see, there's a wom - an right ___ next to you. ___ We say;

✛Coda
C   D♭

Now we ain't mak - in' sto - ries and

B♭   D♭

we ain't lay - in' plans. ___ Don't you know that a man ___ still ___ loves a

B♭   C   D.%. and Fade

wom - an and a wom - an still ___ loves a man. ___ (Just the same though.) _

763. Sing A Song Of Sixpence

Traditional

Joyfully

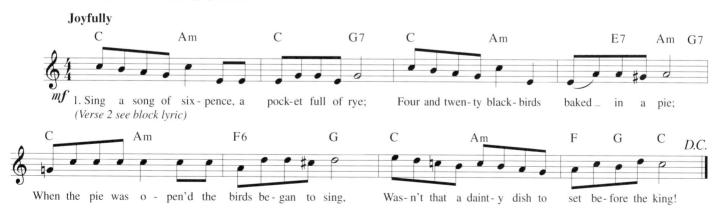

C   Am   C   G7   C   Am   E7   Am   G7

mf 1. Sing a song of six - pence, a pock - et full of rye; Four and twen - ty black - birds baked _ in a pie;
(*Verse 2 see block lyric*)

C   Am   F6   G   C   Am   F   G   C   D.C.

When the pie was o - pen'd the birds be - gan to sing, Was - n't that a dain - ty dish to set be - fore the king!

2. The king was in the counting house counting out his money
The queen was in the parlour eating bread and honey
The maid was in the garden hanging out the clothes
When by came a blackbird and snapped off her nose!

764. Sit Down

Words & Music by Timothy Booth, Lawrence Gott, Gavan Whelan & James Glennie

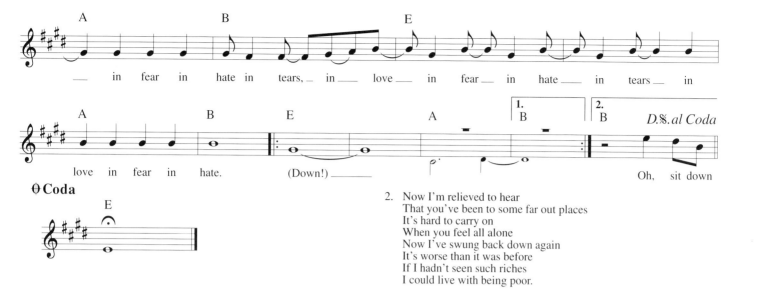

2. Now I'm relieved to hear
That you've been to some far out places
It's hard to carry on
When you feel all alone
Now I've swung back down again
It's worse than it was before
If I hadn't seen such riches
I could live with being poor.

765. She Came In Through The Bathroom Window

Words & Music by John Lennon & Paul McCartney

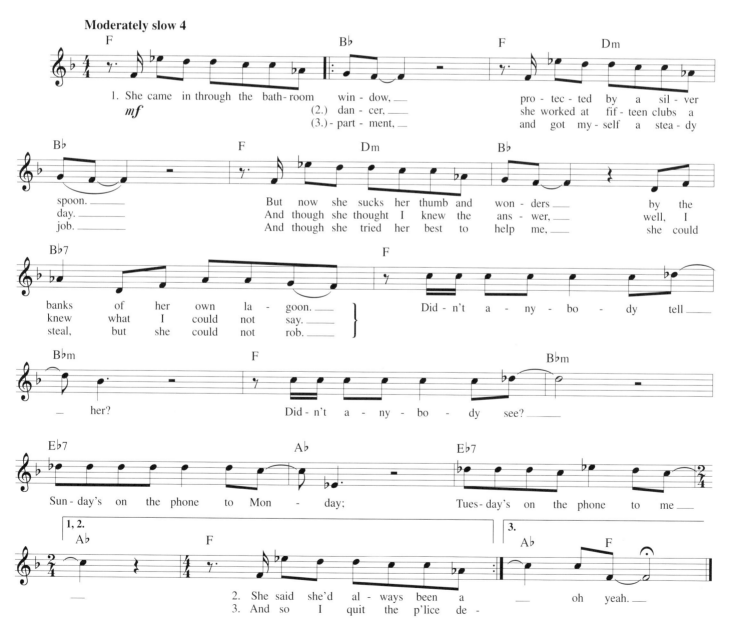

766. Sleepytime

Traditional

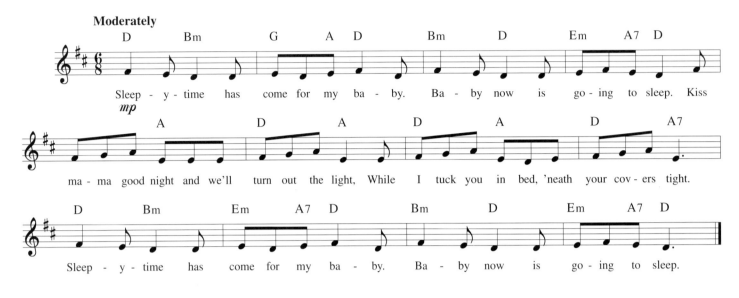

767. She Caught The Train

Words & Music by Joe Monsano

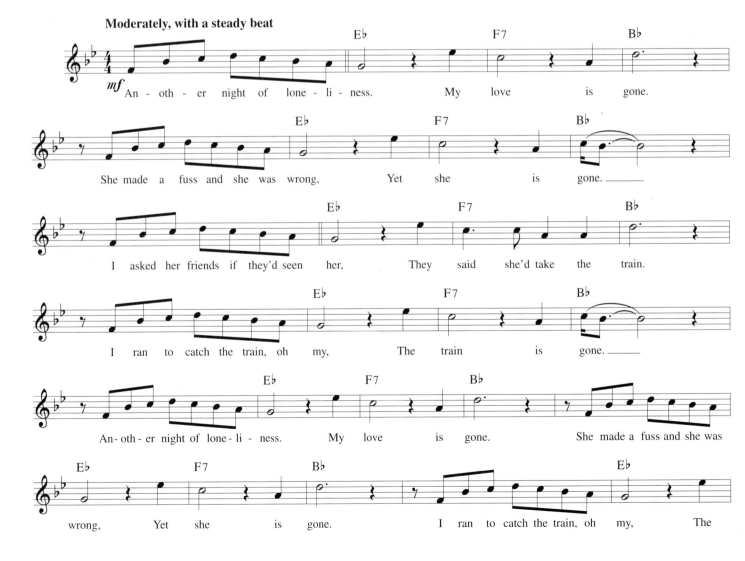

train is gone. ___ Doo doo doo doo. Doo doo doo doo. Doo doo doo

doo. Doo doo doo doo.

Repeat to fade

768. **Shout**

Words & Music by O'Kelly Isley, Ronald Isley & Rudolph Isley

Moderate rock

You know you make me wan-na Come on ___ now, ___ Come on ___ now.

Oh let's Shout now, Hey let's Shout now.

Say ___ you will, Say it right now, Ba-by, say ___

___ you will, Come on, ___ Come on, ___ Say ___ you will, Say it a-gain.

Say ___ you will, Come on ___ now, ___ Say that you love me, Say, say that you

need me, Say, say that you want me, Say you want to please me. Come on ___

___ now, ___ Come on ___ now, Come on ___ now, ___ Come on ___ now.

Repeat to fade

743

769. So Good

Words & Music by Martin Brannigan, Stephen Gately, Ronan Keating,
Michael Graham, Shane Lynch, Keith Duffy & Ray Hedges

Be so — good, be so good now, be so — good.

Coda

oh, — oh, — we're gon - na be so good, — like I knew we would,

you know we're good. —

2. No matter the cost
When we're out on the town getting lazy
I'll show you who's boss
We're just gonna take it all the way
No matter what they say now.

770. **Sphären-Klänge Waltz**

Composed by Johann Strauss

Tempo di valse

771. Some Like It Hot

Words & Music by R. Palmer, A. Taylor & J. Taylor

Some like — it hot, but — you can't tell — how hot till — you try. —

To Coda θ

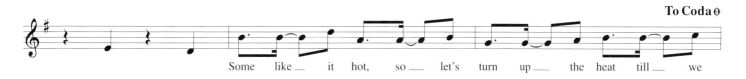

Some like — it hot, so — let's turn up — the heat till — we

1. **2.**

fry. — The girl is

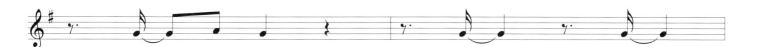

D.%.al Coda

θ Coda

Em7

fry. — Some like — it hot, some like it hot. —

Play 3 times

Some like — it hot, some like it hot. —

2. The girl is on your side; are you gonna do it?
    She wants to be your bride; are you gonna do it?
    She wants to multiply; are you gonna do it?
    I know you won't be satisfied until you do it

    Feel the heat *etc.*

772. Someday

Music by Alan Menken. Lyrics by Stephen Schwartz

773. Small Fry

Words by Frank Loesser. Music by Hoagy Carmichael

774. Something For The Pain

Words & Music by Jon Bon Jovi, Richie Sambora & Desmond Child

Pull me un - der through my veins
(Help I'm

to a place where I feel no pain, be the pil - low un - der my head, cov - er me when I'm in your bed.
fall - - - - ing, night is call - - - - ing.

Take me high - er than I've ev - er been, take me down and back a - gain, come to me, be my dis - guise,
Feels like I'm fly - - ing, Christ I'm

op - en your coat and let me crawl in - side. Come on, come on, come on,
dy - - - - - ing.)

come on, come on, come on, give me some - thing for the pain, give me some - thing for the

blues, give me some - thing for the pain when I feel I'm dang - lin' on a hang - man's

noose. Give me some - thing for the pain, give me some - thing I can

use, to get me through the night, make me feel al - right, some - thing like you.

1.
Give me some - thing for the

2.
Come on, come on, come on, come on, come on, come on, come on, come on, come on, come on.

751

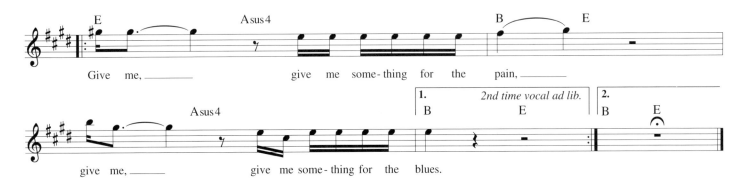

Give me, _____ give me some-thing for the pain, _____

give me, _____ give me some-thing for the blues.

2nd time vocal ad lib.

2. Loneliness has found a home in me
   My suitcase and guitar are my only family
   I've tried to need someone like they needed me
   Well I opened up my heart but all I did was bleed
   I don't need no lover just to get screwed
   They don't make no bandage that's going to cover my bruise.

To Chorus

775. A Spoonful Of Sugar

Words & Music by Richard M. Sherman & Robert B. Sherman

Moderately

In ev-'ry job that must be done there is an el-e-ment of fun; You
feath-er-ing his nest has ver-y lit-tle time to rest While

find the fun and snap the job's a game; _____ And ev-'ry task you un-der-
gath-er-ing his bits of twine and twig. _____ Though quite in-tent in his pur-

take be-comes a piece of cake, A lark! A spree! It's ver-y clear to
suit he has a mer-ry tune to toot; He knows a song will move the job a-

see That a spoon-ful of su-gar helps the med-i-cine go down, The med-i-cine go
long. For a

dow-wown, med-i-cine go down. Just a spoon-ful; of sug-ar helps the med-i-cine go

down In a most de-light-ful way. A rob-in way. _____

776. So Emotional

Words & Music by Billy Steinberg & Tom Kelly

2. I gotta watch you walk in the room, baby;
I gotta watch you walk out
I like the animal way you move
And when you just talk I just watch your mouth.

Oh, I remember the way that we touch;
I wish I didn't like it so much.

777. St James Infirmary

Traditional

Moderate blues

mp ... *mf* I went down to the St. James In-firm-'ry;____ I____

(Verses 2 - 4 see block lyrics)

saw my ba-by there; She was ly-ing on a ta-ble.____ So____ cold, so white,__ so

fair. I went up to see the doc-tor;____ "She's__ ve-ry low," he said. I

went back to see my ba-by.____ And, good God, she was ly-ing there dead.

2. I went down to old Joe's barroom
   On the corner by the square
   The drinks were served as usual
   And the usual crowd was there
   On my left stood Joe MacKennedy
   His eyes were bloodshot red
   He turned to the crowd around him
   And these are the words he said.

3. Let her go, let her go, God bless her
   Wherever she may be
   She may search this wide world over
   But never find another man like me
   Now when I die, please bury me
   In a hightop Stetson hat
   Put a gold piece on my watch chain
   So the gang will know I'm standing pat.

4. Get six gamblers to carry my coffin
   Six chorus girls to sing my song
   Put a jazz band on my tail gate
   To raise hell as we roll along
   And now that you've heard my story
   I'll take another shot of booze
   If anyone should happen to ask you
   I've got the St. James Infirmary blues.

778. A Steel Guitar And A Glass Of Wine

Words & Music by Paul Anka

Moderately

Just give__ me a steel gui-tar and a glass of wine,__ And let me
And let me toast her just one more time,__

drink__ to a love__ I thought was mine,__ A love I thought was true to me.__
Oh, can-dle glow, be-fore you dim,

But now I'm drink-ing to a mem-o-ry.__ A steel gui-tar and a
Tell her what_____ a fool she's been.__ And one more thing,__ be-

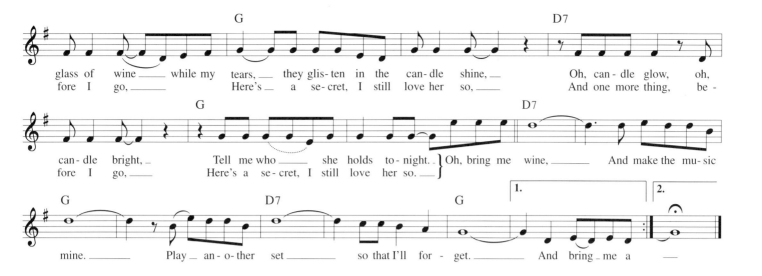

glass of wine ____ while my tears, ____ they glis-ten in the can-dle shine, ____ Oh, can-dle glow, oh,
fore I go, ____ Here's ____ a se-cret, I still love her so, ____ And one more thing, be -

can-dle bright, ____ Tell me who ____ she holds to-night. Oh, bring me wine, ____ And make the mu-sic
fore I go, ____ Here's a se-cret, I still love her so. ____

1.
mine. ____ Play ___ an-o-ther set ____ so that I'll for-get. ____ And bring ___ me a ____
2.

779. Schindler's List

By John Williams

780. Stack-O-Lee

Words & Music by Louis Busch

781. Sorrowful Blues

Words & Music by Bessie Smith

With a blues feel

2. I got nineteen men and won't want more
   I got nineteen men and won't want more
   If I had one more I'd let that nineteen go.

3. I'm gonna tell you, Daddy, like Solomon told the Jew
   I'm gonna tell you, Daddy, like Solomon told the Jew
   If you don't likee me, I sure don't likee you.

4. It's hard to love another woman's man
   It's hard to love another woman's man
   You can't catch him when you want him,
      you got to catch him when you can.

5. Have you ever seen a preacher throw a sweet potato pie?
   Have you ever seen a preacher throw a sweet potato pie?
   Just step in my back yard and taste a piece of mine.

782. Stanley Road

Words & Music by Paul Weller

and on the cor-ner   a   dream   to   meet, _____   yeah, _ go - ing

on   and   on. _____

θ **Coda**

on   and   on, _____   go - ing   on   and   on, _____   it   goes

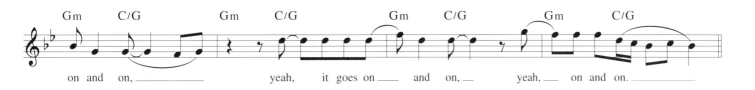

on   and   on, _____   yeah,   it   goes   on ____ and   on, __   yeah, ___ on   and   on.

2. The summer nights that seemed so long   And it's still in the distance
   Always call me back to return   And it shines like the sun
   As I re-write this song   Like silver and gold
   The ghosts of night, the dreams of day   It goes on and on
   Make me swirl and fall and hold me   It goes on and on
   In their sway.   It goes on and on
                                     It goes on and on.

783. **Stars**

Words & Music by Simon Fung

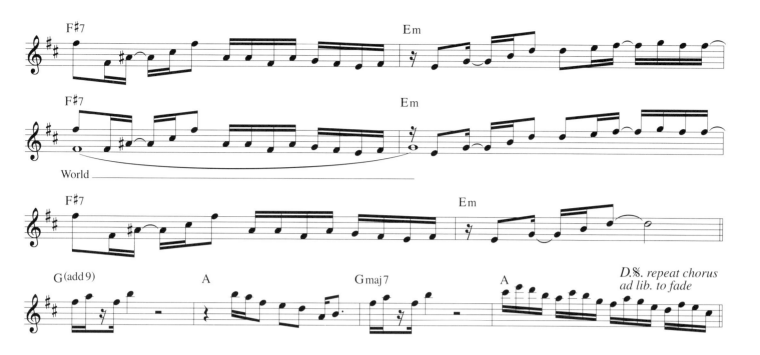

2. Should have warned you
   Is it how you thought it turned out now
   And our future
   No one knows where future paths may go.

784. Stay

Words & Music by Maurice Williams

Dance just a lit-tle bit long-er, please, please, please, please tell me that you're go-in' to. Now your dad-dy don't mind, and your mom-my don't mind, could we have an-oth-er dance, dear, just-a one more, one more time? Oh, won't you stay just a lit-tle bit long-er, please let me dance, please say that you will.

785. Star Trek (TV Theme)

By Alexander Courage

Moderately

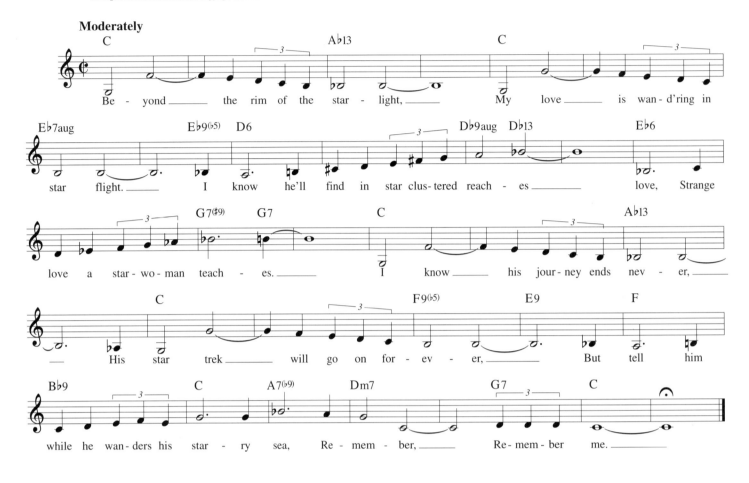

Be - yond the rim of the star - light, My love is wan - d'ring in
star flight. I know he'll find in star clus - tered reach - es love, Strange
love a star - wo - man teach - es. I know his jour - ney ends nev - er,
His star trek will go on for - ev - er, But tell him
while he wan - ders his star - ry sea, Re - mem - ber, Re - mem - ber me.

786. Secretly

Words & Music by Al Hoffman, Dick Manning & Mark Markwell

Moderately slow

1. Why must I meet you in a se - cret ren - dez - vous? Why must we steal a - way to
2. Why must we wait un - til we're danc - ing cheek to cheek, To whis - per all the words of

steal a kiss or two? Why must we wait to do the things we want to do?
love we long to speak? Why must our love be like a game of hide - and - seek?

Why, oh, why, oh, why, oh, why, oh, why? Wish we did - n't have to meet se - cret -

- ly, Wish we did - n't have to kiss se - cret - ly; Wish we did - n't have to be a - fraid To

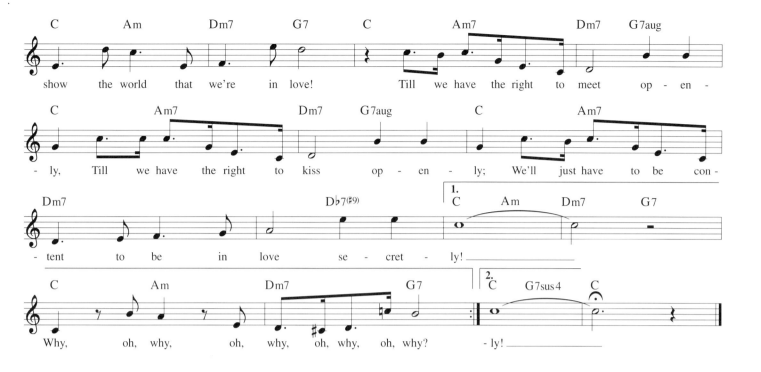

787. Speak Softly Love

Music by Nino Rota. Words by Larry Kusik

788. Theme From Star Trek (The Movie)

By Jerry Goldsmith

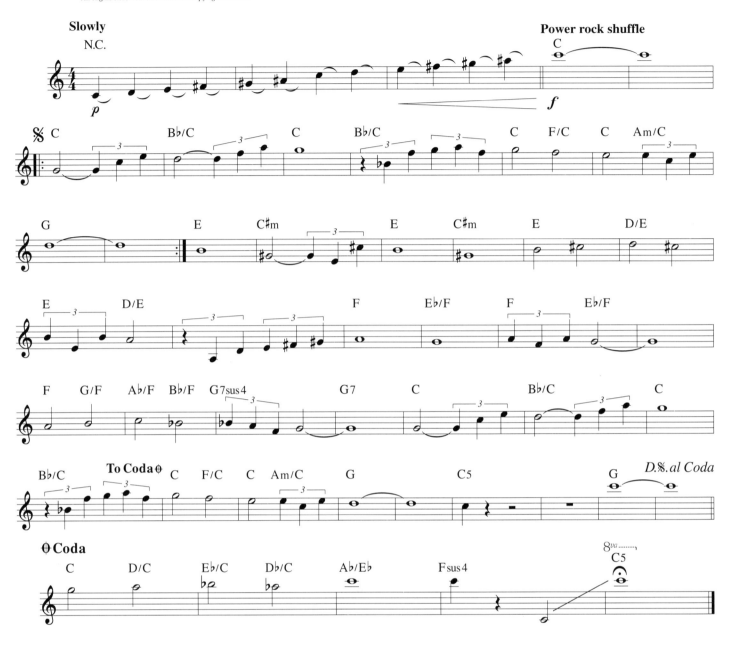

789. Splish Splash

Words & Music by Bobby Darin & Jean Murray

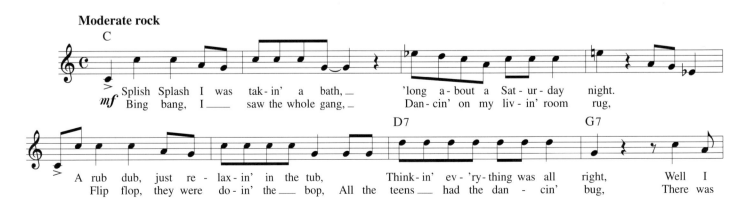

stepped out the tub, put my feet on the floor, I wrapped the towel a - round me and I
a Lol - li - pop with Peg - gy Sue, Good gol - ly Miss ___ Mol - ly was - a

O - pened the door, And then a Splish Splash, I ___ jumped back in the bath, ___ Well
ev - en there too, A well - a Splish Splash I for - got a - bout the bath, ___ I

1.
how was I to know there was a par - ty go - ing on?

2.
on. I was a -

went and put my danc - in' shoes ___

- splish - in' and a - splash - in', I was a - roll - in' and a - stroll - in', I was a -

Repeat to fade
- mov - in' and a - groov - in', I was a - reel - in' with the feel - in', I was a -

790. Sweet And Low

Music by Joseph Barnby. Words by Alfred, Lord Tennyson

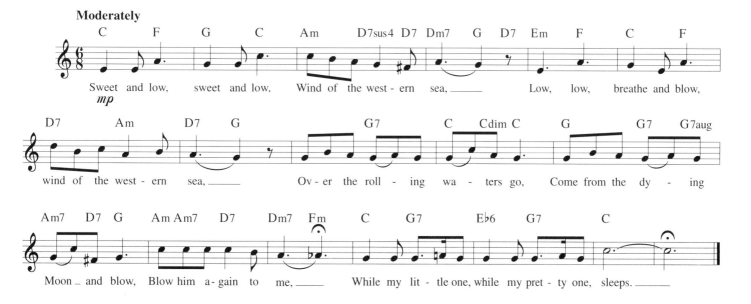

Sweet and low, sweet and low, Wind of the west - ern sea, ___ Low, low, breathe and blow,

wind of the west - ern sea, ___ Ov - er the roll - ing wa - ters go, Come from the dy - ing

Moon ___ and blow, Blow him a - gain to me, ___ While my lit - tle one, while my pret - ty one, sleeps. ___

Extra verse Sleep and rest, sleep and rest,
Father will come to thee soon
Rest, rest on mother's breast
Father will come to thee soon
Father will come to his babe in the nest
Silver sails all out of the west
Under the silver moon
Sleep, my little one, sleep my pretty one, sleep.

791. Stars And Stripes Forever

Music by John Philip Sousa

792. Since I Don't Have You

Words by James Beaumont, Janet Vogel & Joseph Verscharen.
Music by Walter Lester, John Taylor, Lennie Martin & J Rock

793. Stay Another Day

Words & Music by Mortimer, Kean & Hawken

2. I touch your face while you are sleeping
   And hold your hand
   Don't understand what's going on
   Good times we had return to haunt me
   Though it's for you
   All that I do seems to be wrong.

794. Spring Will Be A Little Late This Year

Words & Music by Frank Loesser

795. Stay With Me Baby

Words & Music by Jerry Ragovoy & George Weiss

2. Who did you touch
   When you needed tenderness
   I gave you so much
   And in return I found happiness
   Baby what did I do

   Maybe I was too good
   Just too good for you
   No no, I can't believe
   You'd really leave
   Stay with me *(etc.)*

796. The Story Of My Life

Music by Burt Bacharach. Words by Hal David

797. Stereotypes

Words & Music by Damon Albarn, Graham Coxon, Alex James & David Rowntree

time to time you know, you should go on an-oth-er ben-der, be-fore you come to an end-er.

2. The suburbs they are sleeping
   But he's dressing up tonight
   She likes a man in uniform he loves to wear it tight
   They are on the lover's sofa, they are on the patio
   And when the fun is over watch themselves on video.

   The neighbours may be staring
   But they are just past caring.

798. Song For A Winter's Night

Words & Music by Gordon Lightfoot

Moderately

The lamp is burn-ing low up-on my ta-ble top, the snow is
The smoke is ris-ing in the shad-ows ov-er-head, my glass is
The fire is dy-ing now, my lamp is grow-ing dim, the shades of

soft-ly fall-ing. The air is still in the si-lence of my
al-most emp-ty. I read a-gain be-tween the lines on the
night are lift-ing. The morn-ing light steals a-cross my win-dow

room, I hear your voice soft-ly call-ing. If I could
page, the words of love you sent me. If I could
pane, where webs of snow are drift-ing. If I could

on-ly have you near to breathe a sigh or two
know with-in my heart that you were lone-ly, too
on-ly have you near to breathe a sigh or two

I would be hap-py just to hold the hands I love on this win-ter's night with you.

and to be once a-gain with you, And to be once a-gain with you.

773

799. Stop

Words & Music by Victoria Aadams, Emma Bunton, Melanie Brown,
Melanie Chisholm, Geri Halliwell, Andy Watkins & Paul Wilson

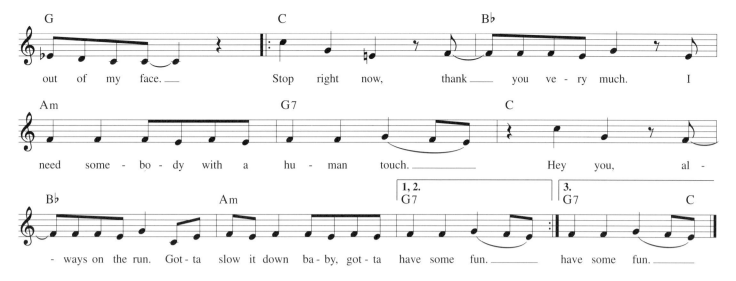

out of my face. ___ Stop right now, thank ___ you ve - ry much. I

need some - bo - dy with a hu - man touch. ___ Hey you, al -

- ways on the run. Got - ta slow it down ba - by, got - ta have some fun. ___ have some fun. ___

1, 2. G7   **3.** G7

2. Do do do do
   Do do do do
   Do do do do, always be together
   Ba da ba da
   Ba da ba da
   Ba da ba, stay that way forever.

   And we know that you could go and find some other
   Take or leave it 'cos we've always got each other
   You know who you are and yes you're gonna break down
   You've crossed the line so you're gonna have to turn around.

   Don't you know *(etc.)*

800. See The Conquering Hero Comes
(from 'Judas Maccabaeus')

Composed by George Frideric Handel

Maestoso

801. St Patrick's Day Parade

Words & Music by Johnny Lange & Hy Heath

802. Somewhere Somehow

Words & Music by Wet Wet Wet

2. Went out walkin' in the morning
   Standing in the pouring rain
   Let it run all over me.

   Stayed up late last night
   Tryin' to put all the things right
   Then your tears roll over me.

3. If you're there and you care
   You will get a million kisses from me
   Somewhere, somehow.

   And if you feel like I feel
   Love cuts the deepest part of me
   Somewhere, somehow.

803. Stormy Weather

Words by Ted Koehler. Music by Harold Arlen

804. Sweetheart Darlin'

Words by Gus Kahn. Music by Herbert Stothart

805. Summer Green, Autumn Gold

Words & Music by Paul Francis Webster & Maurice Jarre

806. The Swan
(from 'Carnival Of The Animals')

Composed by Camille Saint-Saëns

807. The Sweeney

By Harry South

782

808. Sweet Surrender

Words & Music by John Denver

809. Symphony No.40 in G Minor
Theme from 1st Movement

Composed by Wolfgang Amadeus Mozart

810. Stuck On You

Words & Music by Aaron Schroeder & J. Leslie McFarland

785

811. Stella By Starlight

Music by Victor Young. Words by Ned Washington

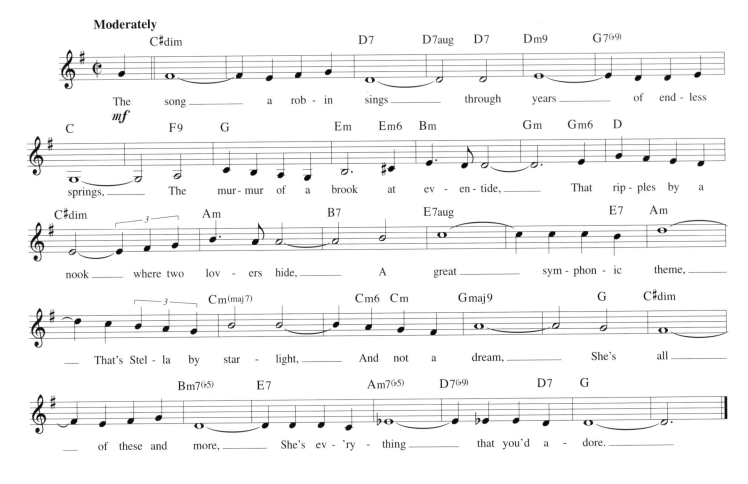

The song a rob-in sings through years of end-less springs, The mur-mur of a brook at ev-en-tide, That rip-ples by a nook where two lov-ers hide, A great sym-phon-ic theme, That's Stel-la by star-light, And not a dream, She's all of these and more, She's ev-'ry-thing that you'd a-dore.

812. Stomp, Look And Listen

By Duke Ellington

813. Tell Me When

Words & Music by Geoff Stephens & Les Reed

814. Summer Green And Winter White

Words & Music by Nat Simon & Charles Tobias

815. Take Good Care Of Her

Words & Music by Arthur Kent & Ed Warren

816. This Old Man

Traditional

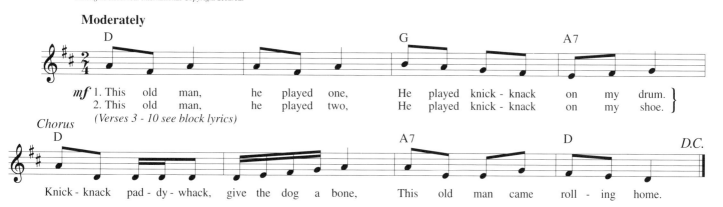

3. This old man, he played three
    He played knick-knack on my knee. *(Chorus)*

4. This old man, he played four
    He played knick-knack on my door. *(Chorus)*

5. This old man, he played five
    He played knick-knack on my hive. *(Chorus)*

6. This old man, he played six
    He played knick-knack on my sticks. *(Chorus)*

7. This old man, he played seven
    He played knick-knack up to heaven. *(Chorus)*

8. This old man, he played eight
    He played knick-knack at the gate. *(Chorus)*

9. This old man, he played nine
    He played knick-knack on my line. *(Chorus)*

10. This old man, he played ten
    He played knick-knack over again. *(Chorus)*

817. Symphony No.94 in G (Surprise)
Theme from 2nd Movement

Composed by Joseph Haydn

818. Sunshine Girl

Words & Music by John Carter & Geoff Stephens

Sun - shine girl I feel your eyes on me ___ Your looks ex - cite me ___ I won - der
Sun - shine girl now I must go a - way ___ 'Cos this was on - ly ___ a sum - mer

can it be ___ Do you in - vite me ___ To hold you tight - ly. ___ How you de - light me
hol - i - day; But one day I'll be ___ re - turn - ing, You'll see ___ a - cross the blue sea ___

___ my sun - shine girl. ___ To - night, to - night and ev - er - y night. _
___ my sun - shine girl. ___ To - night, to - night and ev - er - y night, _

I wan - na be be - side ___ you, To - night, to - night and ev - er - y night. _ I'll be the one to
I'm gon - na dream a - bout ___ you, To - night, to - night and ev - er - y night. _ How can I live with-

guide ___ you, As the wind blows gent - ly on ___ the blue la - goon ___ I'll hide you, Sun - shine girl,
out ___ you, When I'm home then ev - 'ry one ___ will hear a - bout my lit - tle sun - shine girl,

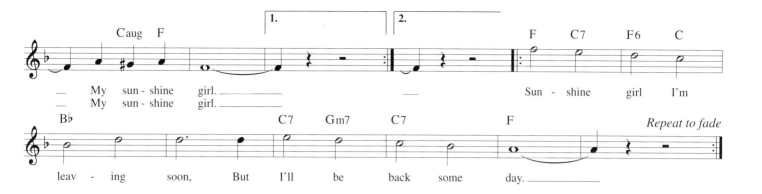

819. Thank You Baby

Words & Music by Hugo Peretti, Luigi Creatore & George David Weiss

820. Take Her To Jamaica (Where The Rum Come From)

Words by Jack Edwards. Music by Irving Fields

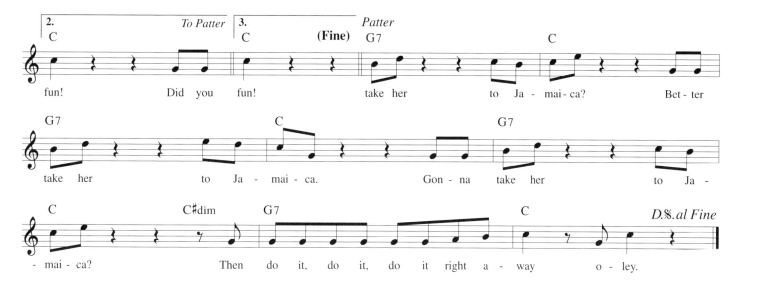

fun! Did you fun! take her to Ja - mai - ca? Bet - ter

take her to Ja - mai - ca. Gon - na take her to Ja -

- mai - ca? Then do it, do it, do it right a - way o - ley.

821. (They Call It A) Teenage Crush

Words & Music by Audrey & Joe Allison

Moderate slow rock

They call it a Teen-Age Crush,

They don't know how I feel, They call it a Teen-Age Crush, They can't be-lieve this is

real, They've for-got-ten when they were young, And the way they tried to be

free, All they say is this young ge-ne-ra-tion is

not just the way it used to be; I know that I know my own heart,

But you say I'm try-ing to rush,

Please don't try to keep us a-part, Don't call it a Teen-Age Crush.

822. Take My Breath Away

Words by Tom Whitlock. Music by Giorgio Moroder

794

2. Watching, I keep waiting, still anticipating love
   Never hesitating to become the fated ones
   Turning and returning to some secret place to hide
   Watching in slow motion as you turn to me and say
   "Take my breath away."

3. Watching every motion in this foolish lover's game
   Haunted by the notion somewhere there's a love in flames
   Turning and returning to some secret place inside
   Watching in slow motion as you turn my way and say
   "Take my breath away."

823. To Each His Own

Words & Music by Jay Livingston & Ray Evans

824. Tangerine

Music by Victor Schertzinger. Words by Johnny Mercer

Moderately

Tan - ger - ine, She is all they claim, With her eyes of night and lips as bright as flame, Tan - ger - ine, When she danc - es by, — Se - ño - ri - tas stare and ca - bal - ler - os sigh. And I've seen toasts to Tan - ger - ine raised in ev - 'ry bar a - cross the Ar - gen - tine, Yes she has them all on the run, But her heart be - longs to just one, Her heart be - longs to Tan - ger - ine.

825. A Taste Of Honey

Words by Ric Marlow. Music by Bobby Scott

Moderately slow

Winds may blow o'ver the ic - y sea, — I'll take with me the —
leave be - hind my — heart to wear And may it e'er re -
ne'er came back to his love so fair And so she died dream - ing

warmth of thee, A taste of hon - ey. A taste much sweet - er than
mind you of A taste of hon - ey, — A taste much sweet - er than
of his kiss. His kiss was hon - ey, — A taste much sweet - er than

wine. _____ I will re- turn, _____ I'll _____ re- turn, I'll come

back for the hon- ey and you. _____ *mp* I'll you, _____ I'll come back for the
He *mp*

hon- ey and you, _____ I'll come back for the hon- ey, hon- ey and you. _____
mf *f*

826. Toyland

Music by Victor Herbert. Words by Glen MacDonough.

Moderately slow

1. When you've grown up, my dears ____ And are as old as I _____ You'll oft- en pon- der
mp 2. you've grown up, my dears ____ There comes a drear- y day _____ When 'mid the locks of

on the years That roll so swift- ly by, my dears, that roll so swift- ly by _____ And
black ap- pears The first pale gleam of gray, my dears, the first pale gleam of gray. _____ Then

of the ma- ny lands _____ You will have jour- neyed through _____ You'll oft re- call The
of the past you'll dream _____ As gray- haired grown ups do _____ And seek once more It's

best of all, The land your child- hood knew! _____ Your child- hood knew! Toy- land!
phan- tom shore, The land your child- hood knew! _____ Your child- hood knew. Toy- land!
mf

Toy- land! Lit- tle girl and boy- land, While you dwell with- in it _____ You are

ev- er hap- py then. Child- hood's Joy- land, Mys- tic mer- ry Toy- land!

Once you pass its bor- ders you can ne'er re- turn a- gain _____ 2. When - gain. _____

827. The Teddy Bears' Picnic

Music by John W. Bratton. Words by Jimmy Kennedy

2. Ev'ry teddy bear who's been good
   Is sure of a treat today
   There's lots of marvellous things to eat
   And wonderful games to play
   Beneath the trees where nobody sees
   They'll hide and seek as long as they please
   'Cause that's the way the teddy bears have their picnic

3. If you go down in the woods today
   You'd better not go alone
   It's lovely down in the woods today
   But safer to stay at home
   For ev'ry bear that ever there was
   Will gather there for certain, because
   Today's the day the teddy bears have their picnic.

828. Telephone Man

Words & Music by Meri Wilson

Spoken: *I rented my apartment on a Monday at one*
Singing do la li la li shiki bum shiki bum
Started moving in it on a Tuesday at two
Singing do la li la li shiki do shiki do

Wednesday at three I called the phone company
Singing, hey baby, put a phone in for me
Thursday at four
He came a-knocking on my door singing

Sung: Hey baby, I'm your telephone man
You just show me where you want it and
I'll put it where I can
I can put it in the bedroom
I can put it in the hall
I can put it in the bathroom
I can hang it on the wall
You can have it with a buzz
You can have it with a ring
And if you really want it
You can have a ding-a-ling
Because hey, baby, I'm your telephone man.

Spoken: *Can you believe that and then he says*
Now when other fellas call
You tell 'em how it all began.

My heart began a-thumping
And my mind began to fly
And I knew I wasn't dealing with no ordinary guy
So while he was a-talking I was thinking up my plan
Then my fingers did the walking
on the telephone man
Singing hey la li la li, hey la li la li
Hey la li la li, get it any way you can.

Right? So.....

I got it in the bedroom
And I got it in the hall
And I got it in the bathroom
And he hung it on the wall
I got it with a buzz and I got it with a ring
And when he told me what my number was
I got a ding-a-ling
Singing hey la li la li, hey la li la li, hey la li la li
Just a-doing my thing.

I never did anything like this before.

829. (Let Me Be Your) Teddy Bear

Words & Music by Kal Mann & Bernie Lowe

830. That's Amoré

Words & Music by Jack Brooks & Harry Warren

Hearts will play, tip-py-tip-py-tay, tip-py-tip-py-tay, like a gay tar-an-

-tel-la. When the stars make you drool just like pas-ta fa-

-zool, that's a-mo-ré, When you dance down the street with a

cloud at your feet, you're in love. When you walk in a dream but you

know you're not dream-ing, Sig-no - ré, 'Scuz-za me, but you

see, back in old Na-po - li, that's a-mo - ré.

831. Trout Quintet
Theme from 4th Movement

Composed by Franz Schubert

Andantino

832. Tell Him

Words & Music by Linda Thompson, Walter Afanasieff & David Foster

I'm scared, so a-fraid to

show I care, will he think me weak if I trem-ble when I

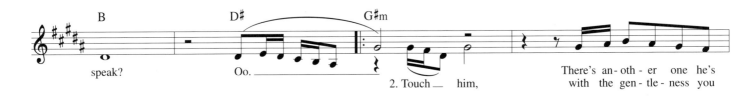

speak? Oo. 2. Touch ___ him, There's an-oth-er one he's with the gen-tle-ness you

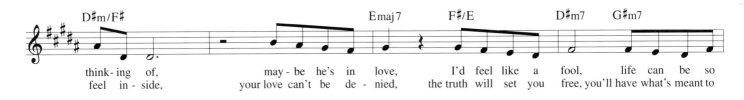

think-ing of, may-be he's in love, I'd feel like a fool, life can be so
feel in-side, your love can't be de-nied, the truth will set you free, you'll have what's meant to

cruel, I don't know what to do. ___ I've been there
be, all in time you'll see. ___ I love him, (then

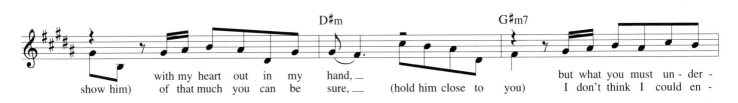

show him) with my heart out in my hand, ___ (hold him close to you) but what you must un-der-
of that much you can be sure, ___ I don't think I could en-

- stand, you can't let the chance to love him pass you by. ___
- dure, if I let him walk a-way when I have so much to say. ___

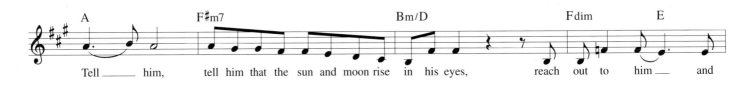

Tell ___ him, tell him that the sun and moon rise in his eyes, reach out to him ___ and

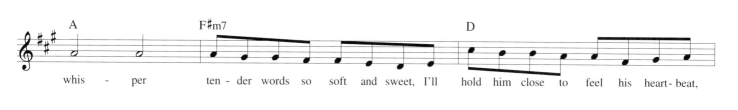

whis - per ten - der words so soft and sweet, I'll hold him close to feel his heart - beat,

love will be the gift you give your - self. ____ - self. ____

Love is like na - ture in love in the hearts of those who know, it's a step that made them

grow. ____ Feed the fire with all the pass - ion you can show, to - night

love will as - sume its place, this mem - 'ry time can - not e - rase, your faith will lead love where it has to

go. ____ Tell ____ him, tell him that the sun and moon rise in his eyes, reach

out to him ____ and whis - per, whis - per words so soft and sweet, ____

hold him close to feel his heart - beat, love will be the gift you give your - self, ____

____ oo, ____ nev - er let him go.

833. Tell Me Marianne

English Adaptation by Bob Musel. Music by Edgardo Donato

834. Thanks For The Memory

Words & Music by Leo Robin & Ralph Rainger

835. Theme From Terms Of Endearment

Words & Music by Michael Gore

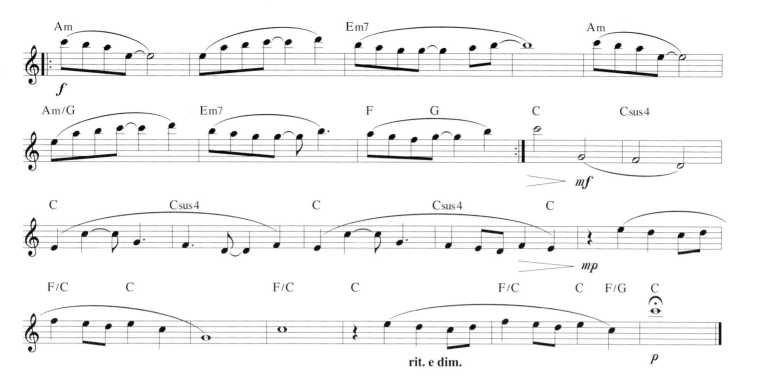

836. Tell Me The Old, Old Story

Music by W. H. Doane. Words by Kate Hawkes

3. Tell me the story softly
   With earnest tones and grave
   Remember, I'm the sinner
   Whom Jesus came to save.
   Tell me the story always
   If you would really be
   In any time of trouble
   A comforter to me.
   Tell me the old, old story *etc.*

4. Tell me the same old story
   When you have cause to fear
   That this world's empty glory
   Is costing me too dear
   Yes, and when that world's glory
   Is dawning on my soul
   Tell me the old, old story
   "Christ Jesus makes thee whole."
   Tell me the old, old story *etc.*

837. Thank U Very Much

Words & Music by Michael McGear

Moderately

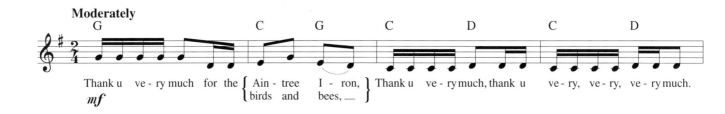

Thank u ve-ry much for the {Ain-tree I-ron, / birds and bees,__} Thank u ve-ry much, thank u ve-ry, ve-ry, ve-ry much.

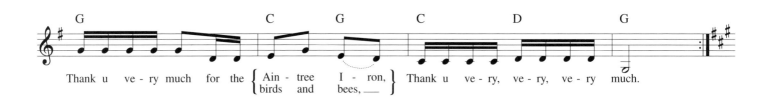

Thank u ve-ry much for the {Ain-tree I-ron, / birds and bees,__} Thank u ve-ry, ve-ry, ve-ry much.

Thank u ve-ry much for the fam-'ly cir-cle, Thank u ve-ry much, thank u ve-ry, ve-ry, ve-ry much.

Thank u ve-ry much for the fam-'ly cir-cle, Thank u ve-ry much, thank u

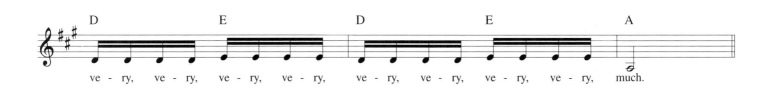

ve-ry, ve-ry, ve-ry, ve-ry, ve-ry, ve-ry, ve-ry, ve-ry, much.

Slightly slower

You don't know how much__ they all mean,_____ They seem
It was sim-ply spif-fing and true,_____ Let me

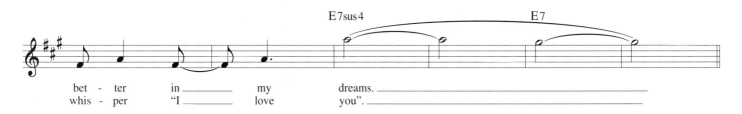

bet-ter in__ my dreams._____
whis-per "I__ love you"._____

838. That Old Black Magic

Music by Harold Arlen. Words by Johnny Mercer

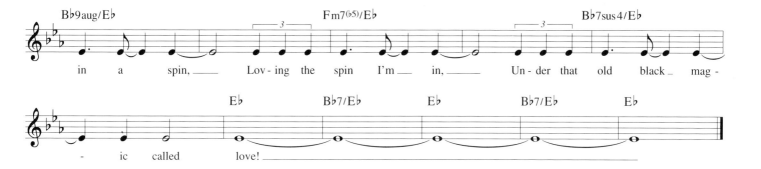

839. Together We Are Beautiful

Words & Music by Ken Leray

840. That Tired Routine Called Love

Words & Music by Matt Dennis & Ted Steele

841. That's Life

Words & Music by Dean Kay & Kelly Gordon

842. That Warm Christmas Feeling Is Here

Words & Music by John Neary & Dick Charles

843. Those Lazy Hazy Crazy Days Of Summer

Words by Charles Tobias. Music by Hans Carste

844. That Would Be Something

Words & Music by Paul McCartney

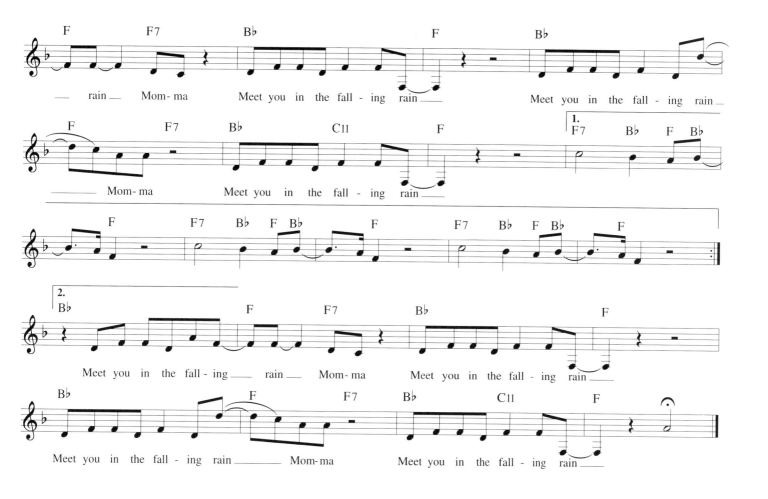

rain ___ Mom- ma Meet you in the fall - ing rain ___ Meet you in the fall - ing rain

Mom- ma Meet you in the fall - ing rain

Meet you in the fall - ing ___ rain ___ Mom- ma Meet you in the fall - ing rain

Meet you in the fall - ing rain ___ Mom- ma Meet you in the fall - ing rain

845. Two Hearts In Love (Emperor Waltz)

Words & Music by Patrick Michael

Moderately fast

Two hearts in love Beat - ing as one, Know - ing at last Life has be - gun;

Each ten - der kiss We're dream - ing og; Joy is com - plete for two hearts in

love. Two to - geth - er Nev - er - more a - part; Love is sing - ing,

Ring - ing in each heart; Soft eyes shin - ing Match the stars a - bove; Two heads in the

clouds, Two hearts in love! hearts in love!

846. There's Something About A Soldier

Words & Music by Noel Gay

in the Pa - lace Yard you'll see the chang - ing of the guard.

Oh! how you run to see a sol - dier. Be - cause there's

sol - dier that is fine, fine, fine!

847. A Time For Us
(Love Theme from 'Romeo & Juliet')

Music by Nino Rota. Words by Eddie Snyder & Larry Kusik

Slowly and expressively

A time for us, some day there'll be, when chains are torn by cour - age born of a love that's

free, A time when dreams so long de - nied can flour - ish as we un - veil the

love we now must hide, A time for us at last, to see a

life worth - while for you and me, And with our love thro' tears and

thorns we will en - dure as we pass sure - ly thro' ev - 'ry storm. A time for us, some - day there'll

be, a new world, a world of shin - ing hope for you and me.

848. There Goes My Everything

Words & Music by Dallas Frazier

I hear foot-steps slow-ly walk-ing,_____ As they gent-ly walk a-
mem-'ry turns back the pag-es,_____ I can see the hap-py

cross____ a lone-ly floor._____ And a voice____ is soft-ly say-ing:
years____ we had be-fore._____ Now the love____ that kept this old heart beat-ing_____

"Dar-ling, this will be good-bye____ for ev-er-more."_____
Has been shat-tered by the clos-ing of the door._____

There goes my rea-son for liv-ing, There goes the one of my

dreams,_____ There goes my on-ly pos-ses-sion,

1.
There goes my ev-'ry-thing.
2.
2. As my thing._____

849. Three Steps To Heaven

Words & Music by Bob & Eddie Cochran

Now there are three____ steps to hea-ven,_____ just lis-ten and

you will____ plain-ly see,_____ and as I tra-vel on, and things do go

wrong, just call it steps one, two and three._____ Step one____ you

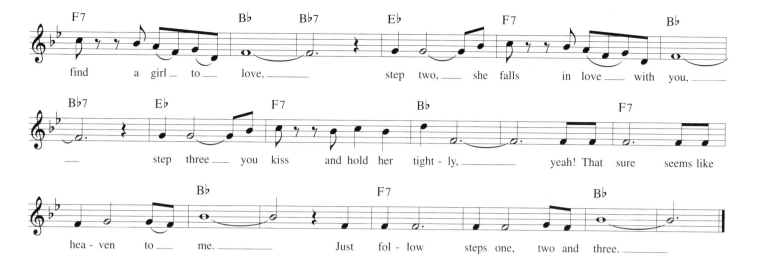

find a girl to love, step two, she falls in love with you,

step three you kiss and hold her tight-ly, yeah! That sure seems like

hea-ven to me. Just fol-low steps one, two and three.

850. That's It, I Quit, I'm Movin' On

Words & Music by Roy Alfred & Del Serino

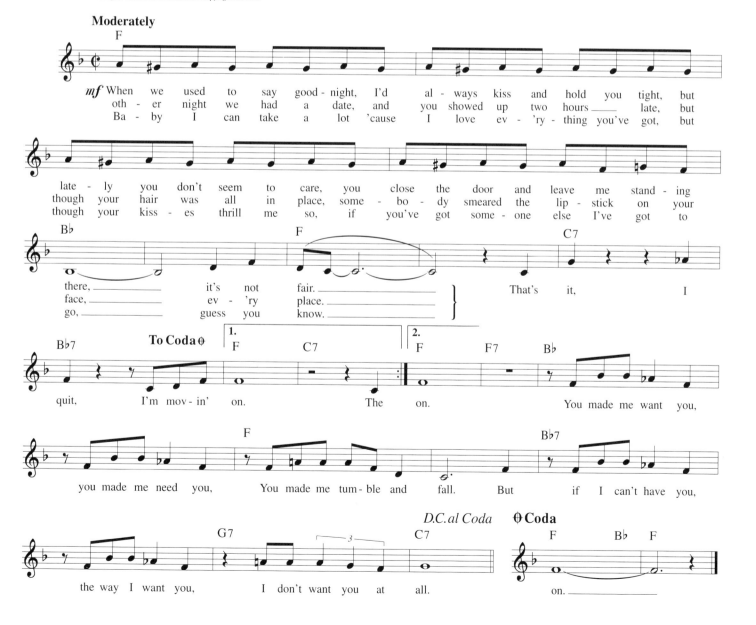

Moderately

mf When we used to say good-night, I'd al-ways kiss and hold you tight, but
oth - er night we had a date, and you showed up two hours late, but
Ba - by I can take a lot 'cause I love ev - 'ry - thing you've got, but

late - ly you don't seem to care, you close the door and leave me stand - ing
though your hair was all in place, some - bo - dy smeared the lip - stick on your
though your kiss - es thrill me so, if you've got some - one else I've got to

there, it's not fair. That's it, I
face, ev - 'ry place.
go, guess you know.

To Coda ⊕

quit, I'm mov - in' on. The on. You made me want you,

you made me need you, You made me tum - ble and fall. But if I can't have you,

D.C. al Coda ⊕ **Coda**

the way I want you, I don't want you at all. on.

851. There Must Be An Angel (Playing With My Heart)

Words & Music by A. Lennox & D. A. Stewart

Must be talk-ing to an an-gel,   must be talk-ing to an an-gel,   must be talk-ing to an an-gel.

Must be talk-ing to an an-gel,   must be talk-ing to an an-gel,

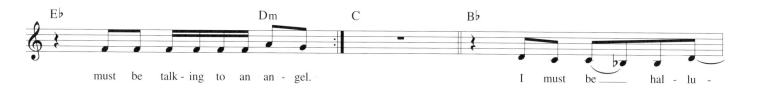

must be talk-ing to an an-gel.   I must be hal-lu-

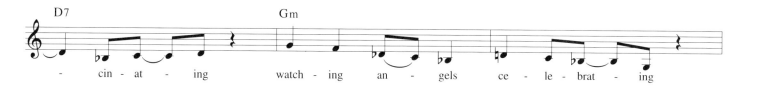

-cin-at-ing watch-ing an-gels ce-le-brat-ing

could this be re-act-ti-va-ting all my sens-es dis-lo-cat-ing?

This must be a strange de-cep-tion by cel-est-ial in-ter-ven-tion

D.𝄋. to Fade on Chorus

leav-ing me the re-col-lec-tion of your hea-ven-ly con-nec-tion.

2. No one on earth could feel like this
   I'm thrown and over blown with bliss
   There must be an angel
   Playing with my heart.
   And when I think that I'm alone
   It seems there's more of us at home
   It's a multitude of angels
   And they're playing with my heart.

852. These Days

Words & Music by Jon Bon Jovi & Richie Sambora

853. Till The End Of The World

Words & Music by Vaughn Horton

854. Think Twice

Words & Music by Andy Hill & Pete Sinfield

2. Baby, think twice for the sake of our love, for the memory
   For the fire and the faith that was you and me
   Baby, I know it ain't easy when your soul cries out for higher ground
   'Cos when you're halfway up, you're always halfway down
   But baby, this is serious
   Are you thinking 'bout you or us?
   (To Chorus:)

Chorus 4:
Don't do what you're about to do
My everything depends on you
And whatever it takes, I'll sacrifice
Before you roll those dice
Baby, think twice.

826

855. Three Wheels On My Wagon

Music by Burt Bacharach. Words by Bob Hilliard

856. This Ain't A Love Song

Words & Music by Jon Bon Jovi, Richie Sambora & Desmond Child

828

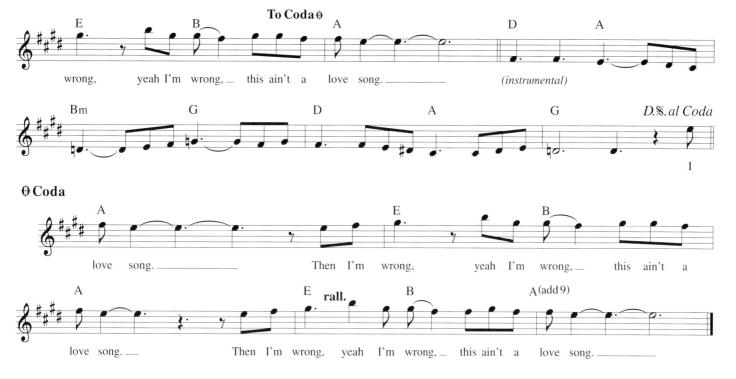

wrong, yeah I'm wrong, — this ain't a love song. _____ (instrumental)

I

Θ Coda

love song. _____ Then I'm wrong, yeah I'm wrong, — this ain't a

love song. ___ Then I'm wrong, yeah I'm wrong, — this ain't a love song. ___

2. Baby I thought you and me would stand the test of time
   Like we got away with the perfect crime
   But we were just a legend in my mind
   I guess that I was blind
   Remember those nights dancing at the masquerade
   The clowns wore smiles that wouldn't fade
   You and I were renegades
   Some things never change.

   It made me so mad 'cause I wanted it bad for us baby
   And now it's so sad that whatever we had ain't worth saving.

857. **The Untouchables**

By Ennio Morricone

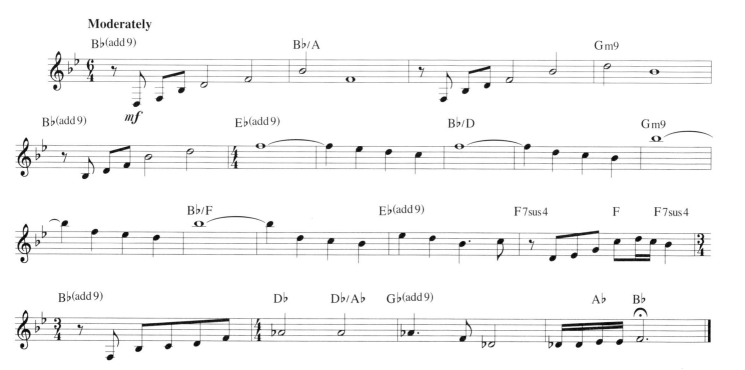

858. The Three Caballeros

Music by Manuel Esperon. Spanish Lyric by M. Cortazan. English Lyric by Ray Gilbert

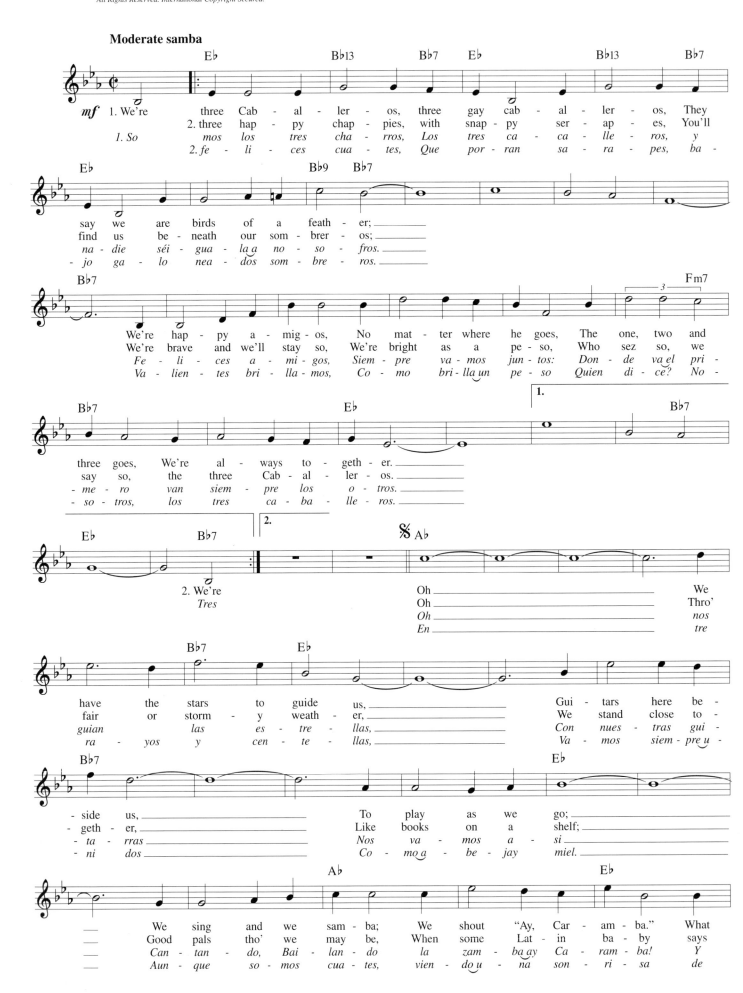

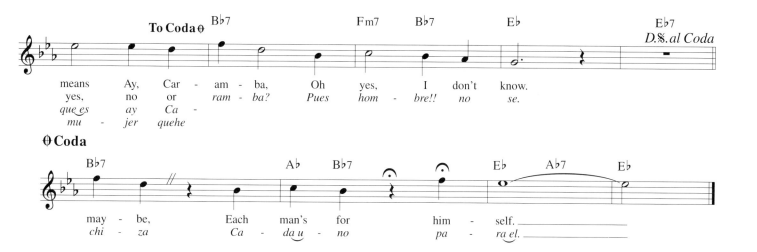

means   Ay,   Car - am - ba,   Oh   yes,   I   don't   know.
yes,   no   or   ram - ba?   *Pues   hom - bre!!*   no   se.
que es   *ay*   *Ca*
mu - jer   *quehe*

⊕ Coda

may - be,   Each   man's   for   him - self. _____
chi - za   *Ca - da u - no*   *pa - ra el.* _____

859. Turkey In The Straw

Traditional

Lively

As ____ I was go - in' ____ down the road, With a
(Verses 2 - 6 see block lyrics)

tir - ed team ____ and a heav - y load, I ____ cracked my whip ____ and the

lead - er sprung, From ____ day to day ____ on the wag - on tongue.   *Chorus*   Tur - key in the hay,

tur - key in the straw,   Tur - key in the hay,   tur - key in the straw,   Roll 'em up, twist 'em up,

High   tuck - a - haw,   And ____ hit 'em up a tune ____ called ____ "Tur - key in the straw."

2. Oh, I went out to milk and I didn't know how
   I milked the goat instead of the cow
   A monkey sittin' on a pile of straw
   A-winkin' at his mother-in-law.
   Chorus

3. Well, I met Mister Catfish comin' downstream
   Says Mister Catfish, "What do you mean?"
   I caught Mister Catfish by the snout
   And turned that catfish wrong side out.
   Chorus

4. Then I came to the river and I couldn't get across
   So, I paid five dollars for an old blind horse
   Well, he wouldn't go ahead and he wouldn't stand still
   So, he went up and down like an old saw mill.
   Chorus

5. As I came down the new cut road
   I met Mister Bullfrog. I met Miss Toad
   And every time Miss Toad would sing
   Ole bullfrog cut a pigeon wing
   Chorus

6. Oh, I jumped in the seat, and I gave a little yell
   The horses run away, broke the wagon all to hell
   Sugar in the gourd and honey in the horn
   I never was so happy since the hour I was born.
   Chorus

860. The Tide Is High

Words & Music by John Holt

tide is high but I'm hold - in' on, I'm gon - na be your num - ber one. The

861. Top Gun Anthem

Music by Harold Faltermeyer

Slowly

(instrumental)

Repeat ad lib. to fade

862. Tobacco Road

Words & Music by John D. Loudermilk

863. Treat Me Nice

Words & Music by Jerry Leiber & Mike Stoller

Medium bright rock

864. Too Bad

Words & Music by Eric Clapton

Moderate blues shuffle

mf

It's too bad ___ I don't love ___ you, for you have wor-ried ___ me night and day. ___

It's too bad I don't love you, for you have wor-ried ___ me night and day, ___

'til my heart ___ be-gins to stam-mer and my hair is turn-ing grey. ___

It's too bad ___ I don't need ___ you, 'cause we get a-long so good. ___

It's too bad ___ I don't need ___ you, be-cause we get a-long so good. ___

You must be think-ing 'bout this time, ___ that my poor heart is made of wood.

Guitar solo
11

It's too bad ___ I don't miss ___ you,

'cause you are al-ways on my mind. ___ It's too bad ___

___ I don't miss ___ you, 'cause you are al-ways on my mind. I want to stay a-

-round, li'l' sil-ly girl, and learn to love ___ you all the time. ___

865. The Town I Loved So Well

Words & Music by Phil Coulter

2. In the early morning the shirt factory horn
   Called women from Creggan, the Moor and the Bog;
   While the men on the dole played a mother's role
   Fed the children, and then walked the dog
   And when times got tough, there was just about enough
   And they saw it through without complaining
   For deep inside was a burning pride
   In the town I loved so well

4. But when I've returned how my eyes have burned
   To see how a town could be brought to its knees
   By the armoured cars and the bombed-out bars
   And the gas that hangs on to every breeze
   Now the army's installed by that old gas yard wall
   And the damned barbed wire gets higher and higher
   With their tanks and their guns, Oh my God what have they done
   To the town I loved so well.

3. There was music there in the Derry air
   Like a language that we all could understand
   I remember the day that I earned my first pay
   When I played in a small pick-up band
   There I spent my youth, and to tell you the truth
   I was sad to leave it all behind me
   For I'd learned about life, and I'd found a wife
   In the town I loved so well.

5. Now the music's gone but they carry on
   For their spirit's been bruised, never broken
   They will not forget, but their hearts are set
   On tomorrow and peace once again
   For what's done is done, and what's won is won
   And what's lost is lost and gone forever
   I can only pray for a bright, brand new day
   In the town I love so well.

866. Too Much

Words & Music by Victoria Aadams, Emma Bunton, Melanie Brown,
Melanie Chisholm, Geri Halliwell, Paul Wilson & Andy Watkins

Too much of no-thing is just as tough, I need to know the way to feel to keep me sat-is-fied.

2. Unwrap yourself from around my finger
   Hold me too tight or left to linger
   Something fine, built to last
   Slipped up there, I guess we're running out of time too fast.

   Yes, my dear you'll know he soothes me (moves me)
   There's no complication, there's no explanation
   It's just a groove in me.

   Too much of something *etc.*

867. **Torches**

Music by John Joubert. Words by J. B. Trend

Tor-ches! Tor-ches! Run with tor-ches all the way to

Beth-le-hem! Christ is born and now lies sleep-ing, Come and sing your

song to Him! Come and sing your song to Him! Ah, Ro-ro, Ro-

- ro, My ba-by, Ah, Ro-ro, My love, Ro-ro. Sleep you well, my

heart's own dar-ling, While we sing you our Ro-ro. Sing my friends and

make you mer-ry, Joy and mirth and joy a-gain, Lo! He lives, The

King of Hea-ven, Now and ev-er-more, A-men. Lo! He lives, The

King of Hea-ven, Now and ev-er-more, A-men.

868. Torero

Words & Music by Renato Carosone, Nisa, Al Hoffman & Dick Manning

lé

O-lé!

869. Tonight Is So Right For Love

Words & Music by Sid Wayne & Abner Silver

Hold me tight, the moon is so bright, To-night is so right for love.
Now's the time to say you'll be mine, To-

-night is so right for love. One by one, the stars ap-pear, they

twink-le in your eyes. Who'd be-lieve that we'd be here so near to

pa-ra-dise. This could be the kiss _____ To un-lock heav-en's

door. _____ That mag-ic of our bliss _____ That we both wait-ed

for, I love you more, and more, and more. But if we could

fly right up to the sky, Do the things we've been dream-ing of. _____ And how

real they would seem. A mid-sum-mer night dream, _____ Can't you

see that to-night _____ is so right _____ for love.

841

870. Trail Of Broken Hearts

Words & Music by Tom Marolda, Richie Sambora & Bruce Foster

Love pass - es by like a small town pa - rade. ___ You watch from the side - walk as love fades a - way. ___ In a

world full of hearts ___ there's on - ly one you can save. ___

ⴲ Coda

Yeah ___ the clock keeps tick - ing and it's run - ning out fast, when you find true ___ love, you bet - ter

make it last, 'cause... Time ___ leaves a trail of ___ bro - ken ___ hearts. You should

know be - fore ___ you ___ start ___ that your heart is on ___ the line. ___

In the end, ___ if you be - lieve ___ in ___ love, my ___ friend, bet - ter

keep your faith 'cause time ___ leaves a trail of ___ bro - ken ___ hearts.

2. Do you know what it's like when you need somebody
   But somebody runs away
   Well, you feel like dying
   But you wish it was in her arms, yeah
   Oh, you'd pay any bail just break that jail
   'Cause you're scared that you're there to stay
   Well, the clock keeps ticking and it's running out fast
   When you find real love, you better make it last 'cause...

871. **Trash**

Words & Music by Brett Anderson & Richard Oakes

2. Oh maybe, maybe it's the things we say
   The words we've heard and the music we play
   Maybe it's our cheapness
   Oh maybe, maybe it's the times we've had
   The lazy days and the cribbies and the fags
   Maybe it's our sweetness
   But we're trash, etc.

3. *Instrumental*

   We're trash, you and me
   We're the lovers on the street
   We're the litter on the breeze
   Just trash, me and you
   It's ev'rything we do
   It's ev'rything we do.

Chorus 2: Just trash, me and you
          It's ev'rything we do
          It's ev'rything we do.

872. That's The Way I've Always Heard It Should Be

Words & Music by Carly Simon & Jacob Brackman

2. My friends from college, they're all married now; they have their houses and their lawns
   They have their silent noons, tearful nights, angry dawns
   Their children hate them for the things they're not; they hate themselves for what they are
   And yet they drink, they laugh, close the wounds, hide the scar.

3. You say that we can keep our love alive. Babe, all I know is what I see
   The couples cling and claw and drown in love's debris
   You say we'll soar like two birds through the clouds, but soon you'll cage me on your shelf
   I'll never learn to be just me first, by myself.

873. Tresor Waltz

Composed by Johann Strauss

874. Things Ain't What They Used To Be

Words by Ted Persons. Music by Duke Ellington

Moderately

1. Got so wear-y of be-in' noth - in'. Felt so drear-y just do-in' noth-
2. No use be-in' a doubt-in' Thom - as, No ig-nor-in' that ro-sy prom-

— in', — Did-n't care ev-er get-tin' noth - in'. Felt so low
— ise, — Now I know there's a hap-py sto - ry yet to come;

— now my eye's on the far ho-ri - zon — Can see a glow — an-
— It's the dawn of the day of glo - ry; — Mil-len-ni-um. — I

nounc-in' things ain't what they used to be. — Look at the
tell you things ain't what they used to be. —

ar - my — fight-in' to be free, It does-n't bar me! —

Shows me how to go with my head up. — Eyes ain't look-in' low, don't feel

fed up — That's how come I see a vic-to-ry; — Be-

lieve me, things ain't what they used to be. —

Θ Coda

847

875. Tritsch Tratsch Polka

Composed by Johann Strauss

876. Two Sleepy People

Words by Frank Loesser. Music by Hoagy Carmichael

877. True Grit

Music by Elmer Bernstein. Words by Don Black

878. True Blue Lou

Music by Richard Whiting. Words by Leo Robin & Sam Coslow

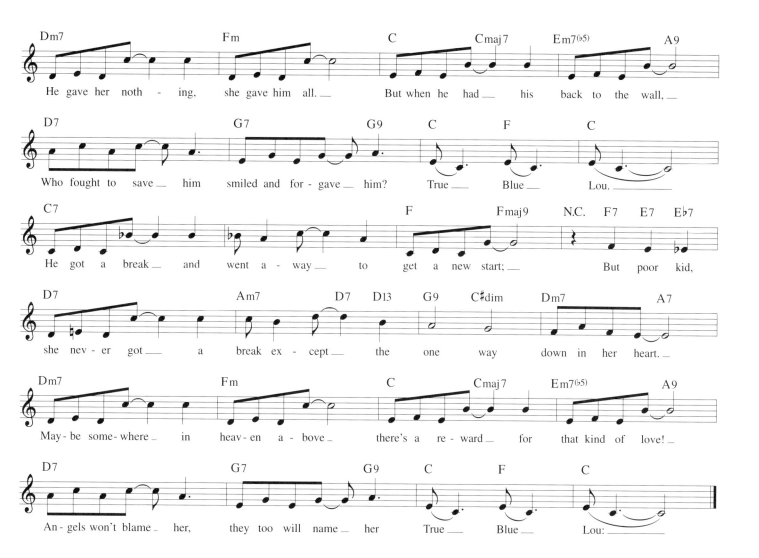

He gave her noth - ing, she gave him all. ___ But when he had ___ his back to the wall, ___

Who fought to save ___ him smiled and for - gave ___ him? True ___ Blue ___ Lou.

He got a break ___ and went a - way ___ to get a new start; ___ But poor kid,

she nev - er got ___ a break ex - cept ___ the one way down in her heart. ___

May - be some - where ___ in heav - en a - bove ___ there's a re - ward ___ for that kind of love! ___

An - gels won't blame ___ her, they too will name ___ her True ___ Blue ___ Lou: ___

879. Trumpet Tune

Composed by Jeremiah Clarke

Allegro moderato

880. 2 Become 1

Words & Music by Victoria Aadams, Melanie Brown, Emma Bunton,
Melanie Chisholm, Geri Halliwell, Matt Rowe & Richard Stannard

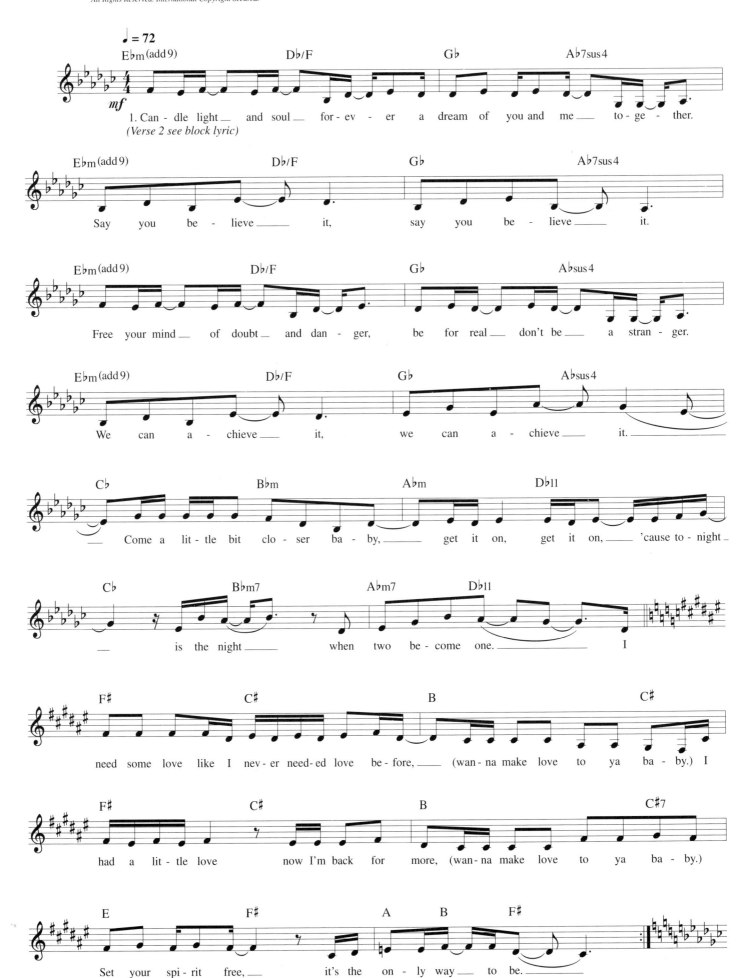

2. Silly games that you were playing, empty words we both were saying
Let's work it out boy, let's work it out boy
Any deal that we endeavour, boys and girls feel good together
Take it or leave it, take it or leave it
Are you as good as I remember baby, get it on, get it on
'Cause tonight is the night when two become one.

I need some love like I never needed love before, (wanna make love to ya baby).
I had a little love, now I'm back for more. (wanna make love to ya baby).
Set your spirit free, it's the only way to be.

881. This Is No Laughing Matter

Words & Music by Buddy Kaye & Al Frisch

882. Theme From Three Days Of The Condor

By Dave Grusin

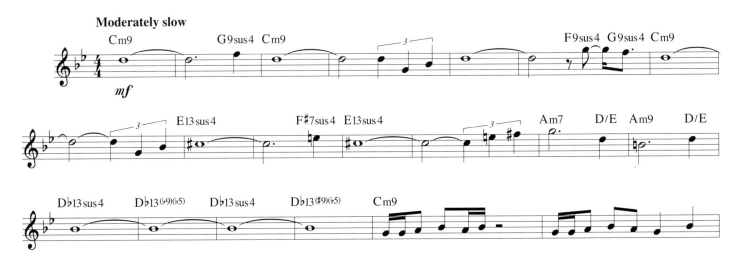

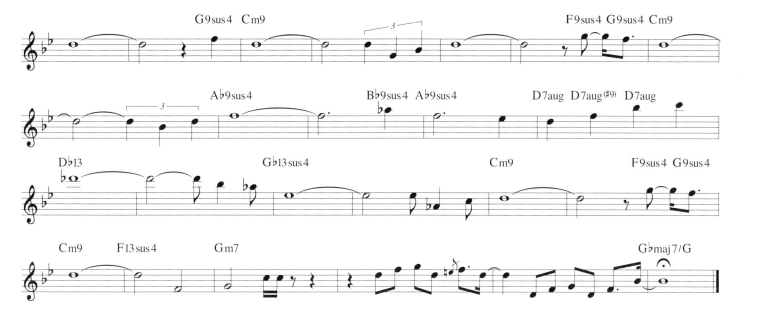

883. Walk, Don't Run

By Johnny Smith

884. Un-Break My Heart

Words & Music by Dianne Warren

857

885. Up Where We Belong

Words & Music by Jack Nitzsche, Will Jennings & Buffy Sainte Marie

886. The Universal

Words & Music by Damon Albarn, Graham Coxon, Alex James & Dave Rowntree

2. No one here is alone
Satelites in every home
The universal's here
Here for everyone.

Every paper that you read
Says tomorrow's your lucky day
Well, here's your lucky day.

859

887. Visions Of A Sunset

Words & Music by Shawn Stockman

Vis- ions __ of a sun- set _____ just ap- pear when I __ close my eyes. ___ Takes me
flee from __ all __ sor- row _____ like the wind __ blows from the sky. ___

clos- er __ to hea- ven when the flute starts to fly ____ and the vi-o-lin cries. ___ I will

1.

2.
vi-o-lin cries. ___

Oh. ___

888. The Very First Christmas Of All

Words by Paddy Roberts. Music by Peter Hart

Moderately

mp

One night when the world was a- sleep, ____ While shep- herds were watch- ing their

sheep, ____ They gazed from a- far at a star they saw, Then fol- lowed that

star to a sta- ble door. A child in a man- ger they found, ____

With gifts made of gold on the ground, ____ And so it be-

- gan, In that hum- ble stall, The ve- ry first Christ- mas of all.

889. Vienna Blood

Composed by Johann Strauss

890. Village Swallows

Composed by Johann Strauss

891. Vienna

Words & Music by M. Ure, B. Currie, W. Cann & C. Allen

892. What's The Use Of Wond'rin'

Music by Richard Rodgers. Words by Oscar Hammerstein II

893. Where The Winds Blow

Words & Music by Terry Gilkyson

got-ta get shot or break the law, Keep a mov-in' on you

durned ol' Char-lie horse, where the winds may blow._____ May-be my

D.%.al Coda

Coda

blow_____ Got to trav-el thro' rain and snow and fol-low the

trail where the moun-tains grow where the winds blow,_____ where the winds

blow,_____ where the winds blow.

894. Whole Lotta Loving

Words & Music by Antoine Domino & Dave Bartholomew

Moderately

I've got a whole lot-ta lov-ing for you,___ true, true lov-ing

for you,___ I've got a whole lot-ta lov-ing for you,_____ I've got a

whole lot-ta kiss-ing for you,___ whole lot-ta kiss-ing

for you,___ I've got a whole lot-ta kiss-ing for you.___ I've got a whole lot

to do,___ a whole lot to do,___ and I'm so glad___ to see you!

895. Viva Las Vegas

Words & Music by Doc Pomus & Mort Shuman

Brightly

mf Bright light ci-ty gon-na set my soul, ___ Gon-na set ___ my soul ___ on
How I wish ___ that ___ there were more ___ than the twen-ty four hours ___ in the

fi-re. Got a whole lot of mon-ey that's ___ rea-dy to burn, ___ So
day, ___ 'Cos ev-en if there ___ were for-ty more, ___ I

get ___ those ___ stakes ___ up high-er. There's a thou-sand pret-ty wo-men ___
would-n't sleep a min-ute a-way. ___ Oh! there's black ___ jack and pok-er and the

wait-in' out there, ___ And they're all ___ liv-in' dev-il-may-care, ___ And
rou-lette ___ wheel, ___ A for-tune won and lost on ev-'ry deal, ___

I'm ___ just the dev-il with ___ love to spare. ___ Vi-va ___ Las
All you need's a strong heart and a nerve of steel. ___

Ve-gas, Vi-va ___ Las Ve-gas. Vi-va Las

Ve-gas with your ne-on flash-in' and your one arm ban-dits crash-in', All those hopes

down the drain! ___ Vi-va Las Ve-gas turn-in' day in-to night-time, turn-in'

night in-to day-time, If you see it once ___ you'll nev-er be the same ___ a-gain.

___ I'm gon-na keep on the run, I'm gon-na have me some

fun if it costs me my ve-ry last ___ dime. ___ If I wind up broke,

Well, I'll al-ways re-mem-ber that I had a swing-in' time.

I'm gon-na give it ev-'ry-thing I've got. ____ La-dy Luck, please let the

dice stay hot, ____ Let me shoot a sev-en with ev-'ry shot!

V-va - Las Ve-gas, Vi-va ____ Las Ve-gas, Vi-va ____ Las

Ve-gas, Vi-va Vi-va ____ Las Ve-gas. ____

896. Waitin' For The Train To Come In

Words & Music by Sunny Skylar & Martin Block

Moderately

Wait-in' for the train to come in, ____ Wait-in' for my {gal/man} to come home; ____ I've

count-ed ev-'ry min-ute of each live-long day, _ Been so mel-an-chol-y since {she/he} went a-way. _ I've

shed a mil-lion tear-drops or more, ____ Wait-in' for the one I a-dore; ____ I'm

wait-in' in the de-pot by the rail-road track, Look-in' for the choo-choo train that brings {her/him} back; ____ I'm

wait-in' for my life to be-gin, ____ Wait-in' for the train to come in. ____

897. Westward Ho The Wagons

Words by Tom Blackburn. Music by George Bruns

898. The Virginia Company
(from Walt Disney Pictures' "Pocahontas")

Music by Alan Menken. Lyrics by Stephen Schwartz.

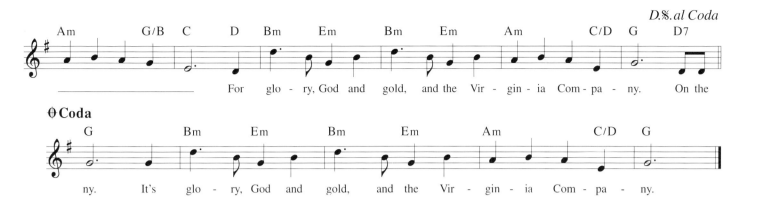

For glo - ry, God and gold, and the Vir - gin - ia Com - pa - ny. On the

⊕ Coda

ny. It's glo - ry, God and gold, and the Vir - gin - ia Com - pa - ny.

899. **Under The Double Eagle**

Music by J. F. Wagner

900. Walking The Floor Over You

Words & Music by Ernest Tubb

1. You left me and you went a - way You said that you'd be
   dar - ling, you know I love you well Love you more than
   some - day you may be lone - some, too Walk - ing the

   back in just a day You've bro - ken your pro - mise and you left me here a -
   I can ev - er tell I thought that you want - ed me and al - ways would be
   floor is good for you Just keep right on walk - ing and it won't hurt you to

   lone, I don't know why you did, dear, but I do know that you're gone. I'm
   mine, But you went and left me here with trou - bles on my mind.
   cry, Re - mem - ber that I love you and I will the day I die.

   walk - ing the floor o - ver you I can't sleep a wink, that is

   true I'm hop - ing and I'm pray - ing as my heart breaks right in two,

   walk - ing the floor o - ver you. 2. Now you.
   3. Now

901. The Waiter And The Porter And The Upstairs Maid

Words & Music by Johnny Mercer

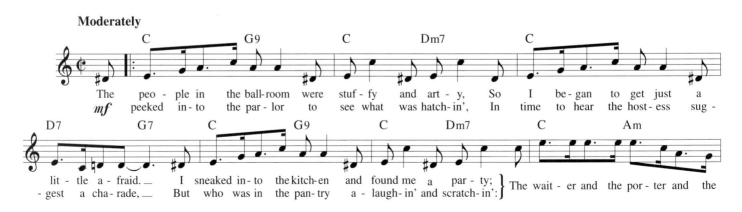

The peo - ple in the ball - room were stuf - fy and art - y, So I be - gan to get just a
peeked in - to the par - lor to see what was hatch - in', In time to hear the host - ess sug -

lit - tle a - fraid. I sneaked in - to the kitch - en and found me a par - ty;
- gest a cha - rade, But who was in the pan - try a - laugh - in' and scratch - in': The wait - er and the por - ter and the

second story maid. I upstairs maid. When they heard the music that the orchestra played, The

waiter and the porter grabbed a hold of the maid Then they all proceeded to go into a clog

Hot dig-ge-ty dog! If ev-er I'm in-vit-ed to some fud-dy dud-dy's I

ain't a gon-na watch an-y har-le-quin-ade, You'll find me in the kitch-en ap-

-plaud-in' my bud-dies; The wait-er and the por-ter and the up-stairs maid.

902. With The Wind And The Rain In Your Hair

Words & Music by Jack Lawrence & Clare Edwards

Last night we met and I dream of you yet } With the wind and the
I held you tight as you whis-pered "Good-night"

rain in your hair. hair. Now it will

be my fav-'rite me-mo-ry That vi-sion of you stand-ing

there There in the mist how you sighed when we

kissed With the rain and the wind in your hair.

903. **Waltz** (from 'Faust')

Composed by Charles Gounod

904. Welcome Home (Vivre)

Music by S. Beldone. French Words by Jean Dupre. English lyrics by Bryan Blackburn

905. Waltz (from 'Swan Lake')

Composed by Peter Ilyich Tchaikovsky

906. War And Peace

Music by Nino Rota. Words by Wilson Stone.

of love _____ Heav-en and earth were mine. _____ Oh, what emp-ty things are the

dreams of kings when love's all that's worth dream-ing of. _____ Cries of war and

peace have their day and cease, but we win the world when we love! _____

907. When The Saints Go Marching In

Traditional

With spirit

mf I am just a wea-ry pil-grim, _____ Plod-ding through this world of

(Verses 2 & 3 see block lyrics)

sin, _____ Get-ting read-y for that day, _____ When the saints go

Chorus

march - ing in. _____ Oh, when the saints go march-ing in,

Oh, when the saints go march-ing in, Lord, I want to

be in that num-ber, _____ When the saints go march-ing in. _____

2. So I pray each day to heaven
   For the strength to help me win
   Want to be in that procession
   When the saints go marching in.
   Chorus

3. Come and join me in my journey
   'Cause it's time that we begin
   And we'll be there for the judgement
   When the saints go marching in.
   Chorus

Alternative Choruses
I want to join the heav'nly band
I want to join the heav'nly band
Want to hear the trumpets a-blowing
When the saints go marching in.

I want to wear a happy smile
I want to wear a happy smile
Want to sing and shout "Hallelujah"
When the saints go marching in.

I want to see those pearly gates
I want to see those pearly gates
Want to see those gates standing open
When the saints go marching in.

908. A Wand'ring Minstrel

Words by W.S. Gilbert. Music by Sir Arthur Sullivan

Moderately

A wan-d'ring min-strel I, a thing of shreds ___ and patch-es, Of bal-lads, songs and

snatch-es, And dream-y lul-la by. ___ My cat-a-logue is long, thro' ev-'ry

pas-sion rag-ing, And to your hu-mors chang-ing, I tune ___ my sup-ple

song! ___ I tune ___ my sup - - - - - ple song! ___

909. What A Wonderful Life

Words & Music by Sid Wayne & Jay Livingston

Moderately bright shuffle (with feel)

It's a won-der-ful life, this life I'm liv-in', What a won-der-ful life,
road, this road I'm trav-'lin', It's a won-der-ful road,

mf

liv-in' a life of ease, ___ oh-ho-ho. ___ Well, I got no ___ job to ___ wor-ry me, ___ no
head-in' be-yond the hill, ___ oh-ho-ho. ___ oh, it may go ___ straight or it may de-tour, ___ but

big bad ___ boss ___ to ___ hur-ry me. ___ } It's a won-der-ful life, ___ Life's good to me.
one thing that I ___ know for sure, ___ }

1. It's a won-der-ful

2. I don't know where I'm go-ing, don't care where I'm go-ing, Like the

four winds are blow-ing, I go on. Laugh-in' the day a-way, lov-in' the night ___ a-way

910. We Are The Sons Of The Desert

Words & Music by T. Marvin Hatley

911. Wannabe

Words & Music by Matt Rowe, Richard Stannard, Melanie Brown, Victoria Aadams,
Geri Halliwell, Emma Bunton & Melanie Chisholm

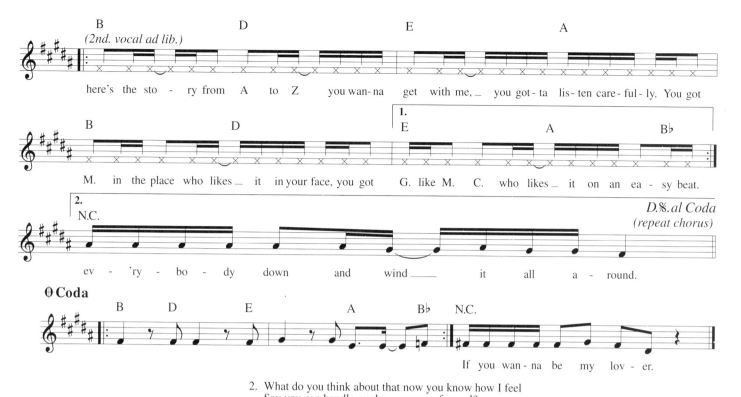

(2nd. vocal ad lib.)

here's the sto - ry from A to Z you wan-na get with me,_ you got-ta lis-ten care-ful-ly. You got

1.

M. in the place who likes _ it in your face, you got G. like M. C. who likes _ it on an ea - sy beat.

2.

N.C.

D.%.al Coda
(repeat chorus)

ev - 'ry - bo - dy down and wind _____ it all a - round.

⊕ Coda

If you wan - na be my lov - er.

2. What do you think about that now you know how I feel
Say you can handle my love, are you for real?
I won't be hasty, I'll give you a try
If you really bug me then I'll say goodbye.

912. We Plough The Fields And Scatter

Music by Johann Schulz. Words by Matthias Claudius

Joyfully

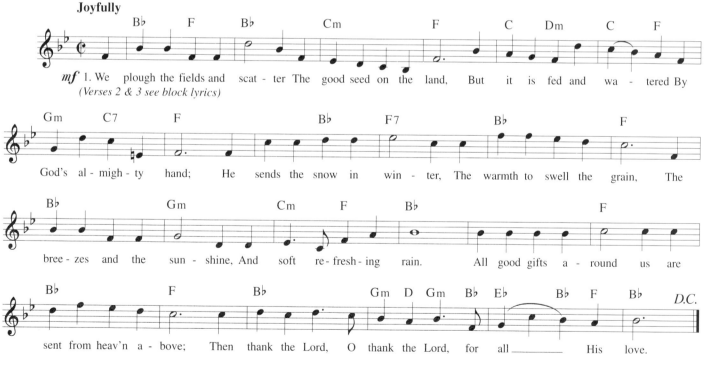

mf 1. We plough the fields and scat - ter The good seed on the land, But it is fed and wa - tered By
(Verses 2 & 3 see block lyrics)

God's al - migh - ty hand; He sends the snow in win - ter, The warmth to swell the grain, The

bree - zes and the sun - shine, And soft re - fresh - ing rain. All good gifts a - round us are

sent from heav'n a - bove; Then thank the Lord, O thank the Lord, for all _____ His love.

2. He only is the maker
Of all things near and far
He paints the wayside flower
He lights the evening star
The winds and waves obey Him
By Him the birds are fed;
Much more to us, His children
He gives our daily bread
All good gifts *etc.*

3. We thank Thee then, O Father
For all things bright and good;
The seed-time and the harvest
Our life, our health, our food
No gifts have we to offer
For all Thy love imparts
But that which Thou desirest
Our humble, thankful hearts
All good gifts *etc.*

913. Were You There

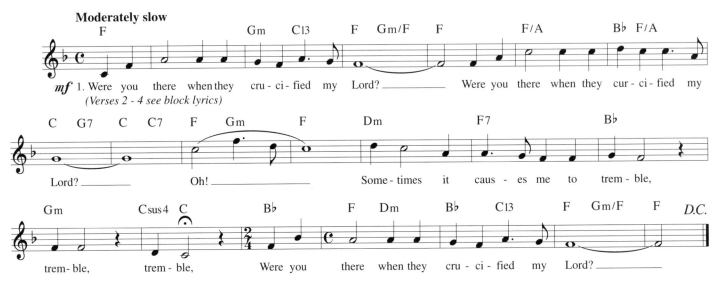

Moderately slow

mf 1. Were you there when they cru-ci-fied my Lord? _____ Were you there when they cur-ci-fied my

(Verses 2 - 4 see block lyrics)

Lord? _____ Oh! _____ Some-times it caus-es me to trem-ble,

trem-ble, trem-ble, trem-ble, Were you there when they cru-ci-fied my Lord? _____

2. Were you there when they nailed Him to the tree?
Were you there when they nailed Him to the tree?
Oh! Sometimes it causes me to tremble, tremble, tremble;
Were you there when they nailed Him to the tree?

3. Were you there when they laid Him in the tomb?
Were you there when they laid Him in the tomb?
Oh! Sometimes it causes me to tremble, tremble, tremble;
Were you there when they laid Him in the tomb?

4. Were you there when God raised Him from the dead?
Were you there when God raised Him from the dead?
Oh! Sometimes it causes me to tremble, tremble, tremble;
Were you there when God raised Him from the dead?

914. The Wonder Of You

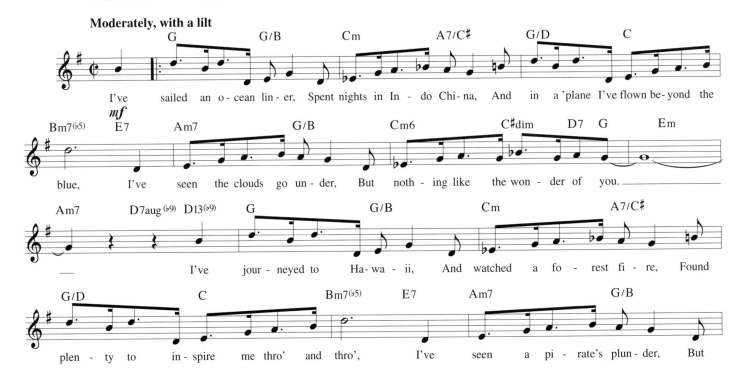

Moderately, with a lilt

mf I've sailed an o-cean lin-er, Spent nights in In-do Chi-na, And in a 'plane I've flown be-yond the

blue, I've seen the clouds go un-der, But noth-ing like the won-der of you. _____

I've jour-neyed to Ha-wa-ii, And watched a fo-rest fi-re, Found

plen-ty to in-spire me thro' and thro', I've seen a pi-rate's plun-der, But

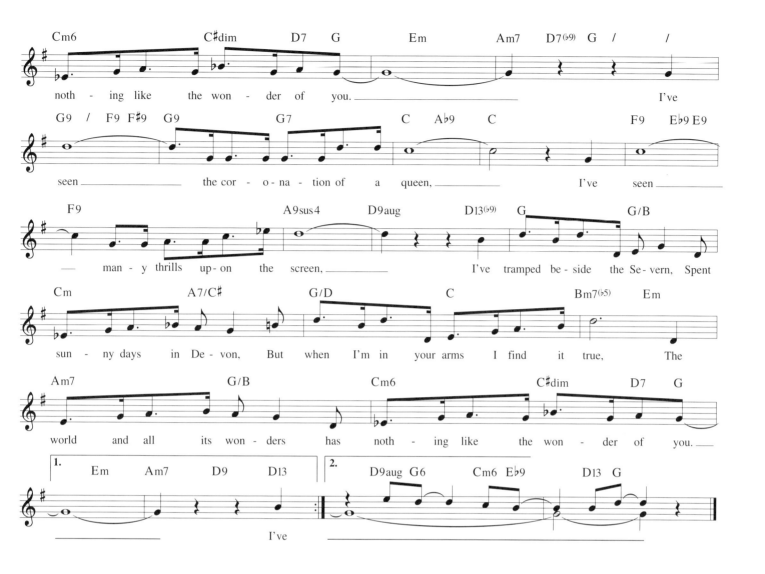

noth - ing like the won - der of you. _____ I've
seen _____ the cor - o - na - tion of a queen, _____ I've seen _____
— man - y thrills up - on the screen, _____ I've tramped be - side the Se - vern, Spent
sun - ny days in De - von, But when I'm in your arms I find it true, The
world and all its won - ders has noth - ing like the won - der of you. _____

1. _____ I've

2.

915. The Westminster Waltz

Composed by Robert Farnon

916. What's Another Year

Words & Music by Shay Healy

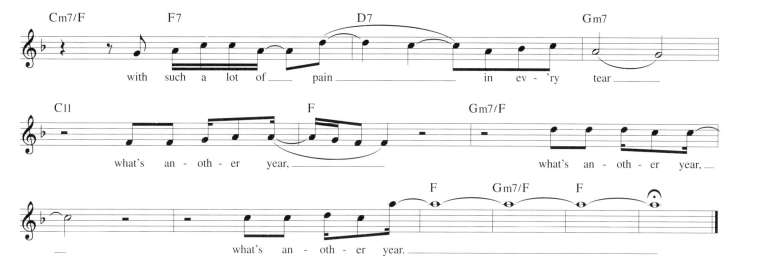

917. What A Party!

Words & Music by Pearl King & Dave Bartholomew

2. It was so dark in that cozy little place
   Du wah du wah, du wah du wah
   You couldn't see a hand before your face
   Du wah du wah wah
   What a party! *(etc.)*

3. The neighbours called the cops about half past four
   Du wah du wah, du wah du wah
   They came in rough and broke down the door
   Du wah du wah wah
   What a party! *(etc.)*

918. When Christmas Comes

Words & Music by Joe Seiferth & Dick Charles

919. When I Take My Sugar To Tea

Words & Music by Irving Kahal, Sammy Fain & Pierre Norman Connor

886

never take her where the gang goes, __ When I take my sug-ar to tea.

Ev-'ry Sun-day af-ter-noon, __ We for-get a-bout our cares, __ Rub-bing el-bows

at the Ritz __ With those mil-lion - aires. __ When I take my sug-ar to

tea, __ I'm as Ritz-y as I can be, __ 'Cause I nev-er take her where the

gang goes, __ When I take my sug-ar to tea. __ When I tea. __

920. What A Friend We Have In Jesus

Music by Charles Converse. Words by Joseph Scriven

Moderately

mf 1. What a friend we have in Je - sus, All our sins and griefs to bear! __
(Verses 2 & 3 see block lyrics)

What a priv-il-ege to car - ry Ev - 'ry-thing to God in prayer! __

O what peace we of-ten for - feit, O what need-less pain we bear, __

All be-cause we do not car - ry Ev - 'ry-thing to God in prayer!

D.C.

2. Have we trials and temptations
   Is there trouble anywhere?
   We should never be discouraged
   Take it to the Lord in prayer
   Can we find a friend so faithful
   Who will all our sorrows share?
   Jesus knows our every weakness
   Take it to the Lord in prayer.

3. Are we weak and heavy-laden
   Cumbered with a load of care?
   Precious saviour, still our refuge
   Take it to the Lord in prayer!
   Do thy friends despise, forsake thee?
   Take it to the Lord in prayer
   In His arms he'll take and shield thee
   Thou will find a solace there.

921. When I Need You

Words & Music by Albert Hammond & Carole Bayer Sager

When I need you, I just close my eyes and I'm with you, and all that I so want to

(Verse 3 see block lyric)

give you is on-ly a heart-beat a-way. When I need love, I hold out my hands and I

(Verses 2 see block lyrics)

touch love, I nev-er knew there was so much love, it's keep-ing me warm night and

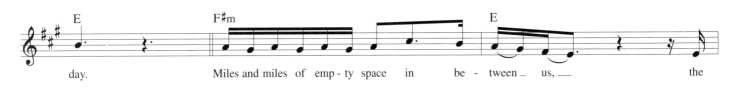

day. Miles and miles of emp-ty space in be-tween us, the

te-le-phone can't take the place of your smile. But you

know I won't be tra-vel-ling for ev-er, it's cold out but hold out and do like I do. (2.) When I

do like I do, oh I need you.

D.%. to fade

When I

2. When I need you
I just close my eyes and I'm with you
And all that I so want to give you, baby
Is only a heartbeat away.

It's not easy when the road is your driver
But honey that's a heavy load that we bear
But you know I won't be travelling a lifetime
It's cold out, but hold out and do like I do, oh I need you.

3. (D.%.) When I need love
I hold out my hands and I touch love
I never knew there was so much love
It's keeping me warm night and day.

I just hold out my hand... and I'm with you darling...
(To fade)

888

922. When Santa Got Stuck Up The Chimney

Words & Music by Jimmy Grafton

923. When I Survey The Wondrous Cross

Music by Edward Miller. Words by Isaac Watts

Moderately

mf 1. When I ___ sur- vey the won- drous cross, On which the Prince of Glo- ry died, ___ My
(Verses 2 - 5 see block lyrics)

rich- est gain I count ___ but loss, And pour con- tempt on all ___ my pride.

2. Forbid it, Lord, that I should boast
   Save in the death of Christ my God
   All the vain things that charm me most
   I sacrifice them to His blood.

3. See from His head, His hands, His feet
   Sorrow and love flow mingled down
   Did e'er such love and sorrow meet
   Or thorns compose so rich a crown?

4. His dying crimson, like a robe
   Spreads o'er His body on the tree
   Then am I dead to all the globe
   And all the globe is dead to me.

5. Were the whole realm of nature mine
   That were a present far too small
   Love so amazing, so divine
   Demands my soul, my life, my all.

924. A Whiter Shade Of Pale

Words & Music by Keith Reid & Gary Brooker

We skipped the light fan-
She said, "There is no

- dan- go   And turned cart- wheels 'cross the   floor.   I was feel- ing kind of
rea- son,   And the truth is ___ plain to   see." ___   But I wan- dered through my

sea- sick,   But the crowd called ___ out for more,   The room was hum- ming
play- ing cards   And would not ___ let her be.   One of six- teen vest- al

har- der   As the cei- ling flew a- way. ___   When we called out for a-
vir- gins   Who were leav- ing for the coast, ___   And al- tho' my eyes were

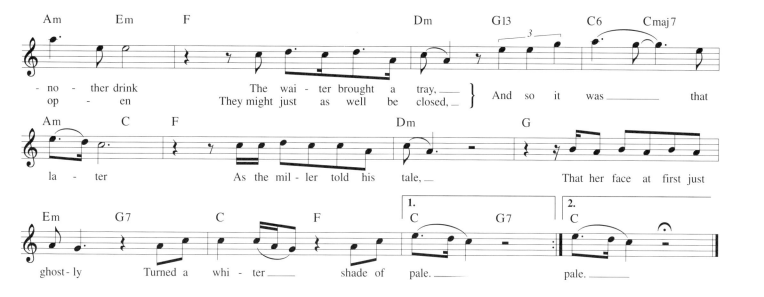

no - ther drink / op - en — The wai - ter brought a tray, — They might just as well be closed, — And so it was — that la - ter As the mil - ler told his tale, — That her face at first just ghost - ly Turned a whi - ter — shade of pale. — pale.

925. The Yellow Rose Of Texas

Traditional

Lively

mf 1. There's a yel - low rose in Tex - as, I'm go - ing there to see, No
(Verses 2 & 3 see block lyrics)

oth - er fel - la knows her, no - bod - y else but me, She — cried so when I left her, it

near - ly broke my heart, And if we ev - er meet a - gain we nev - er more will part. She's the

sweet - est rose of col - our a fel - la ev - er knew, Her eyes are bright as

dia - monds, they spark - le like the dew, You may talk a - bout your dear - est maids, And

sing the Ros - a - lie, But the yel - low rose of Tex - as beats the belles of Ten - nes - see.

2. Where the Rio Grande is flowing and the stars are shining bright
We walked along the river on a quiet summer night
She said "If you remember, we parted long ago
"You promised you'd come back again and never leave me so."

3. Oh, I'm goin' back to find her because I love her so
We'll sing the songs together we sang so long ago
I'll play the banjo gaily and sing the songs of yore
And the yellow rose of Texas will be mine forever more.

926. When Lights Are Low

Words & Music by Benny Carter & Spencer Williams

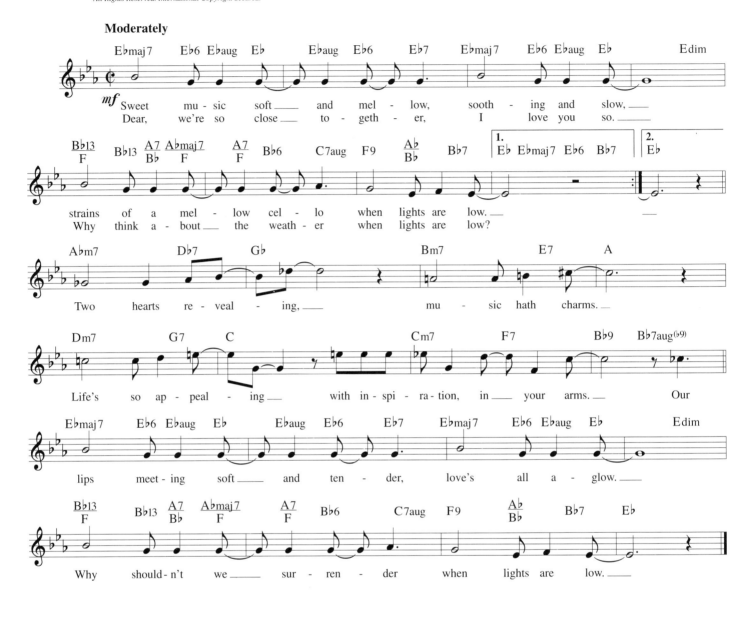

927. Widdecombe Fair

English Traditional Song

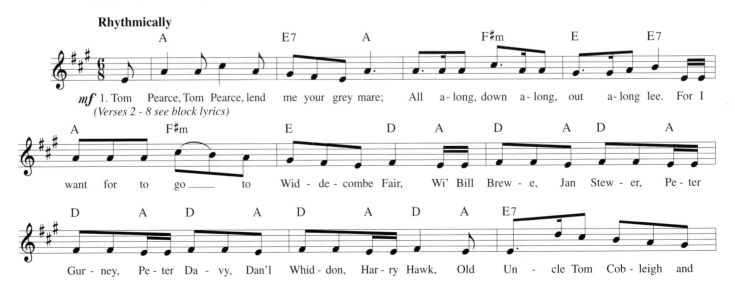

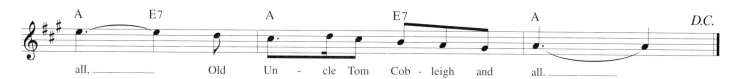

| A | E7 | A | E7 | A | D.C. |

all, _____ Old Un - cle Tom Cob - leigh and all. _____

2. And when shall I see again my grey mare
   All along, down along, out along lee
   By Friday soon or Saturday noon
   With Bill Brewer, *etc.*

3. Then Friday came and Saturday noon
   All along, down along, out along lee
   But Tom Pearce's old mare hath not trotted home
   With Bill Brewer, *etc*

4. .So Tom Pearce he got to the top of the hill
   All along, down along, out along lee
   And he see'd his old mare down a-making her will
   With Bill Brewer, *etc.*

5. So Tom Pearce's old mare her took sick and died
   All along, down along, out along lee
   And Tom he sat down on a stone and he cried
   With Bill Brewer, *etc.*

6. But this isn't the end o' this shocking affair
   All along, down along, out along lee
   Nor, tho' they be dead, of the horrid career
   Of Bill Brewer, *etc.*

7. When the wind whistles cold on the moor of a night
   All along, down along, out along lee
   Tom Pearce's old mare doth appear ghastly white
   With Tom Brewer, *etc.*

8. And all the night long be heard skirling and groans
   All along, down along, out along lee
   From Tom Pearce's old mare in her rattling bones
   With Bill Brewer, *etc.*

928. When The Children Are Asleep

Music by Richard Rodgers. Words by Oscar Hammerstein II

Moderately

When the chil-dren are a-sleep, we'll sit and dream _____ The things that ev-'ry oth-er

mf

dad and moth-er dream. _____ When the chil-dren are a-sleep and lights are

low, _____ If I still love you the way I love you to -

- day, You'll par-don my say - ing "I told you so!" When the chil-dren are a-

- sleep, I'll dream with you _____ We'll think what fun we have had and be

1. glad that it all came true!

2. true! _____

929. When Love And Hate Collide

Words & Music by Joe Elliott & Rick Savage

2. I don't wanna fight no more
I don't know what we're fighting for
When we treat each other, baby
Like an act of war
I could tell a million lies
And it would come as no surprise

When the truth is like a stranger
Hits you right between the eyes
There's a time and a place and a reason
And I know I've got a love to believe in
All I know, got to leave this town.

930. When The Stars Begin To Fall

Traditional

Moderately

931. When You Tell Me That You Love Me

Words & Music by Albert Hammond & John Bettis

932. When They Sound The Last All Clear

Words & Music by Hugh Charles & Louis Elton

933. When You Trim Your Christmas Tree

Words & Music by William Carey, Sonny Burke & Ed Powell

934. Where Everybody Knows Your Name
(Theme from "Cheers")

Music by Gary Portnoy. Words by Judy Hunt Angelo

and they're al - ways glad you came. ___ You want to go where you can see our

troub - les are all the same. ___ You want to go where ev - 'ry - bo - dy knows

your name. You want to go where peo - ple know peo - ple are all the same. ___

You want to go where ev - 'ry - bo - dy knows your name.

935. When You Wish Upon A Star

Words by Ned Washington. Music by Leigh Harline

When you wish up - on a star, makes no diff - 'rence who you are, An - y - thing your

heart de - sires will come to you. If your heart is in your dream, no re - quest is

too ex - treme, When you wish up - on a star as dream - ers do. Fate is kind,

She brings to those who love, the sweet ful - fill - ment of their se - cret long - ing.

Like a bolt out of the blue, Fate steps in and sees you through, When you wish up -

1.
on a star your dream comes true.

2.
dream comes true.

936. When You're In Love

Music by Carl Fischer. Words by Frankie Laine

937. Wish Me A Rainbow

Words & Music by Jerry Livingston & Ray Evans

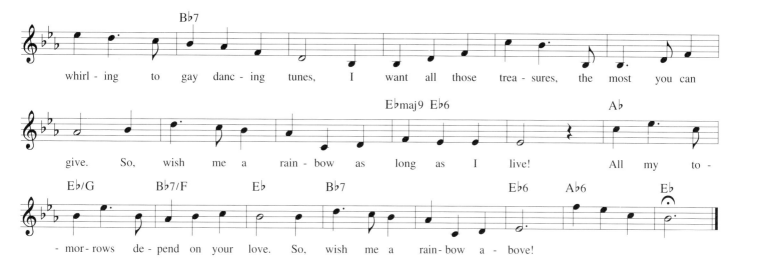

whirl - ing to gay danc - ing tunes, I want all those trea - sures, the most you can

give. So, wish me a rain - bow as long as I live! All my to -

- mor - rows de - pend on your love. So, wish me a rain - bow a - bove!

938. Whistling In The Dark

Music by Dana Suesse. Words by Allen Boretz

Moderately

mf

Whist - ling in the dark, _____ I see the lights all o - ver town, _____ and I keep

walk - ing up and down, _____ while I am whist - ling in the dark. Whist - ling like a lark, _____

— my song goes float - ing on the air, _____ I en - vy ev - 'ry lov - ing pair, _____ while I am

whist - ling in the dark. Who cares what I am say - ing in my song? _____

— Who knows that I am pray - ing some one will come a - long?

Strol - ling in the park, _____ with - out a sin - gle thing to do, _____ the night is

black and I am blue, _____ that's why I'm whist - ling in the dark.

939. Where Do I Begin
(Theme from 'Love Story')

Music by Francis Lai. Words by Carl Sigman

Moderately slow

mp Where do I be - gin _____ to tell the sto - ry of how great a love can be,
With her first hel - lo _____ she gave a mean - ing to this emp - ty world of mine, _____

__ The sweet love sto - ry that is old - er than the sea, The sim - ple truth a - bout the
__ There'd nev - er be an - oth - er love an - oth - er time, She came in - to my life and

1. love she brings to me? _____ Where do I start? _____
made the liv - ing fine. _____

2. __ She fills my *mf*

heart, _____ She fills my heart _____ with ve - ry spe - cial things, __ With an - gel

songs, _____ With wild im - ag - in - ings, _____ She fills my soul _____ with so much

love that an - y - where I go _____ I'm nev - er lone - ly, _____ With her a -

- long, _____ who could be lone - ly? _____ I reach for her hand, _____ it's al - ways there. _____

__ How long does it last? _____ Can love be meas - ured by the hou - rs in a day? *mp*

__ I have no an - swers now, but this much I can say: I know I'll need her till the

stars all burn a - way, _____ and she'll be there. _____

902

940. While My Guitar Gently Weeps

Words & Music by George Harrison

903

941. Where The Streets Have No Name

Words & Music by U2

2. I want to feel sunlight on my face
   See that dust cloud disappear without a trace
   I want to take shelter from the poison rain
   Where the streets have no name.

3. The city's a flood
   And our love turns to rust
   We're beaten and blown by the wind
   Trampled in dust
   I'll show you a place
   High on a desert plain
   Where the streets have no name.

942. What's She Really Like?

Words & Music by Sid Wayne & Abner Silver

943. Who Do You Think You Are?

Words & Music by Victoria Aadams, Emma Bunton, Melanie Brown,
Melanie Chisholm, Geri Halliwell, Andy Watkins & Paul Wilson

who? _____ Some kind of su - per - star, you _____ have got _____ to

swing it, shake it, move it, make it, who do you think you are? _____

Trust it, use it, prove it, groove it, show me how good you are. _____

Play 7 times

Swing it, shake it, move it, make it,

who do you think you are? _____ Trust it, use it, prove it, groove it, show me how good you prove it!

2. You're swelling out in the wrong direction
You've got the bug, superstar you've been bitten
Your trumpet's blowing for far too long
Climbing the snake of the ladder, but you're wrong.

I said who do you think you are?
Some kind of superstar
You have got to swing it, shake it, move it, make it, who do you think you are?
Trust it, use it, prove it, groove it, show me how good you are
Swing it, shake it, move it, make it, who do you think you are?
Trust it, use it, prove it, groove it, show me how good you are.

944. We Are The Champions

Words & Music by Hal Shaper & Mike Berry

Moderately

[Clapping]

We are the cham - pions, we are the cham - pions.

We are the cham - pions, great - est of them all. We are the cham - pions, al - ways on the ball.

Right through the sea - son you'll hear us call, home or a - way we're gon - na win them all.

We are the cham - pions to - geth - er we stand. We are the cham - pions, great - est in the land.

Right from the kick - off you'll see us try 'cos we're the team and no - one can de - ny that,

Repeat to fade

we are the cham - pions, we are the cham - pions

945. Who's That Girl?

Words & Music by A. Lennox & D. A. Stewart

Who's that ___ girl?

The lang - uage of
lang - uage of

love ___ slips from my lov-er's tongue ___ cool - er than ice - cream and
love ___ has left me sto-ney grey ___ tongue - tied and twist - ed at the

warm - er than the sun, ___ dumb hearts get bro - ken just like chin - a cups.
price I've had to pay ___ your care-less no - tions have sil - enced these e - mo -

The lang - uage of love ___ has left me brok - en on the
tions. Look at all ___ the fool - ish - ness your lov-er's talk ___ has done.

1.
rocks. ___ But there's just one thing, just one thing, ___ but there's

just one thing and I real - ly wan - na know. ___

Who's that ___ girl run - ning a - round with you, ___ Tell me Who's that

girl run - ning a - round with you, ___ tell me who's that girl, ___

To Coda
run - ning a - round with you, ___ tell me who's that girl ___ The

908

946. When A Child Is Born

Music by Zacar. Words by Fred Jay

947. Wichita Lineman

Words & Music by Jim Webb

948. Wooden Heart

Words & Music by Fred Wise, Ben Weisman, Kay Twomey & Berthold Kaempfert

910

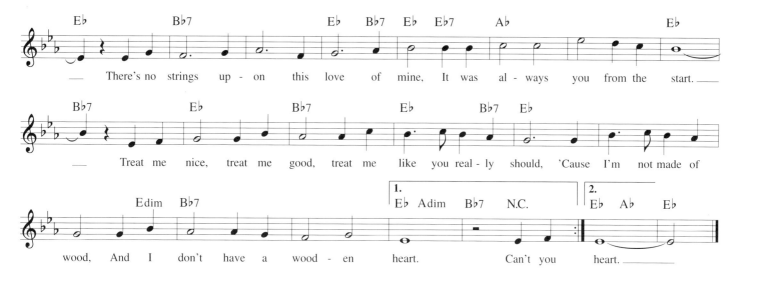

There's no strings up-on this love of mine, It was al-ways you from the start. ___

Treat me nice, treat me good, treat me like you real-ly should, 'Cause I'm not made of

wood, And I don't have a wood-en heart. Can't you heart. ___

949. Whole Lotta Shakin'

Words & Music by Dave Williams & Sunny David

Moderate rock

Come on ov-er ba-by, ___ whole lot-ta shak-in' goin' on. ___

Come on ov-er ba-by, ___ an' ba-by you can't go wrong, ___

ain't no-bo-dy fak-in', ___ whole lot-ta shak-in' goin' on. ___

Come on ov-er ba-by, ___ whole lot-ta kick-in' in the barn, come on ov-er ba-

-by, ___ we got the bull by the horn, ev-'ry-thing is tak-in', ___

whole lot-ta shak-in' goin' on. ___ Whole lot-ta shak-in' goin' on. ___

___ Whole lot-ta shak-in' goin' on. ___

950. The World Is Mine

Music by Victor Young. Words by Stanley Adams

mf The world is mine for you are the world to me. The world is mine as far as my heart can see. Your eyes are my stars that shine. Your lips are my rose. Your arms are my bound-'ry line where my dreams re - pose, My world is bright when - ev - er your smile ap - pears, And there's no light when - ev - er I see your tears. But when you whis - per so low just say that you love me so, then I know that the whole wide world is mine.

951. We Sail The Ocean Blue

Music by Sir Arthur Sullivan. Words by W. S. Gilbert

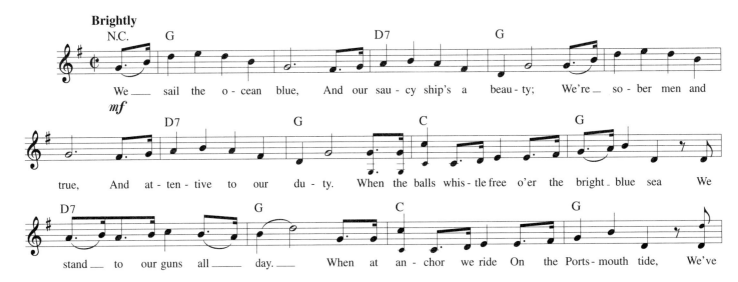

We sail the o - cean blue, And our sau - cy ship's a beau - ty; We're so - ber men and true, And at - ten - tive to our du - ty. When the balls whis - tle free o'er the bright blue sea We stand to our guns all day. When at an - chor we ride On the Ports - mouth tide, We've

plen - ty of time for play, A-hoy! A-hoy! The balls whis-tle free A-hoy! A-hoy! O'er the bright blue sea. We stand to our guns, to our guns all day. We sail the o-cean blue, And our sau-cy ship's a beau-ty; We're so-ber men and true, And at-ten-tive to our du-ty; Our sau-cy ship's a beau-ty, We're at-ten-tive to our du-ty; We're so-ber men and true, We sail the o - - - cean blue.

952. Who Killed Cock Robin?

Traditional

Moderately

Who killed Cock Ro - bin? "I," said the spar-row with my bow and ar - row "I killed Cock Ro - bin." Then the birds of the air Fell a - sigh - ing and a - sob - bing when they heard of the death of poor Cock Ro - bin When they heard of the death of poor Cock Ro - bin.

953. Willow Weep For Me

Words & Music by Ann Ronell

954. The Wisdom Of A Fool

Words & Music by Roy Alfred & Abner Silver

955. Winter Draws On

Words & Music by Harper & Haines

956. Winter World Of Love

Words & Music by Les Reed & Barry Mason

1. My love, the days are cold - er, so let me take your hand and
-cause the nights are long - er, we'll have the time to say such

lead you through a snow-white land, oh oh, oh oh. My love the year is
ten - der things be - fore each day, oh oh, oh oh. And then when love is

old - er, so let me hold you tight and while a - way this win - ter night, oh oh.
strong - er, per - haps you'll give your heart and prom - ise me we'll nev - er part, oh no.

I see the fire - light in your eyes, come kiss me now be - fore it dies.
And at the end of ev - 'ry year, I'll be so glad to have you near.

We'll find a win - ter world of love 'cause love is warm - er in De - cem - ber,

my dar - ling stay here in my arms till sum - mer comes a - long,

and in our win - ter world of love you'll see we al - ways will re -

1.
- mem - ber, that as the snow lay on the ground we found our win - ter world of

2.
love. 2. Be - found our win - ter world of love.

957. Wishing I Was Lucky

Words & Music by Graeme Clark, Tom Cunningham, Neil Mitchell & Marti Pellow

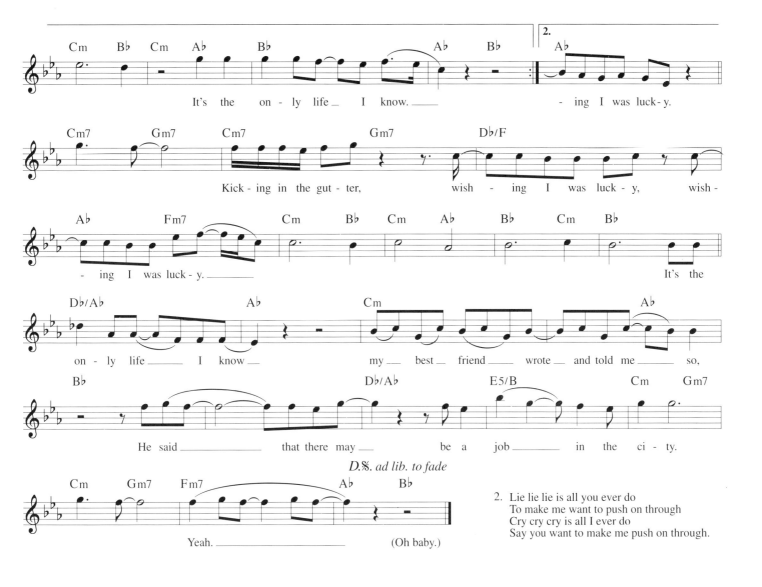

It's the on-ly life _ I know. _____ -ing I was luck-y.

Kick-ing in the gut-ter, wish-ing I was luck-y, wish-

- ing I was luck-y. _____ It's the

on-ly life _____ I know _____ my _ best _ friend _____ wrote _ and told me _____ so,

He said _____ that there may _____ be a job _____ in the ci-ty.

D.%. ad lib. to fade

Yeah. _____ (Oh baby.)

2. Lie lie lie is all you ever do
   To make me want to push on through
   Cry cry cry is all I ever do
   Say you want to make me push on through.

958. Woke Up This Morning (With My Mind On Freedom)

Traditional

Moderately

I woke up this morn-ing with my mind, _____ it was stayed on

mf

free-dom, _____ I woke up this morn-ing with my mind, _____ it was stayed on

free-dom, _____ I woke up this morn-ing with my mind, _____ it was stayed on

free-dom, _____ Hal-le-lu, _____ hal-le-lu, _____ hal-le-lu- _____ jah!

959. With Or Without You

Words & Music by U2

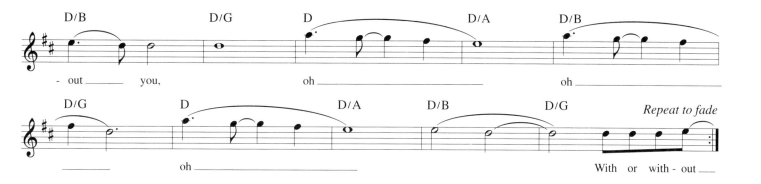

960. Wear My Ring Around Your Neck

Words & Music by Bert Carroll & Russell Moody

961. Without You

Words & Music by Peter Ham & Tom Evans

962. Wives And Lovers

Words by Hal David. Music by Burt Bacharach

963. The Wonderful Thing About Tiggers

Words & Music by Richard M. Sherman & Robert B. Sherman

With a bounce

1, 3. The won-der-ful thing a-bout tig-gers ___ is tig-gers are won-der-ful things! Their
won-der-ful thing a-bout tig-gers ___ is tig-gers are won-der-ful chaps! They're

tops are made out of rub-ber ___ their bot-toms are made out of springs. They're boun-cy, troun-cy,
loaded with vim and with vig-our ___ they love ___ to leap in your laps. They're jump-y, bump-y,

floun-cy, poun-cy, } Fun! Fun! Fun! Fun! Fun! But the most won-der-ful thing a-bout tig-gers is
clump-y, thump-y, }

I'm the on-ly one! 2. Oh, the one! one! ___ Tig-gers are cud-dl-y fel-las ___

tig-gers are aw-ful-ly sweet. Ev-'ry-one else ___ is jea-lous. ___ That's why I re-peat and re-peat. The

964. The White Bearded Old Gentleman

Words & Music by Moira Heath & Ray Martin

Moderately

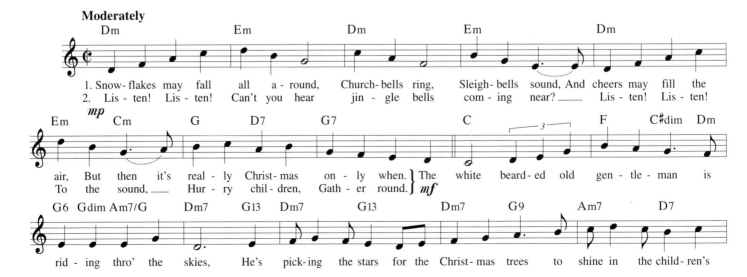

1. Snow-flakes may fall all a-round, Church-bells ring, Sleigh-bells sound, And cheers may fill the
2. Lis-ten! Lis-ten! Can't you hear jin-gle bells com-ing near? ___ Lis-ten! Lis-ten!

air, But then it's real-ly Christ-mas on-ly when. } The white beard-ed old gen-tle-man is
To the sound, ___ Hur-ry chil-dren, Gath-er round. }

rid-ing thro' the skies, He's pick-ing the stars for the Christ-mas trees to shine in the child-ren's

eyes, There's a bag-ful of trea-sure up - on his back, Things for you and me, There's a

dream-full of plea-sure in - side his sack, Just you wait and see! For the white beard-ed old

gen - tle - man is com - ing soon to town, He's just like he looks in the Christ-mas books,

Wrapped in his scar - let gown, So go to sleep child-ren as fast as you can, And close your dream - y

eyes, 'Cos the white beard-ed old gen - tle - man is rid - ing thro' the skies.

965. You'll Never Walk Alone

Music by Richard Rodgers. Words by Oscar Hammerstein II

Moderately slow

When you walk through a storm, hold your head up high And don't be a - fraid of the

dark, _____ At the end of the storm is a gold - en sky And the sweet sil - ver

song of a lark. _____ Walk on through the wind, Walk on through the rain, Tho' your

dreams be tossed and blown _____ Walk on, walk on, with hope in your heart, And you'll nev - er

walk a - lone. _____ You'll nev - er walk a - lone! _____ When you lone! _____

966. You've Got The Wrong Rhumba

Words & Music by Maurice Sigler, Al Goodhart & Al Hoffman

967. The White World Of Winter

Words & Music by Hoagy Carmichael & Mitchell Parish

968. Ya Got Class

Words & Music by Jay Livingston & Ray Evans

969. You Are Beautiful

Words & Music by Hugo Peretti, Luigi Creatore & George David Weiss

970. Year Of The Cat

Words & Music by Al Stewart & Peter Wood

971. You Moved Right In

Words & Music by Harold Adamson & Jimmy McHugh

972. Yeh Yeh

Words & Music by John Hendricks, Roger Grant & Pat Patrick

973. YMCA

Words & Music by J. Morali, H. Belolo & V. Willis

3. Young man, are you listening to me?
   I said, young man what do you want to be?
   I said, young man you can make real your dreams
   But you've got to know this one thing.

4. No man does it all by himself.
   I said young man put your pride on the shelf.
   And just go there to the Y.M.C.A.
   I'm sure they can help you today.
   (To chorus)

5. Young man I was once in your shoes
   I said, I was down and out and with the blues.
   I felt no man cared if I were alive.
   I felt the whole world was so jive.

6. That's when someone come up to me
   And said, "Young man, take a walk up the street.
   It's a place there called the Y. M. C. A.
   They can start you back on your way."
   (To chorus)

933

974. You And Your Beautiful Eyes

Music by Jay Livingston. Words by Mack David

975. You're Nobody 'Til Somebody Loves You

Words & Music by Russ Morgan, Larry Stock & James Cavanaugh

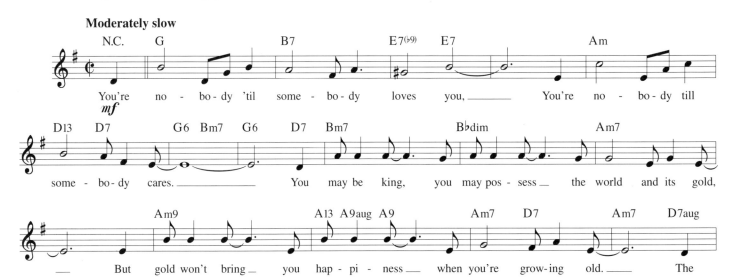

world still is the same, you'll nev- er change it, _____ As sure as the stars _____ shine a- bove, _____ You're no - bo- dy 'til some- bo- dy loves _____ you, So find your- self some - bo- dy to love. _____

976. You Leave Me Breathless

Music by Frederick Hollander. Words by Ralph Freed

You leave me breath- less, you heav- en- ly thing. _____ You look so won- der- ful, _____ you're like a breath of spring, _____ You leave me speech- less, I'm just like the birds, _____ I'm filled with me- lo- dy, _____ but at a loss for words. _____ That lit- tle grin of yours, _____ that fun- ny chin of yours, does so much to my heart. _____ Oh! give your lips to me, _____ for, dar- ling, that would be _____ the fin- al touch to my heart. You leave me breath- less, that's all I can say. _____ I can't say more, be- cause _____ you take my breath a - way. You leave me way. _____

977. You Can't Chop Your Poppa Up In Massachusetts

Words & Music by Michael Brown

978. You'd Never Know The Old Place Now

Music by Matt Dennis. Words by Marve Fisher

979. You Can Fly! You Can Fly! You Can Fly!

Words by Sammy Cahn. Music by Sammy Fain

980. You Came A Long Way From St. Louis

Music by John Benson. Words by Bob Russell

981. You Do Something To Me

Words & Music by Paul Weller

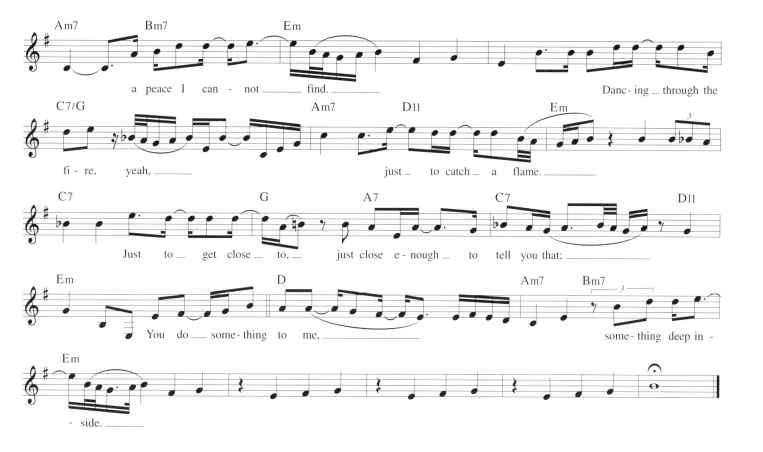

a peace I can - not ____ find. Danc - ing ____ through the fi - re, yeah, ____ just ____ to catch ____ a flame. ____ Just to ____ get close ____ to, ____ just close e - nough ____ to tell you that; ____ You do ____ some-thing to me, ____ some - thing deep in - side. ____

982. Ya Ya

Words & Music by Clarence L. Lewis & Morris Levy

Moderately

Oh, well I'm sit-tin' on my la ____ la, Wait - in' for my Ya ____ Ya, Ah, hm. Ah,
hm. Sit - tin' on my la ____ la, Wait - in' for my Ya ____ Ya, Ah, hm. Ah,
hm. It may sound fun - ny, I don't be - lieve {he's she's} ev - er com - in' home. ____ Ah,
hm. Ba - by, hur - ry. Don't make me wor - ry, Ah, hm. Ah,
hm. Yeah, ba - by hur - ry, Don't make me wor - ry, Ah, hm. Ah,
hm. You know that I love you, Oh, how I love you Ah, hm. Ah, hm.

D.%. and fade

983. You Make Me Feel Brand New

Words & Music by Thom Bell & Linda Creed

942

984. You're So Vain

Words & Music by Carly Simon

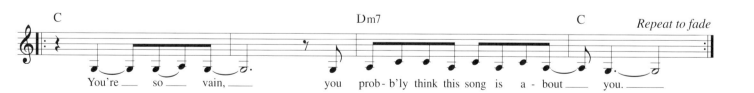

2. You had me several years ago, when I was still quite naive
Well, you said that we make such a pretty pair
    and that you would never leave
But you gave away the things you loved
    and one of them was me
I had some dreams
They were clouds in my coffee, clouds in my coffee and...

3. Well, I hear you went up to Saratoga
    and your horse naturally won
Then you flew your Lear jet up to Nova Scotia
    - to see the total eclipse of the sun
Well, you're where you should be all the time
And when you're not you're with some underworld spy
Or the wife of a close friend, wife of a close friend, and...

985. You Say You Care

Music by Jule Styne. Words by Leo Robin

986. You Can't Catch Me

Words & Music by Chuck Berry

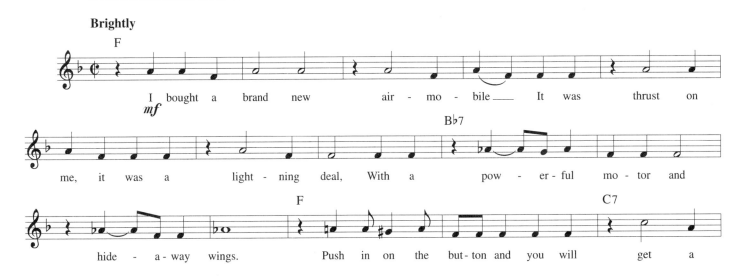

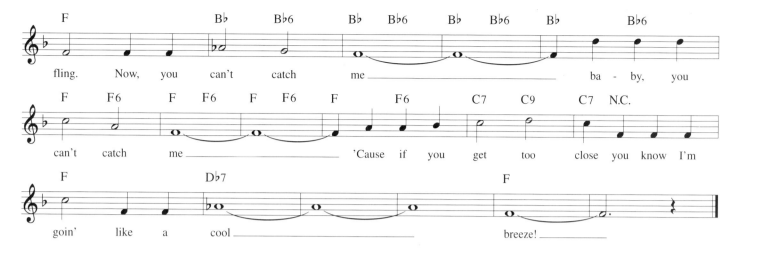

987. You're Mine, You

Music by John Green. Lyrics by Edward Heyman.

Moderately slow

988. You're No Good

Words & Music by Clint Ballard

989. You Brought A New Kind Of Love To Me

Words & Music by Sammy Fain, Irving Kahal & Pierre Norman Connor

990. You're Still The One

Words & Music by Shania Twain & Robert John "Mutt" Lange

2. Ain't nothing better
    We beat the odds together
    I'm glad we didn't listen
    Look at what we would be missing.

    They said, I bet
    They'll never make it
    But just look at us holding on
    We're still together, still going strong.

948

991. Young At Heart

Music by Johnny Richards. Words by Carolyn Leigh

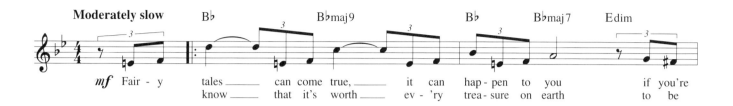

mf Fair-y tales can come true, it can hap-pen to you if you're
know that it's worth ev-'ry trea-sure on earth to be

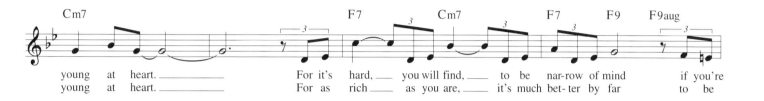

young at heart. For it's hard, you will find, to be nar-row of mind if you're
young at heart. For as rich as you are, it's much bet-ter by far to be

young at heart. You can go to ex-tremes with im-
young at heart. And if you should sur-vive to a

pos-si-ble schemes, you can laugh when your dreams fall a-part at the seams and
hun-dred and five look at all you'll de-rive out of

life gets more ex-cit-ing with each pas-sing day, and love is ei-ther in your heart or

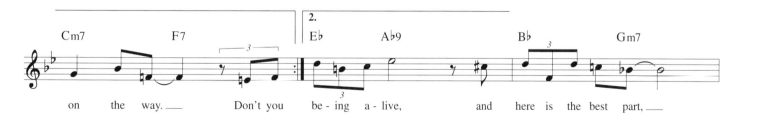

on the way. Don't you be-ing a-live, and here is the best part,

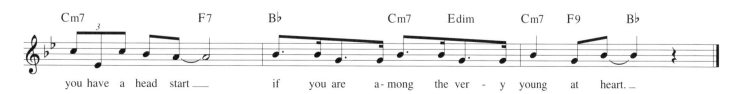

you have a head start if you are a-mong the ver-y young at heart.

992. You're The One That I Want

Words & Music by John Farrar

993. Young At Heart

Words & Music by Robert Hodgens, Siobhan Fahey, Keren Woodward & Sarah Dallin

994. You've Changed

Words by Bill Carey. Music by Carl Fischer

995. Yours (Quierme Mucho)

Music by Gonzalo Roig. Original Words by Agustin Rodriguez. English Words by Jack Sher

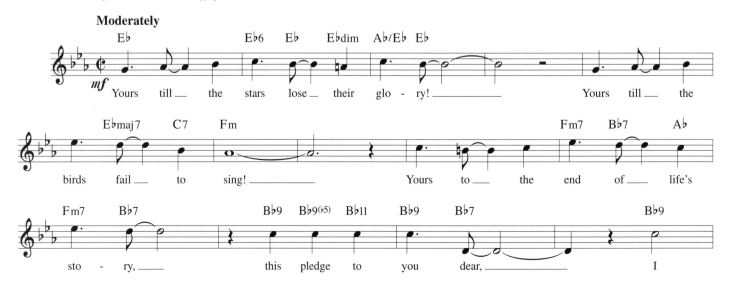

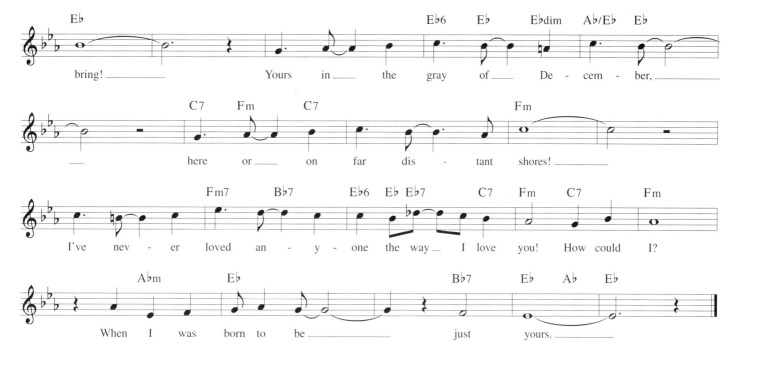

996. You'll Answer To Me

Words & Music by Sherman Edwards & Hal David

997. You Are Not Alone

Words & Music by Robert Kelly

though you're far — a - way, — I am here — to stay. — But you are not — a - lone,

— but I am here — with you, — though we're far — a - part, — you're al - ways in — my heart.

— But you are not — a - lone, — I am here — with you, —

— though you're far — a - way, — I am here — to stay. —

— But you are not — a - lone, — but I am here — with you, — though we're far — a - part, —

— you're al - ways in — my heart. — You are not — a - lone. —

Repeat to fade

(Spoken) You are not alone...   you are not alone...   not alone,
You just reach out for me girl...   in the morning in the evening not alone...not alone...   you and me, not alone...
Together...

2. You are not alone
    I am here with you
    Though you're far away
    I am here to stay
    You are not alone
    I am here with you
    Though wew're far apart
    You're always in my heart
    But you are not alone.

3. Just the other night
    I thought I heard you cry
    Asking me to go
    And hold you in my arms
    I can hear your breaths
    Your burdens I will bear
    But first I need you here
    Then forever can begin.

4. You are not alone
    I am here with you
    Though you're far away
    I am here to stay
    But you are not alone
    I am here with you
    Though we're far apart
    You're always in my heart
    But you are not alone.

955

998. You Hit The Spot

Music by Harry Revel. Words by Mack Gordon

Moderately

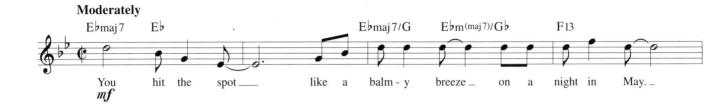

You hit the spot ___ like a balm-y breeze ___ on a night in May. ___

You hit the spot ___ like a cool mint ju - lip on a sum-m'ry day. ___ You hit a new

high in my es - ti - ma - tion. I had to fall _____ 'cause

you've got so much on the ball. Oh! You hit the spot ___ like the

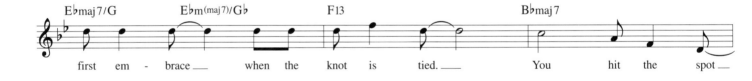

first em - brace ___ when the knot is tied. ___ You hit the spot ___

___ like a pipe and slip - pers by a fire - side. ___ Mat - ter of fact - ly,

don't know ex - act - ly what it is ___ that you've got, but ooh - ooh - ooh

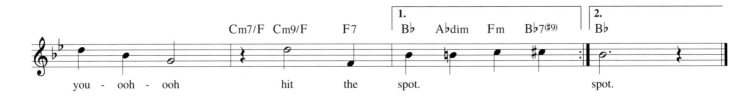

you - ooh - ooh hit the spot. spot.

999. You're Not In My Arms Tonight

Words & Music by Ned Washington & Victor Young

Moderately slow

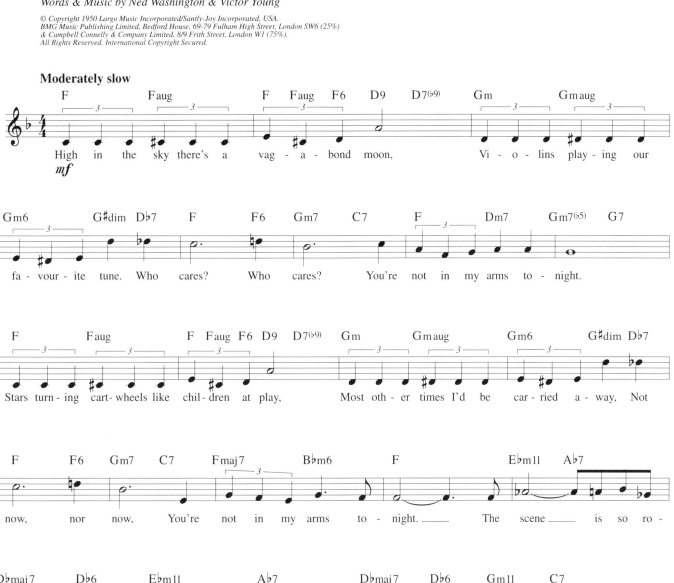

High in the sky there's a vag-a-bond moon, Vi-o-lins play-ing our fa-vour-ite tune. Who cares? Who cares? You're not in my arms to-night.

Stars turn-ing cart-wheels like chil-dren at play, Most oth-er times I'd be car-ried a-way, Not

now, nor now, You're not in my arms to-night. The scene is so ro-

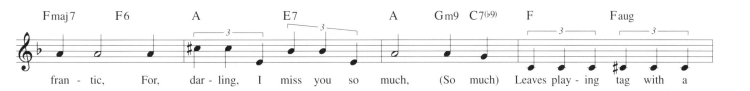

man-tic, it all has a mys-ti-cal touch. And I am near-ly

fran-tic, For, dar-ling, I miss you so much, (So much) Leaves play-ing tag with a

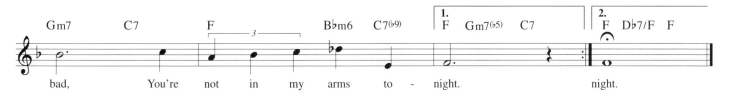

run-a-way breeze, Ma-gic like this leaves you weak in the knees. Too bad, Too

bad, You're not in my arms to-night. night.

1000. Zombie

Words & Music by Dolores O'Riordan

oh,___ oh,___ oh,___ oh,___ oh,___ oh,___ hey,___ oh,___ ya, ya.___

1001. Zing A Little Zong!

Music by Harry Warren. Words by Leo Robin

Moderately

mf Zing, zing, zing a lit-tle zong with me,___ I know we're not be-side the Zui-der Zee,___
Zing, zome zen-ti-men-tal me-lo-dy___ a-bout a chap-el or an ap-ple tree,___

but when you're zit-tin' by the zide of me,___ I want to zing a lit-tle zong.
a-bout a cou-ple liv-in' hap-pi-ly___ and I'll be glad to zing a

long. It ain't the zea-son that has me kind-a zill-y, you real-ly are a dol-ly, a dol-ly and a

dil-ly, You've got a rea-son to cud-dle sort-a close to me___ and we could

do a ve-ry clev-er bit of close har-mo-ny.___ Zing, zing, zing, it's get-ting late, my pet,___

we've got a most im-por-tant date to set.___ I'm sure that we could make a

great du-et___ and we could zing a lit-tle love zong all night long.

959

New from Music Sales - the one-and only, ultimate busker book! It's *the* book to take to a party... to a gig... on your holiday... or to that famous desert island!

It's packed with literally hundreds and hundreds of the best-loved songs of all time... from vintage standards of the 30s right through to the latest pop hits.

"The Suitcase Book"!

The Busker's Fake Book
1001
All-Time Hit Songs

For piano, organ, guitar, all electronic keyboards and all 'C' instruments. With an easy-to-use A-Z title finder plus a classified 'song type' index. As a taster, here's just a quarter of the titles in this unique bumper songbook...

'A' You're Adorable	Hello, Goodbye	Ruby Don't Take Your Love To Town
A Fine Romance	Here, There And Everywhere	Satin Doll
A Fool Such As I	Hey Jude	Scarborough Fair
A Hard Day's Night	Hey, Good Lookin'	Shake Rattle And Roll
A Man And A Woman	Honeysuckle Rose	She Loves You
A Teenager In Love	I Came I Saw I Conga'd	Singing The Blues
Act Naturally	I Don't Want To Spoil The Party	Sixteen Tons
Against All Odds	I Dreamed A Dream	Sloop John B
Ain't Misbehavin'	I Feel Pretty	Smoke Gets In Your Eyes
All I Have To Do Is Dream	I Fought The Law	Solitude
All My Loving	I Left My Heart In San Francisco	Something
America	I Saw Her Standing There	Somewhere
An American In Paris	I'm A Loser	Spanish Eyes
An Old Fashioned Love Song	I'm Beginning To See The Light	Standing On The Corner
Angel Eyes	I'm Still Standing	Stars Fell On Alabama
Another Suitcase In Another Hall	If I Had A Hammer	Stranger In Paradise
As Time Goes By	If I Were A Bell	Strangers In The Night
Band On The Run	In The Air Tonight	Streets Of London
Barbara Ann	It Never Rains In Southern California	Sugarbush
Baubles Bangles And Beads	It's Not Unusual	Sultans Of Swing
Because	It's So Easy	Summertime Blues
Bennie And The Jets	Jambalaya	Sunshine Of Your Love
Big Girls Don't Cry	Jealous Guy	Sweet Charity
Big Spender	La Ronde De l'Amour	Swing Low, Sweet Chariot
Bird Dog	Lady D'Arbanville	Take Back Your Mink
Blowin' In The Wind	The Lady In Red	Take That Look Off Your Face
Boogie Woogie Bugle Boy	The Lambeth Walk	Take The 'A' Train
Buffalo Gals	The Last Time I Saw Paris	Teen Angel
Bye Bye Love	Layla	The Tender Trap
California Dreaming	Leaning On A Lamp Post	That'll Be The Day
Can't Smile Without You	Let It Be	Theme For A Dream
Candle In The Wind	Let's Twist Again	These Foolish Things
Caravan	The Lion Sleeps Tonight	They Didn't Believe Me
Chantilly Lace	Live And Let Die	This Guy's In Love With You
Come Fly With Me	Long Tall Sally	This Land Is Your Land
Consider Yourself	Love And Marriage	Those Were The Days
Crazy	Lover Man	Three Little Fishies
Cruising Down The River	Lucille	Till There Was You
Dancing Queen	Luck Be A Lady	To Know Him Is To Love Him
Daniel	Lullaby Of Birdland	Tonight
Desafinado	Maple Leaf Rag	True Love Ways
Devil In Disguise	Maria	Tulips From Amsterdam
Diamonds Are A Girl's Best Friend	Me And My Girl	Tutti Frutti
Do You Know The Way To San Jose	Mister Bojangles	Unchained Melody
Don't Cry For Me Argentina	Money For Nothing	Under The Boardwalk
Don't Pay The Ferryman	Mull Of Kintyre	Up, Up And Away
Don't Sleep In The Subway	Never On A Sunday	Uptown Girl
EastEnders	Nights In White Satin	The Very Thought Of You
Ebony And Ivory	Norwegian Wood	Wake Up Little Susie
Eleanor Rigby	Not Fade Away	Walk Tall
Empty Chairs At Empty Tables	O Sole Mio	The Way You Look Tonight
The Entertainer	Oh Pretty Woman	We Can Work It Out
Every Breath You Take	Ol' Man River	We Don't Need Another Hero
First Time Ever I Saw Your Face	Old Shep	We Shall Overcome
Fools Rush In	On A Slow Boat To China	We'll Meet Again
From Me To You	Only The Lonely	What Kind Of Fool Am I
Funiculi, Funicula	P.S. I Love You	Wheels
Für Elise	Peggy Sue	When I'm Sixty Four
Get Back	Pennies From Heaven	When Irish Eyes Are Smiling
Get It On (Bang A Gong)	Penny Lane	When This Lousy War Is Over
The Girl From Ipanema	Pigalle	Where Have All The Flowers Gone
Good Vibrations	Poison Ivy	Witchcraft
Goodbye Yellow Brick Road	The Power Of Love	With A Little Help From My Friends
Guys And Dolls	Raindrops Keep Falling On My Head	Woman
Happy Xmas (War Is Over)	Rave On	Yellow Submarine
Havah Nagilah	Rhapsody In Blue	Yesterday
He Ain't Heavy He's My Brother	Riders On The Storm	Your Cheatin' Heart
Hello Mary Lou	Rock Around The Clock	Your Song

Melody, lyrics and guitar chords to literally hundreds and hundreds of the best songs of all time... from the golden standards through to the great pop hits of today.

While compiling this huge book, editor/arranger Peter Lavender kept all the artwork in a huge suitcase. But now that it's printed, this new mega-bumper busker book is a lot easier to carry around!

Surprisingly portable, in fact, at the usual songbook size of 12" x 9"... with some 656 pages!

As well as the 1,001 songs, the book includes a handy A-Z alphabetical title index *and* a classified index, too!

ISBN 0-7119-2535-4

Wise Publications
Order No. AM 89887